How to Solve **General Chemistry Problems**

PRENTICE-HALL INTERNATIONAL, INC.
London   Tokyo   Sydney   Paris
PRENTICE-HALL OF CANADA, LTD.
PRENTICE-HALL DE MEXICO, S.A.

PRENTICE-HALL CHEMISTRY SERIES

How to Solve
General
Chemistry
Problems
Third Edition

C. H. Sorum
Professor of Chemistry
University of Wisconsin

Prentice-Hall, Inc.
Englewood Cliffs, N.J.

QD
42
.S62
1963

© 1952, 1958, 1963 by
PRENTICE-HALL, INC.
Englewood Cliffs, N. J.

Current printing (last digit):

13   12   11   10   9   8   7   6   5   4

Library of Congress Catalog Number 63–7099

Printed in the United States of America
43416C

Preface

The following changes have been made in this revision:

1. The mole factor approach is emphasized in the solution of all problems. The concept of the mole is presented in Chapter 4 and is stressed throughout the rest of the book.

2. A number of more difficult and more challenging problems, identified by the letter s following the number of the problem, are placed at the end of each chapter. These problems are designed for use in more rigorous courses and for assignment to honors students. The problems in the beginning of each chapter clarify the basic concepts and, in general, are less difficult.

3. The discussions of chemical equilibrium and ionic equilibria have been revised and enlarged. The number of problems dealing with ionic equilibria has been substantially increased.

4. A new chapter, Oxidation Potentials, Chapter 22, has been added.

Complete solutions are given to enough problems in each chapter so that the book will, for the majority of students, be self-teaching. In certain of the problems hints rather than complete solutions are given.

Because each chapter contains problems of all ranges of difficulty, and because as few or as many of the chapters can be covered as the requirements of a course warrant, the book is flexible enough to serve the needs of practically any kind of student and any general chemistry group.

As in the previous edition, answers are given to approximately 50 per cent of the basic problems. Answers are given to all of the s problems. Unanswered problems are designated by an asterisk. A list of answers to the unanswered problems is available; requests for this list should be sent to the publisher or the author.

The author wishes to express his indebtedness to the members of his general chemistry teaching staff for their assistance in the preparation of this revision. He is particularly indebted to Duncan Poland and James Espenson.

C. H. SORUM

Contents

1 How to Solve 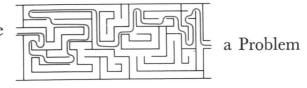 a Problem

Every problem that you encounter, whether it is in chemistry or in some other area, is solved in essentially the same fashion. *First,* you size up the situation carefully, or read the problem carefully, and decide what you are supposed to do and what you have to do it with. *Second,* having determined *what* you are supposed to do and what you have to do it with, you figure out *how* to do it. *Finally,* you go ahead and *do it* according to plan. The first two steps represent the *analysis* of the problem. The third step represents the *arithmetical calculations.* Some problems are knottier than others, but they are all solved by these three fundamental steps.

To be more specific, when you go about solving any problem in this or any other book or in any test or examination:

1. Read the problem carefully. Note exactly what is given and what is sought. Note any and all special conditions. Be sure that you understand the meaning of all terms and units and that you are familiar with all chemical principles that are involved. Every problem in this book is designed to illustrate some principle, some relationship, some law, some definition, or some fact. If you understand the principle, relationship, law, definition, or fact you should have no difficulty solving the problem. The one big reason, the only reason in fact, why students have difficulty with chemistry problems is failure to understand, exactly and well, the chemical principles involved and the meaning and value of all terms and units that are used in the problem.

2. Plan, in detail, just how the problem is to be solved. Get into the habit of visualizing the entire solution before you execute a single step. Insist on knowing what you are going to do and why you are going to do

1

it. Aim to learn to solve every problem in the most efficient manner; this generally means doing it the shortest way, with the fewest steps.

3. When you actually carry out the mathematical operation of solving the problem be sure to **specify definitely what each number represents and the units in which it is expressed.** Don't just write

$$\frac{192}{32} = 6$$

Write

$$\frac{192 \text{ g of sulfur}}{32 \text{ g of sulfur per mole of sulfur}} = 6 \text{ moles of sulfur}$$

or whatever the case may be. Always divide and multiply the *units* as well as the *numbers*. This is one way to give exactness to your thought process and is a very good way to help avoid errors. You should jot down the unit or units in which your answer is to be expressed as the first step in the actual solution. For instance, if you are solving for the number of grams of oxygen in 200 g of silver oxide, you should jot down the fact that the answer will be "= _____ g of oxygen." In reality, every problem is worked backward, since you first focus your attention on the units in which the answer is to be expressed and then plan the solution with these units in mind.

4. Having solved the problem, examine the answer to see if it is reasonable and sensible. The student who reported that 200 g of silver oxide contained 1380 g of oxygen should have known that such an answer was not sensible. When the slide rule is used, errors due to incorrect location of the decimal point are very likely to creep in unless you get into the habit of checking the answer to see if it is of the right order of magnitude.

5. If you do not understand how to solve a problem have it explained to you at the very earliest possible date. To be able to solve the later problems you must understand the earlier ones. After a problem has been explained to you, fix the explanation in your mind by working other similar problems at once, or at least within a few hours, while the explanation is still fresh in your mind.

2 2 2 2 2 2 2 2 2 2 2

Units of Measurement

It will be assumed in this book that every student is familiar, through laboratory experience, with the common units of measure in the metric system and that he has a fair idea of the volume represented by 1 liter, 100 ml, and 1 ml, the mass represented by 10 g, 100 g, or 1 kg, and the length represented by 760 mm, 10 cm, and 1 m, etc. Also, it will be assumed that he is familiar with the centigrade thermometer scale.

It should be recalled that the metric system employs decimal notations in which the prefix, *milli-*, means one thousandth, *centi-* means one hundredth, and *deci-* means one tenth, while *kilo-* means one thousand times.

Conversions of metric units (grams, liters, milliliters, cubic centimeters, centimeters, etc.) to other units (pounds, quarts, inches, feet, etc.) are not often required. The following table will serve where such conversions are called for.

Conversion Units

1 meter (m) = 10 decimeters (dm) = 100 centimeters (cm)
         = 1000 millimeters (mm) = 39.37 inches (in.)
         = 1.09 yards (yd)
1 kilogram (kg) = 1000 grams (g) = 1,000,000 milligrams (mg)
         = 2.2046 pounds (lb)
1 gram (g) = 1000 milligrams (mg)
1 milligram (mg) = 0.001 gram (g)
1 pound (lb) = 453.6 grams (g)

3

1 liter (l) = 1000 milliliters (ml) = 1000.027 cubic centimeters (cc)
   = 0.264 U.S. gallons (gal) = 1.06 U.S. quarts (qt)

1 milliliter (ml) = 1.000027 cubic centimeters (cc)

1 cubic centimeter is the volume of about 20 drops of water

A new U.S. 5-cent piece weighs 5 g

It should be noted that 1 liter is equal to 1000 milliliters (ml) and that 1 liter is also equal to 1000.027 cubic centimeters (cc). One milliliter is therefore equal to 1.000027 cc. For all practical purposes, however, 1 ml and 1 cc are equal to each other. One liter is, for all practical purposes, equal to 1000 cc and will be so considered in this book.

Interconversion of Centigrade and Fahrenheit Temperature Readings

The thermometers used in the laboratory are graduated in centigrade degrees; most household thermometers are graduated in Fahrenheit degrees. The fixed points on both the centigrade and Fahrenheit temperature scales are the boiling point and freezing point of water. On the centigrade scale the freezing point of water is 0° and the boiling point is 100°; the space between the fixed points is divided into 100 units and the space above 100° and below 0° is divided into the same size units. On the Fahrenheit scale the freezing point of water is 32° and the boiling point is 212°; the space between the fixed points is divided into 180 units and the space above 212° and below 32° is divided into the same size units. Since the space between the freezing point and boiling point of water is divided into 100° on the centigrade scale and 180° on the Fahrenheit scale, it follows that 100 centigrade degrees must represent the same temperature change as 180 Fahrenheit degrees. That means that 1 centigrade degree is equal to 1.8 Fahrenheit degrees; or expressing it in fractional form, 1 centigrade degree is equal to $\frac{9}{5}$ Fahrenheit degrees and 1 Fahrenheit degree is equal to $\frac{5}{9}$ of a centigrade degree.

With these facts in mind we see that, if we wish to find the Fahrenheit value of a certain number of centigrade degrees, C, we first multiply the centigrade reading by $\frac{9}{5}$; this gives us $\frac{9}{5}$ C. Since the reference temperature (the freezing point of water) on the F scale is 32° above zero we must add 32° to $\frac{9}{5}$ C in order to get the actual reading on the Fahrenheit scale.

$$\text{Fahrenheit temperature} = \frac{9}{5} \text{ centigrade temperature} + 32$$

or

(1) $$F = \frac{9}{5} C + 32$$

Equation (1) can be transposed to the form,

(2) $$C = \frac{5}{9} (F - 32)$$

Equation (2) tells us that, to find the value, in degrees centigrade, of a Fahrenheit temperature, we first subtract 32° from the Fahrenheit temperature (because the Fahrenheit freezing point reference is 32° above zero) and then take $\frac{5}{9}$ of that answer.

To illustrate the use of the above relationships:

(a) Convert 144°F to a centigrade reading.

In thinking our way through this problem we note that 144°F is (144 − 32) or 112° above the freezing point of water. Since 1 Fahrenheit degree is equal to $\frac{5}{9}$ of a centigrade degree 112 Fahrenheit degrees must be equal to $112 \times \frac{5}{9}$ or 62.2 centigrade degrees. That means that 144°F is 62.2 centigrade degrees above the freezing point of water. Since the freezing point of water is 0°C, 62.2 centigrade degrees above the freezing point of water will be 62.2°C.

(b) Convert 80°C to a Fahrenheit reading.

In thinking our way through this problem we note that 80°C is 80 centigrade degrees above the freezing point of water. Since 1 degree C equals $\frac{9}{5}$ degrees F, 80°C will be $\frac{9}{5} \times 80$ or 144 Fahrenheit degrees above the freezing point of water. But the freezing point of water on the Fahrenheit scale is 32°. Therefore, we must add 32 to our 144 to get the actual Fahrenheit temperature, 176°F.

Problems

2.1 What temperature, in degrees centigrade, is represented by each of the following Fahrenheit temperatures?

(a) 72.0°F

SOLUTION: See solutions of problems given above.

*(b) −20.0°F

2.2 What temperature in degrees Fahrenheit is represented by each of the following centigrade temperatures?

(a) 12.0°C

*(b) −50.0°C

2.3 At what temperature will the readings on the Fahrenheit and centigrade thermometers be the same?

2.4 Suppose you have designed a new thermometer called the X thermometer. On the X scale the boiling point of water is 130°X and the freezing point of water is 10°X. At what temperature will the readings on the Fahrenheit and X thermometers be the same?*

2.5 On a new Jekyll temperature scale water freezes at 17°J and boils at 97°J. On another new temperature scale, the Hyde scale, water freezes at 0°H and boils at 120°H. If methyl alcohol boils at 84°H what is its boiling point on the Jekyll scale?

Exponents

Chemical problems often involve numbers which are either very large or very small. Such numbers are most conveniently expressed in *exponential form*.

To illustrate:

The number, 100, is 10^2, which is 1×10^2; 1000 is 1×10^3 and 1,000,000 is 1×10^6.

The number, 2,000,000, is $2 \times 1,000,000$, which is 2×10^6.

The number, 324,000,000, is $3.24 \times 100,000,000$, which is 3.24×10^8; but it is also $32.4 \times 10,000,000$, which is 32.4×10^7, and $324 \times 1,000,000$, which is 324×10^6. In other words, 324,000,000 may be represented as either 3.24×10^8, 32.4×10^7, or 324×10^6. The first of these, in which there is only one digit to the left of the decimal point in the non-exponential factor, is the preferred form.

Note that, in the above example in which we are dealing with numbers *larger* than 1, a decimal point is placed to the *right* of the first digit in the number; the resulting expression is then multiplied by 10 raised to a positive power equal to the number of terms to the *right* of the decimal point.

To illustrate:

$$602,000,000,000,000,000,000,000 = 6.02 \times 10^{23}$$

and

$$31,730,000 = 3.173 \times 10^7$$

7

The number 0.0001 is one tenthousandth, which is 1/10,000, which is $1/10^4$.

Keeping in mind that (a) $1 = 10^0$, (b) the fraction, $1/10^4$, means 1 divided by 10^4, and (c) in division of exponential numbers the exponent of the denominator is subtracted from the exponent of numerator, then

$$\frac{1}{10^4} = \frac{10^0}{10^4} = 10^{0-4} = 10^{-4} = 1 \times 10^{-4}$$

Likewise,

$$0.00002 = 2 \times \frac{1}{100,000} = 2 \times \frac{1}{10^5} = 2 \times 10^{-5}$$

and

$$0.00000038 \text{ is } 3.8 \times \frac{1}{10,000,000} = 3.8 \times \frac{1}{10^7} = 3.8 \times 10^{-7}$$

Note that, in dealing with numbers *less* than 1, a decimal point is placed to the *right* of the first term to the right of the zeros and the resulting expression is then multiplied by 10 raised to a *negative* power equal to the number of terms to the *left* of this decimal point.

Thus

$$0.00000257 = 2.57 \times 10^{-6}$$

and

$$0.000016 = 1.6 \times 10^{-5}$$

Just as 3.24×10^8, 32.4×10^7, and 324×10^6 all represent the same number so 2.57×10^{-6}, 25.7×10^{-7} and 257×10^{-8} are all the same number and 48×10^{-6} is equivalent to 4.8×10^{-5}.

Note that, in changing 48×10^{-6} to its equal, 4.8×10^{-5}, and in changing 32.4×10^7 to 3.24×10^8, we *divide* the first factor (48 and 32.4) by 10 and *multiply* the second factor (10^{-6} and 10^7) by 10. Likewise, in changing 0.23×10^{-4} to 2.3×10^{-5} we *multiply* the first factor (0.23) by 10 and *divide* the second factor (10^{-4}) by 10. Since, in each example, we multiply one factor by 10 and divide the other by 10, the value of the number is not changed.

Thus

$$2.36 \times 10^{-5} = 23.6 \times 10^{-6} = 236 \times 10^{-7} = 0.236 \times 10^{-4}$$

and

$$4.92 \times 10^5 = 49.2 \times 10^4 = 492 \times 10^3 = 0.492 \times 10^6$$

The use of exponents makes it quite easy to determine the correct number of digits in the answer to an operation involving multiplication and division of many numbers. Thus, if the expression

$$\frac{417,000 \times 0.0036 \times 15,300,000}{0.000021 \times 293 \times 183,000}$$

is changed to the form

$$\frac{4.17 \times 10^5 \times 3.6 \times 10^{-3} \times 1.53 \times 10^7}{2.1 \times 10^{-5} \times 2.93 \times 10^2 \times 1.83 \times 10^5}$$

it can be determined, at a glance, that the answer is approximately 2×10^7.

Likewise, when the expression

$$\frac{0.0045 \times 0.082 \times 600}{204 \times 23}$$

is changed to the form

$$\frac{4.5 \times 10^{-3} \times 8.2 \times 10^{-2} \times 6 \times 10^2}{2.04 \times 10^2 \times 2.3 \times 10^1}$$

it can be seen that the answer is approximately

$$48 \times 10^{-6} \quad \text{or} \quad 4.8 \times 10^{-5}$$

Problems

3.1   Express each of the following numbers in exponential form:

(a) 21,000,000,000

*(b) 760

(c) 0.0027

*(d) 0.0000018

(e) 0.10

3.2   Carry out each of the following operations; first write each number in exponential form:

(a) $\dfrac{136,000 \times 0.000322 \times 273}{0.082 \times 4200 \times 129.2}$

*(b) $\dfrac{120 \times 309 \times 800}{273 \times 600}$

3.3   Solve each of the following:

(a) $\dfrac{1.76 \times 10^{-3}}{8.0 \times 10^2}$

*(b) $\dfrac{0.0234 \times 10^{-3}}{3.6 \times 10^{-4}}$

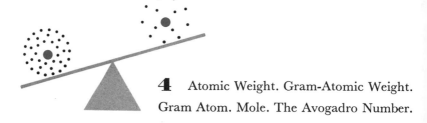

4 Atomic Weight. Gram-Atomic Weight.
Gram Atom. Mole. The Avogadro Number.

Atomic Weight

The atomic weight of an element is a number which tells us how the weight of an *average atom* of that element compares with the weight of a standard reference atom. In the modern system of atomic weights, adopted in 1961, the atom of carbon-12 (^{12}C) is the reference standard and is assigned a value of exactly 12. The atomic weight of gold, listed in the table on the inside back cover, is 196.967. This means that the weight of an *average atom* of gold is to the weight of an atom of ^{12}C as 196.967 is to 12. Likewise, the weight of an average atom of calcium (whose atomic weight is 40.08) is to the weight of an atom of ^{12}C as 40.08 is to 12, and so on down the list of elements. Since all atomic weights are referred to the same standard it must follow that these atomic weights are the relative weights of the average atoms of all the elements. That is, the weight of the average gold atom is to the weight of the average calcium atom as 196.967 is to 40.08, and the weight of the average calcium atom is 40.08/196.967 times the weight of the average gold atom, and so on.

Gram-Atomic Weight

Atomic weight, as defined above, is simply a number. To give it more precise meaning we can say that the ^{12}C atom has a mass of 12 *atomic*

10

weight units (awu) and not be concerned about what these units represent. The atomic weight of calcium then becomes 40.08 awu, of gold, 196.967 awu, and so on.

But we would like to use these atomic weights for solving problems, and since the most commonly employed unit of mass (weight) is the gram, it will be most convenient if atomic weights can be expressed in units of grams. To do this we take a large enough "handful" of atoms of a given element so that its weight, in grams, is exactly equal to the atomic weight of the element. For oxygen the handful weighs 15.9994 g, for sulfur it weighs 32.064 g, for magnesium it weighs 24.312 g, for helium it weighs 4.0026 g, etc. *This weight in grams of an element equal to its atomic weight is called one gram-atomic weight* of the element.

It has been determined that one gram-atomic weight of helium (4.0026 g) contains 6.023×10^{23} helium atoms. A similar figure has been obtained in numerous experiments with other elements. From these data it can be concluded that *one gram-atomic weight of any element consists of* 6.023×10^{23} *atoms of that element.*

The argument that one gram-atomic weight of any element contains 6.023×10^{23} atoms runs like this: The atomic weight of helium is 4.0026 and of sulfur is 32.064. That means that 1 atom of helium is 4.0026/32.064 times as heavy as 1 atom of sulfur. Therefore, 10 atoms of helium must be 4.0026/32.064 times as heavy as 10 atoms of sulfur and 6.023×10^{23} atoms of helium must be 4.0026/32.064 times as heavy as 6.023×10^{23} atoms of sulfur. But 6.023×10^{23} atoms of helium weigh 4.0026 g. Therefore, 6.023×10^{23} atoms of sulfur must weigh 32.064 g. Since 4.0026 g is one gram-atomic weight of helium and 32.064 g is one gram-atomic weight of sulfur, and since the above argument can be applied to each of the other 101 elements, it can be concluded that one gram-atomic weight of any element consists of 6.023×10^{23} atoms.

Gram Atom

The term, gram-atomic weight, is abbreviated to *gram atom*. "*One gram atom*" of an element means one gram-atomic weight of that element.

Mole

The quantity, 6.023×10^{23} atoms, is referred to as one *gram mole* of atoms or, simply, one *mole*. It follows from what has been stated above that one mole of atoms means one gram atom or one gram-atomic weight. As we proceed, we shall learn that *"mole"* is a very widely used term. It is applied to molecules, ions, clusters of atoms, and electrons as well as to atoms. *One mole of a species is* 6.023×10^{23} *units of that species.*

The Avogadro Number

The number, 6.023×10^{23}, which represents the number of units in one mole of a substance, is referred to as the *Avogadro Number*, in honor of the Italian scientist who first postulated its existence. It is denoted by the letter N.

Review

Since, as has been noted above, gram atom is an abbreviation for gram-atomic weight, since one gram-atomic weight of an element is 6.023×10^{23} atoms, since one mole of atoms means 6.023×10^{23} atoms, and since the number, 6.023×10^{23}, is the Avogadro Number, N, it follows that, when applied to a particular element, the terms

> one mole of atoms
>
> one gram atom
>
> one gram-atomic weight
>
> 6.023×10^{23} atoms
>
> N atoms

all mean the same thing.

Specifically, 32.064 g of sulfur is

> one mole of sulfur atoms
>
> one gram atom of sulfur
>
> one gram-atomic weight of sulfur
>
> 6.023×10^{23} atoms of sulfur
>
> N atoms of sulfur

Symbol

The name of an element is commonly represented by an abbreviation, referred to as the *symbol* for that element. Thus the symbols for sodium and oxygen are, respectively, Na and O.

When the symbol for an element is used in any chemical formula or equation it is understood that it refers to one gram atom of the element. Since, as has already been noted, one gram atom means *one mole* of atoms, it follows that *the symbol for an element, when used in any chemical formula or equation, refers to one mole of atoms of that element.* This is a very important fact to remember; it is a basic fact in the solution of most chemical problems.

Pound-Atomic Weight, Ton-Atomic Weight, Pound Atom, Ton Atom, Pound Mole, Ton Mole

It has been pointed out that, because the weight of 1 atom of sulfur is to the weight of 1 atom of helium as 32.064 is to 4.0026, the weight of any number, X, atoms of sulfur is to the weight of the same number, X, atoms of helium as 32.064 is to 4.0026. If we take 6.023×10^{23} atoms of helium they will weigh 4.0026 g; therefore, if we take 6.023×10^{23} atoms of sulfur they will weigh 32.064 g. Suppose X atoms of helium weigh 4.0026 *pounds*. If X atoms of helium weigh 4.0026 lb, X atoms of sulfur will then weigh 32.064 lb, X atoms of hydrogen will weigh 1.00797 lb, X atoms of sodium will weigh 22.9898 lb, and so on down the list of elements. Likewise, if Y atoms of helium weigh 4.0026 *tons*, Y atoms of hydrogen will weigh 1.00797 tons, Y atoms of sodium will weigh 22.9898 tons, Y atoms of sulfur will weigh 32.064 tons, and so on. The quantity, 4.0026 pounds of helium, is one *pound-atomic weight*, one *pound atom*, or one *pound mole* of He. The quantity, 32.064 tons of sulfur, is one ton-atomic weight, one ton atom, or one ton mole of S. In other words, just as we have gram-atomic weights, so we can have *pound-atomic weights, ton-atomic weights, pound atoms, ton atoms, pound moles* and *ton moles*. A pound-atomic weight is a weight in pounds of an element equal to its atomic weight and a ton-atomic weight is a weight in tons of an element equal to its atomic weight. One pound mole of S is 32.064 pounds and one ton mole of Ag is 107.870 tons. Since the atomic weight table tells us how the weights of the atoms of the elements *compare* with each other, the numerical values of the atomic weights will be the same regardless of the unit in which they are being expressed.

It should be noted, however, that the number of individual atoms in a pound mole of an element will not be 6.023×10^{23} atoms. The Avogadro number, 6.023×10^{23}, represents the number of atoms in one *gram atom*, that is, in one *gram mole*. Since 1 ton = 2000 lb and 1 lb = 453.6 g, one pound mole of an element will contain $453.6 \times 6.023 \times 10^{23}$ atoms and one ton mole will contain $2000 \times 453.6 \times 6.023 \times 10^{23}$ atoms.

Problems

4.1 What fraction of a mole of zinc atoms is 12.00 g of Zn?

SOLUTION: The atomic weight of zinc is 65.37. Therefore, 65.37 g
is 1 mole of Zn, and 12.00 g is 12.00/65.37 mole of Zn.
The calculation, in detail, is

$$12.00 \text{ g of Zn} \div 65.37 \text{ g of Zn/mole of Zn} = \frac{12.00}{65.37} \text{ mole of Zn}$$

Since any fraction represents a process of division, the calculation
can take the form

$$\frac{12.00 \text{ g of Zn}}{65.37 \text{ g of Zn/1 mole of Zn}} = \frac{12.00}{65.37} \text{ mole of Zn}$$

Note that g of Zn in the numerator cancels g of Zn in the denominator. The answer is then in moles of Zn.
The solution can also be carried out as follows: We are given 12.00 g
of zinc. We want to know how many moles of zinc this represents.
We reason that, if we multiply

$$\text{g of Zn} \times \frac{\text{moles of Zn}}{\text{g of Zn}}$$

then g of Zn in the numerator and denominator will cancel and the
answer will be in units of moles of Zn. Since 1 mole of Zn weighs
65.37 g the actual calculation will be

$$12.00 \text{ g of Zn} \times \frac{1 \text{ mole of Zn}}{65.37 \text{ g of Zn}} = \frac{12.00}{65.37} \text{ mole of Zn}$$

4.2 A weight of 30.42 g of calcium is what fraction of a mole of calcium
atoms?

4.3 A weight of 120.0 g of helium is how many moles of He atoms?*

4.4 Calculate the weight of 2.32 moles of carbon atoms.

SOLUTION: The atomic weight of carbon is 12.011. Therefore, 1 mole
of C weighs 12.011 g.

2.32 moles × 12.011 g/mole = 27.9 g

(g/mole means "grams per mole")

Note that moles in the numerator and denominator cancel. The
answer is in grams.

4.5 Calculate the weight of 4.72 moles of fluorine atoms.

4.6 Calculate the weight of 0.140 mole of sodium atoms.*

4.7 Calculate the weight of 0.821 gram atom of manganese.

4.8 Calculate the weight of 3.20 ton moles of Si.*

4.9 How many atoms are there in 20.00 g of boron?

SOLUTION: We know that there are 6.023×10^{23} atoms in 1 mole of B. If we know how many moles of B there are in 20 g of B we can then multiply moles of B by 6.023×10^{23} atoms per mole. The atomic weight of boron is 10.811. That means that there are 10.811 g in 1 mole of B. Therefore

(1) $$\frac{20 \text{ g of B}}{10.811 \text{ g of B/mole of B}} = \frac{20}{10.811} \text{ moles of B}$$

(2) $$\frac{20}{10.811} \text{ moles of B} \times 6.023 \times 10^{23} \text{ atoms/mole of B}$$

$$= \frac{20}{10.811} \times 6.023 \times 10^{23} \text{ atoms}$$

$$= 11 \times 10^{23} \text{ atoms}$$

$$= 1.1 \times 10^{24} \text{ atoms}$$

The entire calculation can be combined in one operation:

$$\frac{20 \text{ g}}{10.811 \text{ g/mole}} \times 6.023 \times 10^{23} \text{ atoms/mole} = 1.1 \times 10^{24} \text{ atoms}$$

Note that grams cancel grams and mole cancels mole.

4.10 An amount of 4.63×10^{21} atoms is how many moles of Sn?

SOLUTION: 6.023×10^{23} atoms is 1 mole of Sn. Therefore, 4.63×10^{21} atoms is

$$\frac{4.63 \times 10^{21}}{6.023 \times 10^{23}} \text{ mole of Sn}$$

The detailed calculation would be

$$\frac{4.63 \times 10^{21} \text{ atoms}}{6.023 \times 10^{23} \text{ atoms/mole}} = \frac{4.63 \times 10^{21}}{6.023 \times 10^{23}} \text{ mole}$$

$$= 0.772 \times 10^{-2} \text{ mole}$$

$$= 7.72 \times 10^{-3} \text{ mole}$$

4.11 How many grams of copper will contain 3.22×10^{24} atoms of copper?

SOLUTION: The atomic weight of copper is 63.54. This means that there are 63.54 g of Cu in 1 mole of Cu. If we know how many moles of Cu are represented by 3.22×10^{24} atoms we can multiply these moles by 63.54 g of Cu per mole.

We know that one mole contains 6.023×10^{23} atoms; therefore, 3.22×10^{24} atoms is

$$\frac{3.22 \times 10^{24}}{6.023 \times 10^{23}} \text{ moles}$$

$$\frac{3.22 \times 10^{24}}{6.023 \times 10^{23}} \text{ moles} \times 63.54 \text{ g/mole} = 339 \text{ g}$$

The entire calculation can be carried out in one operation

$$\frac{3.22 \times 10^{24} \text{ atoms}}{6.023 \times 10^{23} \text{ atoms/mole}} \times 63.54 \text{ g/mole} = 339 \text{ g}$$

4.12 How many atoms are there in 120 g of magnesium?

4.13 Calculate the weight in grams of 8.00×10^{23} atoms of iron.*

4.14 How many grams of chromium will contain 4.00×10^{23} atoms of chromium?

4.15 How many atoms of sulfur will weigh 40.0 g?*

4.16 What fraction of a mole of aluminum atoms will contain 4.11×10^{20} atoms?

4.17 How many atoms are there in 125 pound moles of nickel?

SOLUTION: Since 1 lb = 453.6 g, 125 lb moles = 125×453.6 gram moles. One gram mole = 6.023×10^{23} atoms. Therefore, the complete calculation is

125 pound moles $\times$ 453.6 gram moles/pound mole

$\times\ 6.023 \times 10^{23}$ atoms/gram mole $= 3.41 \times 10^{28}$ atoms

4.18 How many atoms are there in 0.0260 ton moles of chromium?

4.19 s A sample of chlorine gas consists of 80.00 mole per cent of ^{35}Cl with atomic mass 35.00 and 20.00 mole per cent of ^{37}Cl with atomic mass 37.00. Calculate the atomic weight of the chlorine in the sample.

4.20 s An element X whose atomic weight is 22.7 is a mixture of two isotopes with atomic masses of 24.1 and 22.5, respectively. Calculate the relative abundance (mole per cent) of each isotope in the mixture.

5 Calculations from Formulas of Compounds HHHHH   OOOOO
Determining the Formula of a Compound HHHH**H** H_2O OOOOO
Rounding Off a Number HHHHH OOOO**O**
Significant Figures **H**HHHH OOOOO

When atoms combine to form compounds they always do so in definite proportions by weight. As a result, the composition of every pure compound is definite and constant. This is the *law of definite composition*.

The definite composition of a particular compound is represented by its *chemical formula*. To illustrate, it has been found by experiments that 22.9898 g of sodium will always combine with 35.453 g of chlorine to form 58.443 g of common salt. From the table of atomic weights we learn that 22.9898 g is 1 gram atom of sodium, while 35.453 g is 1 gram atom of chlorine. That means that sodium combines with chlorine in the *ratio* of 1 gram atom of sodium to 1 gram atom of chlorine to form the compound sodium chloride. We represent 1 gram atom of sodium by the symbol Na and 1 gram atom of chlorine by the symbol Cl. The formula for sodium chloride is therefore NaCl. This formula, NaCl, means that the compound, NaCl, is made up of sodium and chlorine combined in the *ratio* of 1 gram atom of sodium to 1 gram atom of chlorine. Since, as has already been emphasized, the symbol for an element refers to one mole of atoms of that element, the formula, NaCl, means that the compound, NaCl, is made up of sodium and chlorine combined in the ratio of 1 *mole* of Na atoms to 1 *mole* of Cl atoms. The experimentally determined formula for hydrogen sulfide is H_2S, which tells us that in this compound the hydrogen and sulfur are combined in the ratio of 2 moles of H atoms to 1 mole of S atoms.

In many instances the formula of a compound represents the actual composition of a *molecule* of the compound. The term molecule refers to the neutral unit in which the substance exists and displays its characteristic as a pure substance. Thus, the carbon disulfide molecule contains 1 atom

18

of carbon in combination with 2 atoms of sulfur; its actual composition is represented, correctly, by the *true chemical formula*, CS_2. Likewise, H_2S, CO, CO_2, HCl, NH_3, SO_2, CH_4, C_2H_6, and H_2O are true chemical formulas; they represent the actual number of atoms of each component element in a molecule of the compound.

A great many compounds, however, exist as ions, not as molecules in the sense that a molecule is a neutral particle of substance. Thus, every crystal, "pinch," or barrelful of solid sodium chloride and every cubic centimeter of melted $NaCl$ or $NaCl$ solution is made up of many Na^+ and Cl^- ions. For every Na^+ ion there is one Cl^- ion; the mass of salt is neutral. The quantity of sodium chloride and the size of the crystal may vary, but the *ratio* of sodium to chlorine is constant and is correctly represented by the *empirical formula*, $NaCl$. The same is true of the hundreds of other salts, metal oxides, and metal hydroxides. Their formulas are empirical formulas, not true chemical formulas; they represent the ratios in which the elements combine but do not represent the mass of a "molecule." Since, in most problems, the *ratio* in which elements combine is the important thing, the fact that we do not know the true chemical formula of a compound causes no real difficulty.

The sum of the atomic weights represented by the formula of a substance is its *formula weight*. If the true chemical formula of a substance is known the formula weight is also the *molecular weight*. Thus, the formula weights of $NaCl$ and CS_2 are, 58.443 and 76.139, respectively; 76.139 is the molecular weight of CS_2.

The number of *grams* equal, numerically, to the formula weight is the *gram-formula weight*; expressed in pounds or tons it is the *pound-formula weight* or *ton-formula weight*. The formula weight of $NaCl$ is 58.443; 58.443 *grams* is one *gram*-formula weight of $NaCl$, 58.443 *pounds* is one *pound*-formula weight, and 58.443 *tons* is one *ton*-formula weight.

The number of *grams* equal, numerically, to the molecular weight, is the *gram-molecular weight*; expressed in units of pounds or tons it is the *pound-molecular weight* or *ton-molecular weight*. The molecular weight of CH_4 is 16.043; 16.043 *grams* is one *gram*-molecular weight of CH_4, 16.043 *pounds* is one *pound*-molecular weight, and 16.043 *tons* is one *ton*-molecular weight.

Just as the symbol of an element, when used in a formula or an equation, represents one gram-atomic weight of that element, so the formula of a compound, when used in an equation, represents one gram-formula weight of that compound. If the true chemical formula is known, this formula represents one gram-molecular weight.

One gram-molecular weight of any substance contains 6.023×10^{23} *molecules.* The reasoning that leads to this conclusion can be illustrated in the case of the compound whose true chemical formula is CS_2. This formula tells us that 1 atom of C combines with 2 atoms of S to form 1 molecule of CS_2. Therefore 6.023×10^{23} atoms (1 mole) of C must combine with $2 \times 6.023 \times 10^{23}$ atoms (2 moles) of S to yield 6.023×10^{23} molecules of CS_2. Therefore 1 gram-molecular weight of CS_2 must contain 6.023×10^{23} individual molecules. In a similar manner it can be reasoned that 1 gram-molecular weight of any substance whose true chemical formula is known contains 6.023×10^{23} molecules.

But 6.023×10^{23} units is, by definition, one mole. Since the formula represents one gram-molecular weight, since one gram-molecular weight consists of 6.023×10^{23} molecules, and since 6.023×10^{23} molecules is 1 mole, *the chemical formula of a compound, when used in any equation, represents one mole of that substance.*

Use of the Term "Mole"

The symbol or formula for any chemical substance, whether it is an element, a compound, or an ion, when used in a formula or equation, *represents one mole of that substance.* So that there may be no question about the identity of the substance, its symbol or formula should be given. The following statements, each of which represents correct usage of the term *mole*, will illustrate this point:

The formula, $KClO_3$, tells us that 1 mole of $KClO_3$ contains 1 mole of K, 1 mole of Cl, and 3 moles of O.

One mole of $KClO_3$, when heated, will yield 1 mole of KCl and 1.5 moles of O_2.

One mole of Na_2SO_4 will yield 2 moles of Na^+ ions and 1 mole of SO_4^{--} ions.

In the reaction represented by the equation, $C + O_2 = CO_2$, 1 mole of C atoms combines with 1 mole of O_2 molecules to form 1 mole of CO_2 molecules. A mole of CO_2 molecules can be considered to consist of 1 mole of C atoms and 2 moles of O atoms.

In the reaction, $Ag^+ + Cl^- = AgCl$, the Ag^+ ions and Cl^- ions combine in the ratio of 1 mole of Ag^+ ions to 1 mole of Cl^- ions to form 1 mole of AgCl.

If the true chemical formula is known, one mole means one *molecular weight,* expressed in the proper units of mass. If only the empirical formula is known, one mole means one *formula weight.*

Since the unit of mass commonly employed is the gram, the term mole will, unless otherwise stated, be understood to mean *gram mole* and represents either the gram-atomic weight, the gram-molecular weight, or the gram-formula weight. If the unit of mass employed is the pound or ton we will have a *pound mole* or *ton mole.* To illustrate, 1 mole of NaCl is 58.443 g and 1 mole of CS_2 is 76.139 g. One pound mole of CO_2 is 44.01 lb and 1 ton mole of H_2SO_4 is 98.10 tons.

Determining the Formula of a Compound

Attention has already been called, in one of the preceding paragraphs, to the experimental facts and scientific reasoning which lead to the conclusion that the empirical formula for the compound, sodium chloride, is NaCl. The formula of every compound that you will meet in chemistry has been determined experimentally in the same manner and by exactly the same kind of reasoning. Because it is imperative for the solution of all future problems that the significance and meaning of the chemical formula be clearly understood, the method used in the determination of a formula will now be discussed in detail.

Let us remember, first of all, that the chemical formula for a compound gives the ratio of the number of atoms of each of the elements in the compound. Since the ratio of the number of *atoms* of each element in a *molecule* of the compound is the same as the ratio of the number of *moles of atoms* of each element in a *mole* of the compound, what we are trying to do, when we determine the formula of a compound, is to find the number of moles of atoms of each element in one mole of the compound.

Suppose we want to determine the chemical formula for water. First we synthesize pure water (prepare it from pure oxygen and pure hydrogen). We find, by careful experiment, that 15.999 g of oxygen combine with exactly 2.016 g of hydrogen to form exactly 18.015 g of water. We check our results by analyzing (breaking down) these 18.015 g of water, and we find that they yield exactly 15.999 g of oxygen and 2.016 g of hydrogen. The gram-atomic weight of oxygen is 15.999 g and the gram-atomic weight of hydrogen is 1.008 g. That means that 1 gram-atomic weight (1 gram atom) (1 mole) of O has combined with 2 gram-atomic weights (2 gram atoms) (2 moles) of H to form 1 gram-molecular weight of water. The chemical formula for water is therefore H_2O. The subscript to the right and below the H means that there are 2 atoms of hydrogen combined with 1 atom of oxygen. We obtained the 2, representing the number of atoms of H, by dividing the 2.016 g of hydrogen by 1.008 g (the gram-atomic weight of hydrogen). That is,

$$\frac{2.016 \text{ g of H}}{1.008 \text{ g per gram atom of H}} = 2 \text{ gram atoms of H}$$

$$\frac{15.999 \text{ g of O}}{15.999 \text{ g per gram atom of O}} = 1 \text{ gram atom of O}$$

Therefore, the chemical formula is H_2O.

Since 1 gram atom of an element is 1 mole of atoms of that element, the calculation given above can be represented as follows:

$$\frac{2.016 \text{ g of H}}{1.008 \text{ g per mole of H}} = 2 \text{ moles of H}$$

$$\frac{15.999 \text{ g of O}}{15.999 \text{ g per mole of O}} = 1 \text{ mole of O}$$

Summarizing what we did in getting the formula for water, we proceed as follows in determining the empirical formula for any chemical compound.

1. Determine the exact composition of the compound, that is, the weights of each element that combine, or the per cent of each element in the compound, either by analysis or by synthesis.

2. Divide the weight of each element, or the per cent of each element, by its gram-atomic weight. The simplest ratio between the quotients gives the chemical formula.

In Problems 5.1–5.10, which are designed to show how formulas are determined, the results of the experimental analysis or synthesis will be given. Only the subsequent calculations will be required.

Rounding Off Numbers

Up to this point the exact values of the various atomic weights have been used in making calculations. Since it is strongly recommended that a slide rule be used for all calculations, and since the average slide rule reading is not exact beyond three or four digits, nothing is gained by using such exact values. Accordingly, the "rounded off" values given in the table on the inside front cover will be used in all future calculations.

A number is "rounded off" by dropping digits starting from the right. In the case of atomic weights we will round off by dropping enough digits so that there is only one digit to the right of the decimal place. Thus 39.096 becomes 39.1 and 35.457 becomes 35.5.

The following rules govern the rounding-off process:

1. When the digit dropped is less than 5, the next digit to the left remains unchanged. Thus 69.72 becomes 69.7, and 12.011 becomes 12.0.

2. When the digit dropped is greater than 5, the value of the next digit to the left is increased by 1. Thus 65.38 becomes 65.4 and 35.457 becomes 35.5.

3. When the digit dropped is exactly 5, 1 is added to the digit on the left if that digit is odd but nothing is added if that digit is even. Thus 95.95 becomes 96.0 and 51.75 becomes 51.8, but 55.85 becomes 55.8 and 51.65 becomes 51.6.

Significant Figures

Before we proceed further with calculations, it is desirable that we consider the question: To how many decimal places, if any, should we report the answer to a problem? In other words, we would like to know how many *significant figures* our answer should contain. A significant figure is one that is reasonably reliable. Suppose you have a yardstick which is divided into 36 one-inch units and suppose each inch is divided into tenths of an inch, but there are no smaller divisions. Now suppose you wish to measure the length of a table top using this yardstick. You can read the stick accurately to tenths of an inch. Thus, if the length of the table fell exactly on the twenty-eighth and two-tenths mark, you could say the length was 28.2 in. All three of these numbers would be accurate, all three would be significant, and you would say that you had measured the length to *three significant figures*. Suppose, however, that the length of the table doesn't fall exactly on the 28.2 mark but falls somewhere between 28.2 and 28.3. You *estimate* that it falls two-tenths of the distance between 28.2 and 28.3, and you report the length as 28.22. The last digit in this four-digit number is not exact because you had to estimate its value. So your answer still has only three absolutely significant figures, 28.2. If you were asked to report the length to the strictly significant figures only, you would report 28.2, not 28.22. However, experience has shown that estimates of the sort that you made are so close to being exact that they are considered to be significant and can be recorded as such. In other words, in the average careful measurement which involves taking a reading on a graduated scale of discernible length or width, the first estimated digit is considered to be significant and can be recorded. So, under ordinary circumstances, you would be justified in reporting the length of the table top as 28.22 in.

Suppose that this table whose top you have measured happens to stand end to end with a fine stainless-steel bench which you have just received from the National Bureau of Standards. The top of this bench has been carefully machined and has been measured by the Bureau of Standards with a very accurately graduated rule and is certified to be exactly 31.964 in. in length. The Bureau of Standards measurement is of such precision that all five digits in the number 31.964 are significant. Now you are asked to report the combined length of your table and the bench. The question is, will the combined length be reported as 60.184 in. (31.964 + 28.22) or 60.18 in.? The answer is 60.18 in. The rule is that the sum can have no more significant figures than the least significant of its parts. In other words, the sum is no more accurate than its least accurate part.

Now suppose you wish to calculate the area of the above table top. You have already found its length to be 28.22 in. You measure the width and report it, justifiably, as 20.16 in. To get the area in square inches you multiply 28.22 × 20.16 and get 568.9152. The question is, what figure shall you report? The answer is 568.9 sq in., and the rule is that the product shall contain no more significant figures than are present in the multiplier with the least number. In other words, the product can be no more exact than the least exact multiplier. By the same rule the product of 1.56 × 1.78 is reported as 2.78, not as 2.7768. Only three digits are significant, so 2.7768 has been rounded off to 2.78 in accordance with the rules given on page 23.

In division also, we apply the same rule, namely, that the answer can be no more accurate than the least accurate of the terms involved in the operation. It follows, therefore, that the quotient obtained when 76.2 is divided by 47.24 is 1.61 and not 1.613. The quotient obtained when *exactly* 200 is divided by *exactly* 3 is 66.66 . . . 6, because, if the 200 is exactly 200 and the 3 is exactly 3, the numbers can be written 200.000 . . . 0 and 3.0000 . . . 0, respectively. In other words, a whole number has, in reality, an unlimited number of significant figures. The question of significance comes into the picture only when the number is the result, either directly or indirectly, of a physical measurement.

The number 0.00134, assuming that it does in fact represent, correctly, some measured value, has three significant figures, while the number 13.40 has four significant figures. Zeros to the left of a group of digits are not counted as significant figures but zeros to the right are. The zeros at the left serve only to locate the decimal point. The quotient obtained when 0.00134 is divided by 0.023 would be reported as 0.057, not 0.0573, because 0.023 has only two significant figures.

Since 0.00134 has three significant figures, 1.34×10^{-3}, which is equal to 0.00134, also has three significant figures. Likewise 1.5×10^{-20} has two significant figures, and the product of 2.32 and 1.5×10^{-20} will be 3.5×10^{-20}.

The number 6.023×10^{23} has four significant figures. It illustrates the fact that a more realistic picture of the degree of precision can be conveyed by writing large numbers in exponential form.

The question may arise as to why a number as small as 1.22×10^{-15} moles can have as many significant figures as the larger number, 235 g/mole. The answer is that, even though, in the first number, the unit 1×10^{-15}, is very small, we are certain that we have 1.22 such units (not 1.2 or 1.223). In the number, 235, the unit is large, but we are only certain that we have 235 of these units. In an exponential number the exponential term defines the unit of measure while the non-exponential term defines the number of these units; the latter determines the significant figures.

The upshot of all this discussion is that the answer obtained in multiplication or division of fractional or mixed numbers should never have any more digits than the number with the least number of significant digits. The answer obtained in addition or subtraction should never have any more digits to the right of the decimal point than does the number with the least digits to the right of the decimal point.

Certain refinements of the above rules must be considered in specific cases, but they need not concern us in this book.

The answers to all problems in this book are rounded off to the nearest significant figure. It should be stated, also, that all answers in this book have been obtained by slide-rule calculation and are, accordingly, subject to the normal chance of slight variation present in all slide-rule calculations. A student should never feel that he must duplicate the answer to the problem exactly. The correct method of solution is more important than the identically correct answer.

A slide rule should be used when solving problems. Longhand calculations are much too laborious and time-consuming.

Calculation of the Formula of a Compound

Problems

5.1 It was found that 56 g of iron combined with 32 g of sulfur. Calculate the formula of the compound that was formed.

SOLUTION: The formula of a compound gives the number of moles of atoms of each element in one mole of the compound. The atomic weight of iron is 56 and of sulfur is 32. Therefore, 56 g is 1 mole of Fe and 32 g is 1 mole of S. Therefore, Fe and S are combined in the ratio of 1 mole of Fe to 1 mole of S. Since 1 mole of iron atoms is represented by the symbol, Fe, and 1 mole of sulfur atoms by the symbol, S, the empirical formula for the compound, iron sulfide, is FeS.

5.2 When heated, 433.22 g of a pure compound yielded 401.22 g of mercury and 32 g of oxygen. Calculate the empirical formula of the compound.

SOLUTION: To find the number of moles of atoms of each element present, we will divide the weight of each element by the weight of 1 mole of atoms of the element, that is, by the atomic weight of that element.

$$\frac{401.22 \text{ g of Hg}}{200.61 \text{ g of Hg per mole of Hg}} = 2 \text{ moles of Hg}$$

$$\frac{32 \text{ g of O}}{16 \text{ g of O per mole of O}} = 2 \text{ moles of O}$$

The formula would thus appear to be Hg_2O_2. However, since we are interested in getting the simplest formula (the empirical formula), we will take the simplest ratio. Since 2 is to 2 as 1 is to 1, the empirical formula is HgO.

5.3 When burned, 4.04 g of magnesium, combined with 2.66 g of oxygen to form 6.70 g of magnesium oxide. Calculate the empirical formula of the oxide.

SOLUTION: To find the number of moles of Mg in 6.70 g of magnesium oxide we will divide the weight in grams of the magnesium by the gram-atomic weight of Mg and to find the number of moles of O we will divide the weight in grams of the oxygen by the gram-atomic weight of O.

$$\text{moles of Mg} = \frac{4.04 \text{ g of Mg}}{24.3 \text{ g per mole of Mg}} = 0.166 \text{ mole of Mg}$$

$$\text{moles of O} = \frac{2.66 \text{ g of O}}{16.0 \text{ g per mole of O}} = 0.166 \text{ mole of O}$$

Therefore, the magnesium and oxygen are combined in the ratio of 0.166 mole of Mg to 0.166 mole of O. But 0.166 is to 0.166 as 1 is to 1. Therefore, the simplest formula is MgO. The formula represents the simplest *whole-number* ratio of the moles. In this case the simplest ratio is 1 to 1.

5.4   A pure compound was found on analysis to contain 31.9% potassium, 28.9% chlorine, and 39.2% oxygen. Calculate its empirical formula.

SOLUTION: To say that a compound contains 31.9% potassium, 28.9% chlorine, and 39.2% oxygen is equivalent to saying that 100 g of the compound contain 31.9 g of potassium, 28.9 g of chlorine, and 39.2 g of oxygen. Therefore, to find the number of moles of each element in a mole of the compound, we will divide the per cent of each element by its atomic weight.

$$\text{K} = \frac{31.9 \text{ g of K}}{39.1 \text{ g/mole of K}} = 0.815 \text{ mole}$$

$$\text{Cl} = \frac{28.9 \text{ g of Cl}}{35.5 \text{ g/mole of Cl}} = 0.815 \text{ mole}$$

$$\text{O} = \frac{39.2 \text{ g of O}}{16 \text{ g/mole of O}} = 2.45 \text{ moles}$$

The mole ratio of K to Cl to O is 0.815 to 0.815 to 2.45. To simplify this, we divide all three of these numbers by the smallest.

$$\text{K} = \frac{0.815}{0.815} = 1 \qquad \text{Cl} = \frac{0.815}{0.815} = 1 \qquad \text{O} = \frac{2.45}{0.815} = 3$$

The simplest formula of the compound is, therefore, $KClO_3$.

5.5   A sample of 2.12 g of copper was heated in oxygen until no further change took place. The resulting oxide weighed 2.65 g. Calculate the empirical formula of the oxide.

5.6 It was found that 10.0 g of a pure compound contains 3.65 g of K, 3.33 g of Cl, and 3.02 g. of O. Calculate the empirical formula of the compound.*

5.7 A compound contains 29.1% sodium, 40.5% sulfur, and 30.4% oxygen. What is its empirical formula?

5.8 In the laboratory 2.38 g of copper combined with 1.19 g of sulfur. In a duplicate experiment 3.58 g of copper combined with 1.80 g of sulfur. Are these results in agreement with the law of definite composition?*

5.9 A compound was found on analysis to contain 21.6% magnesium, 27.9% phosphorus, and 50.5% oxygen. Calculate the empirical formula of the compound.

5.10 Five pure chemical compounds, when carefully analyzed, gave the results shown below. Calculate the empirical formula for each compound.

*(a) 621.6 g of lead; 64.0 g of oxygen.

(b) 2.24 g of iron; 0.96 g of oxygen.

*(c) 58.5% carbon; 4.1% hydrogen; 26.0% oxygen; 11.4% nitrogen.

(d) 52.3% carbon; 13.0% hydrogen; 34.7% oxygen.

*(e) 14.0% potassium; 9.7% aluminium; 30.2% silicon; 46.1% oxygen.

5.11 Calculate the formula weight of KCl.

SOLUTION: The formula weight is the sum of the atomic weights of the atoms represented by the formula. The atomic weight of K is 39.1. The atomic weight of Cl is 35.5.

$$39.1 + 35.5 = 74.6$$

5.12 Calculate the formula weight of $KClO_3$.

SOLUTION: The formula shows that $KClO_3$ is made up of potassium, chlorine, and oxygen combined in the ratio of 1 atom of potassium to 1 atom of chlorine to 3 atoms of oxygen. The formula weight is the sum of the weights of the atoms represented by the formula.

$$1\ K = 39.1$$
$$1\ Cl = 35.5$$
$$3\ O = \underline{48.0}$$
$$\text{formula weight} = 122.6$$

5.13 Calculate the formula weight of $Al_2(SO_4)_3$.

SOLUTION: The chemical formula, $Al_2(SO_4)_3$, indicates that aluminum sulfate is made up of aluminum, sulfur, and oxygen combined in the ratio of 2 atoms of aluminum to 3 atoms of sulfur to 12 atoms of oxygen. The SO_4^{--} radical is enclosed in parentheses with a subscript 3 outside the parentheses. This means that the radical is taken three times. The subscript 2 applies only to the aluminum atom; the subscript 3 applies only to the SO_4 radical.

$$2\ Al = 54$$
$$3\ S = 96.3$$
$$12\ O = 192$$
$$\text{formula weight} = \overline{342.3}$$

5.14 What is the weight of a mole of H_2SO_4?

SOLUTION: A mole is the weight in grams of the elements represented by the formula of a substance. Therefore, to find the weight of a mole of H_2SO_4 we simply find the sum of the gram-atomic weights of its constituent atoms.

$$2\ H = 2\ g$$
$$1\ S = 32.1\ g$$
$$4\ O = 64.0\ g$$
$$\text{mole of } H_2SO_4 = \overline{98.1\ g}$$

5.15 Calculate the weight of 0.0200 mole of $K_2Cr_2O_7$.

SOLUTION: One mole of $K_2Cr_2O_7$ is 294.2 g.

$$0.0200 \text{ mole} \times 294.2 \text{ g/mole} = 5.88 \text{ g}$$

5.16 What fraction of a mole of CH_4 is 7 g of CH_4?

SOLUTION: One mole of CH_4 is 16.0 g.

$$\frac{7 \text{ g of } CH_4}{16 \text{ g of } CH_4/1 \text{ mole of } CH_4} = \frac{7}{16} \text{ mole of } CH_4$$

5.17 An amount of 20 g of NH_3 is what fraction of a mole of NH_3?

5.18 What fraction of a mole of CO is 12.0 g of CO?*

5.19 An amount of 120 g of CO_2 is how many moles of CO_2?

5.20 How many moles of Na_2SO_4 are there in 240 g of Na_2SO_4?*

5.21 How many moles of P are there in 2.4 moles of P_4O_{10}?

SOLUTION: The formula P_4O_{10} shows that 1 mole of P_4O_{10} contains 4 moles of P.

$$2.4 \text{ moles of } P_4O_{10} \times \frac{4 \text{ moles of P}}{1 \text{ mole of } P_4O_{10}} = 9.6 \text{ moles of P}$$

5.22 How many moles of S are there in 265/310.3 moles of As_2S_5?

SOLUTION: 1 mole of As_2S_5 contains 5 moles of S.

$$\frac{265}{310.3} \text{ moles of } As_2S_5 \times \frac{5 \text{ moles of S}}{1 \text{ mole of } As_2S_5} = 4.27 \text{ moles S}$$

5.23 How many moles of C are there in 0.283 mole of $K_4Fe(CN)_6$?

5.24 How many moles of H are there in 8.6 moles of N_2H_4?*

5.25 How many moles of CCl_4 will contain 2.4 moles of Cl?

SOLUTION:

$$\frac{2.4 \text{ moles of Cl}}{4 \text{ moles of Cl}/1 \text{ mole of } CCl_4} = 0.60 \text{ mole of } CCl_4$$

5.26 How many moles of C_3H_8 will contain 23 moles of H?

5.27 How many molecules are there in 2.70 moles of H_2S?

SOLUTION: One mole of H_2S contains 6.023×10^{23} molecules.

$$2.70 \text{ moles of } H_2S \times \frac{6.023 \times 10^{23} \text{ molecules of } H_2S}{1 \text{ mole of } H_2S}$$

$$= 1.62 \times 10^{24} \text{ molecules}$$

5.28 How many molecules are there in 0.0372 moles of CO?*

5.29 How many moles of CH_4 will contain 4.31×10^{25} molecules of CH_4?

SOLUTION:

$$\frac{4.31 \times 10^{25} \text{ molecules of } CH_4}{6.023 \times 10^{23} \text{ molecules of } CH_4/\text{mole of } CH_4} = 71.5 \text{ moles of } CH_4$$

5.30 How many moles of NH_3 will contain 5.16×10^{20} molecules of NH_3?

5.31 How many molecules of SO_2 are there in 200 g of SO_2?

SOLUTION: The molecular weight of SO_2 is 64.1. Therefore, 200 g of SO_2 is 200/64.1 moles of SO_2.

$$\frac{200}{64.1} \text{ moles of SO}_2 \times 6.023 \times 10^{23} \text{ molecules/mole of SO}_2$$

$$= 1.88 \times 10^{24} \text{ molecules}$$

5.32 How many molecules of CH_4 are there in 1.25 g of CH_4?*

5.33 How many grams of CO_2 will contain 5.10×10^{24} molecules of CO_2?

5.34 Calculate the weight in grams of 9.00×10^{22} molecules of SO_3.*

5.35 The weight of 2.60 moles of a compound is 312 g. Calculate the molecular weight of the compound.

SOLUTION: The molecular weight is the weight in grams of 1 mole.

$$\frac{312 \text{ g}}{2.60 \text{ moles}} = 120 \text{ g/mole}$$

$$\therefore \quad \text{molecular weight} = 120$$

5.36 A 6.2 mole sample of a compound weighed 105.4 g. Calculate the molecular weight of the compound.

5.37 A 0.040 mole sample of a compound weighed 1.2 g. Calculate the molecular weight of the compound.*

5.38 How many grams of sulfur are there in 2.20 moles of H_2S?

SOLUTION: One mole of H_2S contains 1 mole of S. One mole of S weighs 32.1 g.

$$2.20 \text{ moles of H}_2\text{S} \times \frac{1 \text{ mole of S}}{1 \text{ mole of H}_2\text{S}} \times \frac{32.1 \text{ g of S}}{1 \text{ mole of S}} = 70.6 \text{ g of S}$$

Since it is obvious that one mole of H_2S contains 32.1 g of S, the second factor in the above equation can be omitted to give

$$2.20 \text{ moles of H}_2\text{S} \times \frac{32.1 \text{ g of S}}{1 \text{ mole of H}_2\text{S}} = 70.6 \text{ g of S}$$

5.39 How many grams of sulfur are there in 1.67 moles of P_4S_3?

5.40 How many moles of SiO_2 will contain 50.0 g of oxygen?*

5.41 How many moles of O are there in 182 g of $KClO_3$?

SOLUTION:

$$\frac{182 \text{ g of KClO}_3}{122.6 \text{ g of KClO}_3/\text{mole of KClO}_3} \times \frac{3 \text{ moles of O}}{1 \text{ mole of KClO}_3}$$

$$= 4.46 \text{ moles of O}$$

5.42 How many moles of S are there in 0.0142 g of CS_2?

5.43 How many grams of Sb_2S_3 will contain 4.80 moles of S.*

5.44 How many grams of oxygen are there in 120 g of CuO?

SOLUTION: One mole of CuO contains 1 mole of O.
Therefore, moles of O = moles of CuO.
The formula weight of CuO is 79.5. Therefore, 120 g of CuO is
120/79.5 moles of CuO. Therefore, there are 120/79.5 moles of O.

$$\frac{120}{79.5} \text{ moles of O} \times \frac{16.0 \text{ g of O}}{1 \text{ mole of O}} = 24.2 \text{ g of O}$$

The entire calculation can be carried out in one operation.

$$\frac{120 \text{ g of CuO}}{79.5 \text{ g of CuO/mole of CuO}} \times \frac{1 \text{ mole of O}}{1 \text{ mole of CuO}}$$

$$\times \frac{16.0 \text{ g of O}}{1 \text{ mole of O}} = 24.2 \text{ g of O}$$

5.45 How many grams of phosphorus are there in 160 g of P_4O_{10}?

SOLUTION: One mole of P_4O_{10} contains 4 moles of P. Moles of
P = 4 × moles of P_4O_{10}.

$$\frac{160 \text{ g of P}_4O_{10}}{284 \text{ g of P}_4O_{10}/\text{mole of P}_4O_{10}} = \frac{160}{284} \text{ mole of P}_4O_{10}$$

$$\text{moles of P} = \frac{4 \times 160}{284}$$

$$\frac{4 \times 160}{284} \text{ mole of P} \times \frac{31.0 \text{ g of P}}{1 \text{ mole of P}} = 69.8 \text{ g of P}$$

The solution, in one operation, is

$$\frac{160 \text{ g of P}_4O_{10}}{284 \text{ g of P}_4O_{10}/\text{mole of P}_4O_{10}} \times \frac{4 \text{ moles of P}}{1 \text{ mole of P}_4O_{10}}$$

$$\times \frac{31.0 \text{ g of P}}{1 \text{ mole of P}} = 69.8 \text{ g of P}$$

5.46 How many grams of S are there in 0.163 g of $Na_2S_2O_3$?

5.47 How many grams of oxygen are there in 1.64 g of $K_2Cr_2O_7$?*

5.48 How many grams of SO_3 will contain 2.00 g of oxygen?

5.49 Calculate the per cent of carbon in CO_2.

SOLUTION: By definition, per cent means parts per 100 parts by weight. So all we need do in this problem is find how many grams of C there are in 100 g of CO_2; the answer will then be the per cent of C in pure CO_2. A more general definition of per cent is that it is the ratio of the number of parts by weight of the particular thing you want to find to the parts by weight of the whole thing. That is,

$$\text{per cent of C in } CO_2 = \frac{\text{weight of the C in } CO_2}{\text{weight of the } CO_2}$$

A mole of CO_2 weighs 44.0 g and contains 12.0 g of C. Therefore,

$$\text{per cent of C in } CO_2 = \frac{12.0 \text{ g of C}}{44.0 \text{ g of } CO_2} = 0.273$$

This gives a decimal (fractional) per cent. To change this to the standard notation, we simply multiply by 100%. Doing the whole calculation in one operation,

$$\text{per cent of C in } CO_2 = \frac{12.0}{44.0} \times 100\% = 27.3\%$$

The general form of this relationship is:

per cent of an element in a compound

$$= \frac{\text{weight of the element in the compound}}{\text{formula weight of the compound}} \times 100\%$$

5.50 Calculate the per cent of oxygen in:
(a) $Fe_2(SO_4)_3$
*(b) $(NH_4)_2CO_3$

5.51 What is the per cent of chromium in $K_2Cr_2O_7$?

5.52 For the compound $C_6H_5NO_2$ calculate:
(a) moles of $C_6H_5NO_2$ in 200 g of $C_6H_5NO_2$
(b) grams of C in 5.00 moles of $C_6H_5NO_2$
(c) grams of C in 200 g of $C_6H_5NO_2$
(d) grams of C per 10.0 g of N
(e) moles of O in 150 g of $C_6H_5NO_2$
(f) moles of $C_6H_5NO_2$ which contain 5.0 g of N
(g) grams of $C_6H_5NO_2$ which contain 0.500 mole of C
(h) molecules of $C_6H_5NO_2$ in 3.00 g of $C_6H_5NO_2$

(i)   atoms of C in 3.00 g of $C_6H_5NO_2$

(j)   the per cent of carbon

(k)   atoms of N per atom of C

(l)   grams of H per gram of C

(m)   grams of C per mole of H

5.53 How many pounds of combined sulfur are there in 600 lb of Na_2SO_3?

SOLUTION: The formula, Na_2SO_3, tells us that one mole of the compound contains 2 moles of Na, 1 mole of S, and 3 moles of O. Since the atomic weights of Na, S, and O are 23.0, 32.1, and 16.0, respectively, the formula weight of Na_2SO_3 is 126.1. That means that the 3 elements are combined in the ratio of 46.0 parts by weight of Na, to 32.1 parts by weight of S, to 48.0 parts by weight of O to give 126.1 parts by weight of Na_2SO_3. In other words, 126.1 parts by weight of Na_2SO_3 will contain 32.1 parts by weight of S. Now it doesn't matter whether we express the parts by weight as grams or pounds or tons, as long as we use the same units throughout. That is, 126.1 g of Na_2SO_3 will contain 32.1 g of sulfur, 126.1 lb of Na_2SO_3 will contain 32.1 lb of sulfur, while 126.1 tons of Na_2SO_3 will contain 32.1 tons of sulfur. It makes no difference what units of weight we use; it is always true that 126.1 parts by weight of Na_2SO_3 will contain 32.1 parts of the same unit of weight of S, and $32.1/126.1 \times$ any weight of Na_2SO_3 = weight of S. Therefore,

$$\frac{32.1}{126.1} \times 600 \text{ lb} = 153 \text{ lb}$$

5.54 How many tons of Fe_2O_3 will contain 12.0 tons of Fe?*

5.55 Dealer A sells NaClO bleach at 80 cents per pound of NaClO content. Dealer B sells the same identical bleach at $1.00 per pound of ClO content. Which dealer offers the better bargain?

5.56 The element M forms the chloride, MCl_4. This chloride contains 75.0% chlorine. Calculate the atomic weight of M, knowing that the atomic weight of chlorine is 35.5.*

5.57 s The elements X and Y form a compound which is 40% X and 60% Y by weight. The atomic weight of X is twice that of Y. What is the empirical formula of the compound?

5.58 s The metal M forms two chlorides, MCl_a and MCl_b. MCl_a contains 50.9 weight per cent M and 49.1% Cl. MCl_b contains 46.4% M and 53.6% Cl. The atomic weight of Cl is 35.5. Calculate the atomic weight of M and the formulas of the two chlorides.

SOLUTION: a and b are small whole numbers. Calculate the ratio, b/a. The values of a and b and the atomic weight of M can then be calculated.

5.59 s A sample of pure NaCl contains 38.97 weight per cent of sodium. The relative abundance (mole per cent) of the two chlorine isotopes in the sample are: ^{35}Cl, atomic mass 35.00, 80%; ^{37}Cl, atomic mass 37.00, 20%. The sample contains the two isotopes, ^{22}Na, atomic mass 22.00, and ^{23}Na, atomic mass 23.00. Calculate the relative abundance of the two sodium isotopes.

5.60 s Three pure compounds are formed when 1-gram portions of element X combine with, respectively, 0.472 g, 0.630 g and 0.789 g of element Z. The first compound has the formula, X_2Z_3. What are the empirical formulas of the other two compounds? How does the atomic weight of X compare with that of Z?

6 The Gas Laws

Boyle's Law

We know from experience that if pressure is applied to any gas, to the air in a football, basketball, or tennis ball, for example, the volume of the gas will be decreased. As the pressure goes *up* the volume goes *down;* that is an *inverse proportion*. If we double the pressure, keeping the temperature constant, the volume will be reduced one half. We can state, therefore, that, at constant temperature, *the volume of a mass of gas is inversely proportional to the pressure*. This is *Boyle's law*. If we call P_1 the original or first pressure and V_1 the original or first volume, then if the pressure is increased to a second value, P_2, the volume will be decreased to a second value V_2. We can represent the change as follows:

The pressure goes up, from P_1 to P_2; the volume goes down, from V_1 to V_2. As already stated, this is an inverse proportion because as one increases the other decreases. That is,

$$\frac{P_2}{P_1} = \frac{V_1}{V_2}$$

or

$$\frac{V_1}{V_2} = \frac{P_2}{P_1}$$

This is the formula for Boyle's law. It tells us that, at constant temperature, *the volume of a mass of gas is inversely proportional to the pressure.*

Standard Pressure

The pressure on a gas can be recorded in a variety of ways, but it is usually expressed in units of millimeters of mercury. A pressure of 740 mm means the pressure which would be exerted by a column of liquid mercury 740 mm high. At sea level the average pressure of the atmosphere is 760 mm of mercury. A pressure of 760 mm is, therefore, called *standard pressure.* A pressure of 760 mm is referred to as *one atmosphere.*

The following problems will illustrate the application of Boyle's law.

Problems: Boyle's Law

6.1 A gas has a volume of 500 cc at a pressure of 700 mm of mercury. What volume will it occupy if the pressure is increased to 800 mm, the temperature remaining constant?

SOLUTION: One way of solving will be to substitute in the Boyle's law equation

$$\frac{V_1}{V_2} = \frac{P_2}{P_1}$$

The first volume, $V_1 = 500$ cc.

The second volume, V_2, is what we want to find.

The first pressure, $P_1 = 700$ mm.

The second pressure, $P_2 = 800$ mm.

Substituting these values in the formula, we have

$$\frac{500 \text{ cc}}{V_2} = \frac{800 \text{ mm}}{700 \text{ mm}}$$

Solving,

$$V_2 = \frac{500 \text{ cc} \times 700 \text{ mm}}{800 \text{ mm}} = 437 \text{ cc}$$

Solving by substitution in the Boyle's law formula is an acceptable method as long as we understand the formula in the first place and are careful to keep our values straight.

A second way of solving will be to reason that since the volume is going to be changed by the change in pressure, the new volume will be the result of a pressure effect on the old volume. That is,

new volume = old volume × a pressure effect

The "pressure effect" will be the ratio of 800 mm to 700 mm. We know, since the pressure has gone up from 700 to 800, that the volume must have gone down. That is, the answer (the new volume) must be less than 500 cc. If the new volume is going to be less than 500, the "pressure effect" by which we multiply the old volume (500 cc) in the formula

new volume = old volume × pressure effect

must be less than 1. But the pressure effect is the ratio of 800 mm to 700 mm. Now $800/700 = 1.14$, which is greater than 1, and $700/800 = 0.875$, which is less than 1. (If the numerator is greater than the denominator the value of the ratio is greater than 1. If the numerator is smaller than the denominator the value of the ratio is less than 1.) Therefore, to get the correct new volume, we will multiply 500 cc by 700 mm/800 mm. That is,

$$\text{new volume} = 500 \text{ cc} \times \frac{700 \text{ mm}}{800 \text{ mm}} = 437 \text{ cc}$$

This, you will notice, is exactly the same combination of terms as we obtain in the final step of our solution by substitution in the formula.

Of the two methods, the solution by reasoning is the more desirable one.

6.2   The volume of a gas is 800 liters at 750 mm and 20°C. What volume in liters will it occupy at 710 mm and 20°C?

6.3   The volume of a gas is 20 cu ft at 600 mm and 0°C. What volume in cu ft will it occupy at 1000 mm and 0°C?*

6.4   A mass of hydrogen gas has a volume of 1200 liters at a pressure of one atmosphere. To what value in atmospheres must the pressure be changed if the volume is to be reduced to 2.00 liters?

6.5   A steel cylinder in which compressed helium gas is kept has an interior volume of 1.20 cu ft. When it was opened and the gas was allowed to escape into a dry storage tank at a pressure of 800 mm, the gas occupied a volume of 420 cu ft. Under what pressure in mm was the helium gas stored in the cylinder?*

The Effect of Change of Temperature

When a gas is heated it expands. That is, when the temperature goes up the volume increases. This is *direct proportion,* so we can say that *the volume of a gas varies directly as the temperature.* When the temperature increases the volume increases. When the temperature decreases the volume decreases.

Absolute Zero

Suppose we were to take exactly 273 cc of some gas, helium for example, at exactly 0°C and at some constant pressure, say 750 mm. If we cool this gas, keeping the pressure constant, and note how the volume changes, the results obtained will be as summarized in the following table:

WHEN THE TEMPERATURE IS	THE VOLUME OF THE GAS IS
0°C	273 cc
−1°C	272 cc
−2°C	271 cc
−3°C	270 cc
−4°C	269 cc
−5°C	268 cc
−10°C	263 cc
−20°C	253 cc
−100°C	173 cc
−200°C	73 cc
−250°C	23 cc
−270°C	3 cc

Notice that the volume has decreased by $\frac{1}{273}$ of the volume at 0°C for each degree drop in temperature. If the volume were to keep on shrinking at the same rate, then at −273.15°, the volume would be zero. Since cooling below −273.15°C would, on the basis of these data, give a volume less than zero, and since it is reasonable to assume that there is no such thing as negative volume, it can be concluded that −273.15°C is the lowest temperature theoretically possible. Therefore, $-273.15°C$ is designated as *absolute zero*. (The value, $-273°$, is sufficiently accurate for all calculations in this book.) It is represented by the notation, $0°K$. K means degrees Kelvin. Notice that absolute zero is $273°$ below centigrade zero. Zero degrees centigrade is therefore $273°K$, and $273°C$ is $546°K$. In other words, to change centigrade temperature to absolute temperature expressed in degrees Kelvin we simply add $273°$ to the centigrade reading.

Charles's Law

If we had taken the 273 cc of helium gas at $0°C$ and heated it we would have found that, at $273°C$, the volume would have increased to 546 cc. That is, at $0°C$ the volume is 273 cc while at $273°C$ it is 546 cc, or just twice as great. But $0°C$ is the same as $273°K$ (absolute) and $273°C$ is the same as $546°K$. When we double the absolute temperature (from $273°K$ to $546°K$) we double the volume (from 273 cc to 546 cc). That means that *the volume of a mass of gas, at constant pressure, is directly proportional to the absolute temperature. This is Charles's law.* The formula for Charles's law is

$$\frac{V_1}{V_2} = \frac{T_1}{T_2}$$

Standard Temperature

Zero degrees centigrade is referred to as *standard temperature*. Standard temperature $(0°C)$ and standard pressure (760 mm) are commonly referred to by the notation STP.

Problems: Charles's Law

6.6 A gas occupies a volume of 200 cc at $0°C$ and 760 mm. What volume will it occupy at $100°C$ and 760 mm?

SOLUTION: Since the pressure is constant, this is a problem involving temperature change only. We can solve by substituting in the Charles's law formula,

$$\frac{V_1}{V_2} = \frac{T_1}{T_2}$$

$V_1 = 200 \text{ cc}; T_1 = 273°K \ (0 + 273°); T_2 = 373°K \ (100 + 273°).$

$$\frac{200 \text{ cc}}{V_2} = \frac{273°\text{K}}{373°\text{K}}$$

$$V_2 = \frac{200 \text{ cc} \times 373°\text{K}}{273°\text{K}} = 273 \text{ cc}$$

This problem can also be solved by applying the following logical reasoning: since the change of absolute temperature will change the volume, we can say that

new volume = old volume × a temperature effect

The *temperature effect* is the ratio of the old and new *absolute* temperatures. In this particular problem the temperature goes up. Therefore, the volume must increase. To get a larger volume, the old volume must be multiplied by a factor greater than 1. That means that the larger of the two absolute temperatures must go in the numerator. So we write

$$\text{new volume} = 200 \text{ cc} \times \frac{373°\text{K}}{273°\text{K}} = 273 \text{ cc}$$

6.7 The volume of a gas is 600 cc at 12°C. What volume will it occupy at 0°C, pressure remaining constant?

6.8 The volume of a gas is 20.0 cu ft at −20°C and 750 mm. What volume will it occupy at 20°C and 750 mm?*

6.9 A mass of helium gas occupies a volume of 100 liters at 20°C. If the volume occupied by the gas is tripled, to what must the temperature be changed in order to keep the pressure constant?

Change of Pressure and Temperature

By combining the formulas for Boyle's law and Charles's law we get the general formula expressing the change of volume with change of pressure and change of temperature.

(1) $$\frac{V_1}{V_2} = \frac{T_1 \times P_2}{T_2 \times P_1}$$

Equation (1) can be transposed to give Equation (2).

(2) $$\frac{V_1 P_1}{T_1} = \frac{V_2 P_2}{T_2}$$

We can also reason logically that

new volume = old volume × a temperature effect × a pressure effect

Using the combined formula or the combined logic we can calculate volume changes resulting from changes in both pressure and temperature.

It should be noted that no gases obey Boyle's and Charles's laws perfectly over all ranges of temperature and pressure; that is, no gases are "perfect." It will, however, be assumed in the problems in this book that all gases are perfect and that Boyle's and Charles's laws are obeyed.

Problems

6.10 The volume of a gas is 200 liters at 12°C and 750 mm. What volume will it occupy at 40°C and 720 mm?

SOLUTION:

$$12°C = 285°K$$
$$40°C = 313°K$$

new volume = old volume × temperature effect × pressure effect

Since the temperature increases, the volume must thereby be increased. Therefore the temperature effect is greater than 1, so the larger absolute temperature goes in the numerator. The pressure decreases, therefore the volume must be increased, so the larger pressure must go in the numerator of the pressure effect factor. This gives us the relation

$$\text{new volume} = 200 \text{ liters} \times \frac{313°K}{285°K} \times \frac{750 \text{ mm}}{720 \text{ mm}} = 229 \text{ liters}$$

We can also solve by substituting in the general formula

$$\frac{V_1}{V_2} = \frac{T_1}{T_2} \times \frac{P_2}{P_1}$$

$$\frac{200 \text{ liters}}{V_2} = \frac{285°K \times 720 \text{ mm}}{313°K \times 750 \text{ mm}}$$

$$V_2 = 200 \text{ liters} \times \frac{313°K \times 750 \text{ mm}}{285°K \times 720 \text{ mm}} = 229 \text{ liters}$$

6.11 The volume of a dry gas is 50.0 liters at 20°C and 742 mm. What volume will it occupy at STP?

6.12 At what temperature will a mass of gas whose volume is 150 liters at 12°C and 750 mm occupy a volume of 200 liters at a pressure of 730 mm?*

6.13 A gas in a 10.0 liter steel cylinder is under a pressure of 4.00 atm at 22.0°C. If the temperature is raised to 600°C what will be the pressure on the gas

NOTE: From the combined gas law formula

$$\frac{V_1 P_1}{T_1} = \frac{V_2 P_2}{T_2}$$

it follows that, when the volume is kept constant, the pressure exerted by a given mass of gas is directly proportional to the absolute temperature.

6.14 A mass of helium gas contained in a 700 ml vessel at 710 mm pressure and 22°C is transferred to a 1000 ml vessel at 110°C. What is the pressure in the 1000 ml vessel?*

6.15 s A cylinder contains helium gas at a pressure of 1470 lb per sq in. When a quantity of helium gas which occupies a volume of 4 liters at a pressure of 14.7 lb per sq in. is withdrawn, the pressure in the tank drops to 1400 lb per sq in. (Temperature remains constant.) Calculate the volume of the tank.

Molar Volume of a Gas. The Ideal Gas Law Equation.
Density of a Gas. Vapor Pressure.
Dalton's Law of Partial Pressures.
Graham's Law of Diffusion.

One gram-molecular weight (one mole) of any gas occupies a volume of 22.4 liters at standard temperature and pressure (0°C and 760 mm). The figure, 22.4 liters, is referred to as the *molar volume* or the *gram-molecular* volume. Since 1 mole of any gas occupies 22.4 liters at STP, it follows that the weight in grams of 22.4 liters of any gas at STP is the molecular weight of that gas.

Since one mole of any gas occupies a volume of 22.4 liters at STP, and since the gas laws apply equally to all gases, it follows that, *at the same temperature and pressure, equal volumes of all gases contain the same number of moles of gas.*

This leads to the conclusion that, *for different volumes of gases at the same temperature and pressure, the number of moles of a gas is directly proportional to the volume of that gas.* Thus, if at constant temperature and pressure, gas A occupies a volume of 100 liters and gas B occupies a volume of 50 liters, the number of moles of A is twice the number of moles of B.

It can also be concluded that at a given temperature and in a given volume of gas, the pressure is directly proportional to the number of moles of gas. Since the number of moles of gas in a given volume is the *molar concentration* of that gas, it can be stated that, *at a given temperature, the pressure exerted by a gas is directly proportional to its molar concentration.*

The fact that 1 mole of any gas occupies a volume of 22.4 liters at STP enables one, with the aid of Boyle's and Charles's laws, to calculate the weight of any volume of a gas and the volume of any weight of that gas under any conditions of temperature and pressure, provided, of course, that its true chemical formula and, hence, its true molecular weight is known.

It should be noted that He, Ar, Ne, Kr, and Xe are monatomic gases; their molecular weights equal their atomic weights. The other elementary gases, H_2, O_2, N_2, F_2, Cl_2, Br_2, and I_2, form diatomic molecules.

Problems

7.1 What volume in liters will 2.71 moles of He gas occupy at STP?

SOLUTION: The molar volume of a gas at STP is 22.4 liters. That means that 1 mole of He will occupy a volume of 22.4 liters at STP.

$$2.71 \text{ moles} \times \frac{22.4 \text{ liters}}{1 \text{ mole}} = 60.7 \text{ liters}$$

7.2 What volume in liters will 0.362 moles of CO gas occupy at STP?

7.3 A volume of 6.34 liters of CH_4 gas, measured at STP, is what fraction of a mole of CH_4?

SOLUTION: 22.4 liters of CH_4 at STP is 1 mole
Therefore, 6.34 liters is 6.34/22.4 mole = 0.283 mole

$$\frac{6.34 \text{ liters}}{22.4 \text{ liters/mole}} = 0.283 \text{ mole}$$

7.4 A volume of 50.0 liters of H_2S gas, measured at STP, is how many moles of H_2S?

SOLUTION:

$$\frac{50.0 \text{ liters}}{22.4 \text{ liters/mole}} = 2.23 \text{ moles}$$

7.5 How many moles are there in 18.3 liters of HF gas at STP?*

7.6 A volume of 65.2 liters of NO_2 gas, measured at STP, is how many moles of NO_2?

7.7   What volume in liters will 100 g of CH_4 gas occupy at STP?

SOLUTION: In solving this problem our first question is "How many *moles* of CH_4 are there?" We know that one mole of a gas occupies a volume of 22.4 liters at STP. Therefore, if we know how many moles of CH_4 gas there are in 100 g of CH_4, we can multiply this number of moles by 22.4 liters/mole.

The molecular weight of CH_4 is 16. Therefore, 100 g of CH_4 is 100/16 moles.

$$\frac{100}{16} \text{ moles} \times \frac{22.4 \text{ liters}}{1 \text{ mole}} = 140 \text{ liters}$$

The complete calculation, in one operation, is:

$$\frac{100 \text{ g of } CH_4}{16 \text{ g of } CH_4/\text{mole of } CH_4} \times \frac{22.4 \text{ liters of } CH_4}{1 \text{ mole of } CH_4} = 140 \text{ liters of } CH_4$$

7.8   What volume in liters will 40.0 g of HCl gas occupy at STP?*

7.9   Calculate the volume in liters of 0.853 g of CO gas at STP.

7.10   Calculate the weight in grams of 40.0 liters of NO gas at standard conditions.

SOLUTION: In solving this problem our first question is "How many *moles* of NO do we have?". If we know the number of moles, we can multiply this number of moles by the number of grams of NO in 1 mole.

22.4 liters of NO at STP is 1 mole. Therefore, 40.0 liters at STP is 40.0/22.4 moles of NO.

The molecular weight of NO is 30.

Therefore,

$$\frac{40.0}{22.4} \text{ moles of NO} \times \frac{30 \text{ g of NO}}{1 \text{ mole of NO}} = 53.6 \text{ g of NO}$$

The entire solution can be carried out in one operation, as follows:

$$\frac{40.0 \text{ liters of NO}}{22.4 \text{ liters of NO}/\text{mole of NO}} \times \frac{30 \text{ g of NO}}{1 \text{ mole of NO}} = 53.6 \text{ g of NO}$$

7.11   Calculate the weight in grams of 120 liters of CO_2 gas at STP.

7.12   A volume of 62.5 liters of C_2H_2 gas, measured at 0°C and 760 mm, will weigh how many grams?*

7.13 What volume will 65.0 g of NO gas occupy at 27.0°C and a pressure of 700 mm?

SOLUTION: We will first find the volume which 65.0 g of NO will occupy at STP in the manner described in Problem 7.7. We will then convert this volume from STP to 27.0°C and 700 mm by using the combined gas laws in the manner developed in Problem 6.10. The calculations, in one operation, are

$$\frac{65.0 \text{ g of NO}}{30 \text{ g of NO/mole}} \times \frac{22.4 \text{ liters}}{1 \text{ mole}} \times \frac{300°K}{273°K} \times \frac{760 \text{ mm}}{700 \text{ mm}} = 57.8 \text{ liters}$$

7.14 What volume in liters will 27.2 g of CH_4 gas occupy at $-13.0°C$ and 800 mm?

7.15 What volume in liters will 100 g of NH_3 gas occupy at 27.0°C and 730 mm?*

7.16 A quantity of C_2H_4 gas occupies a volume of 100 liters at 37°C and a pressure of 720 mm. Calculate the weight in grams of this gas.

SOLUTION: If we know the volume which this C_2H_4 will occupy at STP, we can then calculate its weight, since we know that 1 mole of C_2H_4 occupies a volume of 22.4 liters at STP.
We will first calculate the volume which 100 liters, measured at 37°C and 720 mm, will occupy at STP in the manner described in Problem 6.10. Knowing the volume at STP, we can calculate the weight of this volume of C_2H_4 in the manner described in Problem 7.10. The calculations, in one operation, are:

$$100 \text{ liters} \times \frac{273°K}{310°K} \times \frac{720 \text{ mm}}{760 \text{ mm}} \times \frac{1 \text{ mole of } C_2H_4}{22.4 \text{ liters}}$$
$$\times \frac{28 \text{ g of } C_2H_4}{1 \text{ mole of } C_2H_4} = 104 \text{ g of } C_2H_4$$

7.17 Calculate the weight in grams of 6.24 liters of CO gas measured at 22°C and 740 mm.

7.18 Calculate the weight in grams of 100 liters of SO_2 gas at 40.0°C and 740 mm.*

7.19 How many grams of nitrogen are there in 100 liters of NO measured at STP?

SOLUTION: In solving this problem we first ask "How many moles of NO are there?". Knowing the number of moles of NO we can easily calculate the number of grams of N, since 1 mole of NO contains 14 g of N. The formula, NO, tells us that there is 1 mole (1 gram-atom) of N in 1 mole of NO. One mole of N weighs 14 g.

100 liters of NO is 100/22.4 moles of NO and 100/22.4 moles of NO contain 100/22.4 moles of N.

$$\frac{100}{22.4} \text{ moles of N} \times \frac{14 \text{ g of N}}{1 \text{ mole of N}} = 62.5 \text{ g of N}$$

The solution, in one operation, is

$$\frac{100 \text{ liters of NO}}{22.4 \text{ liters of NO/mole of NO}} \times \frac{1 \text{ mole of N}}{1 \text{ mole of NO}}$$

$$\times \frac{14 \text{ g of N}}{1 \text{ mole of N}} = 62.5 \text{ g of N}$$

7.20 A volume of 65.0 liters of H_2S, measured at STP, contains how many grams of S?

7.21 How many liters of CO, measured at STP, will contain 10.0 g of oxygen?

SOLUTION:

$$\frac{10.0 \text{ g of O}}{16.0 \text{ g of O/mole of CO}} \times \frac{22.4 \text{ liters of CO}}{1 \text{ mole of CO}} = 14.0 \text{ liters of CO}$$

7.22 How many liters of SO_2, measured at STP, will contain 50.0 g of S?

7.23 A volume of 100 liters of CH_4 gas, measured at 35°C and 0.90 atm, contains how many grams of H?

SOLUTION:

$$100 \text{ liters of CH}_4 \times \frac{273°}{308°} \times \frac{0.90 \text{ atm}}{1.00 \text{ atm}} \times \frac{1 \text{ mole of CH}_4}{22.4 \text{ liters of CH}_4}$$

$$\times \frac{4 \text{ moles of H}}{1 \text{ mole of CH}_4} \times \frac{1 \text{ g of H}}{1 \text{ mole of H}} = 14 \text{ g of H}$$

7.24 A volume of 56.0 liters of C_3H_8 gas, measured at 160°C and 600 mm, contains how many grams of carbon?*

7.25 How many liters of C_2H_2 gas, measured at 25°C and 745 mm, will contain 10.0 g of carbon?

SOLUTION:

$$\frac{10.0 \text{ g of C}}{24.0 \text{ g of C/mole of C}_2\text{H}_2} \times \frac{22.4 \text{ liters of C}_2\text{H}_2}{1 \text{ mole of C}_2\text{H}_2}$$

$$\times \frac{298°}{273°} \times \frac{760 \text{ mm}}{745 \text{ mm}} = 10.4 \text{ liters of C}_2\text{H}_2$$

7.26 How many liters of SO_2 gas, measured at 85.0°C and 500 mm, will contain 52.5 g of oxygen?

7.27 A volume of 2.00 liters of a gas, measured at STP, weighs 5.71 g. Calculate the approximate molecular weight of the gas.

SOLUTION: The molecular weight of a gas is the weight in grams of 1 mole of the gas. One mole of a gas occupies a volume of 22.4 liters at STP. Therefore, the molecular weight of a gas is the weight in grams of 22.4 liters at STP.

$$\frac{5.71 \text{ g}}{2.00 \text{ liters}} \times \frac{22.4 \text{ liters}}{1 \text{ mole}} = 64.0 \text{ g/mole}$$

Since the gas laws are not exact, the molecular weight calculated in this manner is not exact.

7.28 A volume of 6.82 liters of a gas, measured at STP, weighed 9.15 g. Calculate the approximate molecular weight of the gas.*

7.29 A volume of 2.38 liters of a gas, measured at 97°C and 720 mm, weighed 2.81 g. Calculate the approximate molecular weight of the gas.

SOLUTION:

$$\frac{2.81 \text{ g}}{2.38 \text{ liters} \times \dfrac{273°}{370°} \times \dfrac{720 \text{ mm}}{760 \text{ mm}}} \times \frac{22.4 \text{ liters}}{1 \text{ mole}} = 37.8 \text{ g/mole}$$

7.30 A volume of 1.36 liters of a gas, measured at 22° and 740 mm, weighed 2.623 g. Calculate the approximate molecular weight of the gas.

7.31 Twelve liters of dry nitrogen gas, measured at 22°C and 741 mm, weighed 13.55 g. Calculate the formula for a molecule of nitrogen gas.*

7.32 What volume will 100 g of chlorine gas occupy at STP?

SOLUTION: The formula for a molecule of chlorine gas is Cl_2. The atomic weight of chlorine is 35.5 and its molecular weight is 71. Therefore, 100 g of Cl_2 gas is 100/71 moles and occupies a volume of 100/71 × 22.4 liters at STP.

7.33 Flask A contains 20.0 liters of CH_4 gas. Flask B contains 30.0 liters of CO gas. Each volume is measured at the same temperature and pressure. If flask A contains 6.18 moles of CH_4, how many moles of CO are there in flask B?

SOLUTION: At the same temperature and pressure, the number of moles of gas is directly proportional to the volume of the gas.

Since the volume of B is 1.50 times the volume of A the number of moles of CO in B will be 1.50 times the moles of CH_4 in A.

7.34 If 25.0 g of CH_4 gas occupy a volume of 30.0 liters at a certain temperature and pressure, what volume in liters will 50.0 g of CO_2 gas occupy at the same temperature and pressure?

7.35 A volume of 40.0 liters of pure O_2 gas, measured at a certain temperature and pressure, was found to contain 40.0 g of oxygen. A volume of 60 liters of CH_4 gas, measured at the same temperature and pressure, will contain how many grams of CH_4?*

7.36 Two gases, A and B, have molecular weights, M_A and M_B. Suppose a certain number of grams of A is placed in a 100-liter evacuated container and an equal number of grams of B is placed in another 100-liter evacuated container. The gases in both containers are at the same temperature. How are the pressures in the two containers related to the molecular weights of the two gases?

7.37 A certain number of grams of CO gas was placed in one evacuated container. An equal number of grams of CO_2 gas was placed in a second evacuated container whose volume was the same as that of the first. The temperature of the gas in each container was the same. The pressure of the CO was 20.0 mm. What was the pressure of the CO_2 gas?*

The Ideal Gas Law Equation, $PV = nRT$

As has already been stated, the combined effect on the volume of a gas of change of temperature and pressure can be expressed by the equation

$$(1) \qquad \frac{P_0 V_0}{T_0} = \frac{PV}{T}$$

This equation tells us that if we know the volume, V_0, which a specific amount of gas occupies at pressure, P_0, and absolute temperature, T_0, we can calculate the volume, V, which this mass of gas occupies at some other pressure, P, and temperature, T.

As has been pointed out in the early part of this chapter we *do know* that a specific amount, *one mole*, of *an ideal gas* occupies a volume of 22.4 liters at 273°K and 760 mm (1 atm). Since we are assuming in our calculations that all gases are ideal, we can state that *one mole* of *any gas* occupies a volume of *22.4 liters* at *273°K* and *760 mm*. That means that, in Equation (1) above, for one mole of any gas $V_0 = 22.4$ liter, $P_0 = 760$ mm, and $T_0 = 273°$. That means that, for one mole of any gas, P_0V_0/T_0 is always equal to (760 mm × 22.4 liters)/273 deg; that is, P_0V_0/T_0 is constant. If we calculate the value of this constant we find that, when P_0 is 760 mm,

$$\text{the constant} = \frac{22.4 \text{ liters}}{1 \text{ mole}} \times \frac{760 \text{ mm}}{273 \text{ deg}} = 62.4 \frac{\text{liters} \times \text{mm}}{\text{mole} \times \text{deg}}$$

When P_0 is 1 atm

$$\text{the constant} = \frac{22.4 \text{ liters}}{1 \text{ mole}} \times \frac{1 \text{ atm}}{273 \text{ deg}} = 0.082 \frac{\text{liters} \times \text{atm}}{\text{mole} \times \text{deg}}$$

If we call this constant R, then Equation (1) becomes

(2)
$$R = \frac{PV}{T}$$

It was stated that V_0 is the volume occupied by *one mole* at pressure P_0 and absolute temperature T_0. For n moles of gas the volume will be $n \times V_0$. Therefore, for n moles of gas,

(3)
$$\frac{PV}{T} = nR$$

and

(4)
$$PV = nRT$$

Equation (4) is the *Ideal Gas Law Equation*.

Problems

7.38 What volume will 45.0 g of CH_4 gas occupy at 27°C and 800 mm?

SOLUTION: We will solve by substituting in the equation, $PV = nRT$.

$$n = \text{moles of } CH_4 = \frac{45.0 \text{ g}}{16.0 \text{ g/mole}} = \frac{45.0}{16.0} \text{ moles}$$

$$P = 800 \text{ mm}$$

$$T = 300°K$$

$$V = \frac{nRT}{P} = \frac{45.0}{16.0} \text{ moles} \times \frac{62.4 \dfrac{\text{liters} \times \text{mm}}{\text{mole} \times \text{deg}} \times 300 \text{ deg}}{800 \text{ mm}}$$

$$= 65.6 \text{ liters}$$

Note that moles, mm, and deg cancel.

7.39 The hydrogen gas in a 2.00-liter steel cylinder at 25°C was under a pressure of 4.00 atm. How many moles of H_2 were in the cylinder?

SOLUTION:

$$PV = nRT$$

$$n = \frac{PV}{RT} = \frac{4.00 \text{ atm} \times 2.00 \text{ liters}}{0.082 \dfrac{\text{liters} \times \text{atm}}{\text{mole} \times \text{deg}} \times 298 \text{ deg}} = 0.328 \text{ mole}$$

Note that liters, atm, and deg cancel.

7.40 What pressure, in atmospheres, will 26.0 g of He gas exert when placed in a 3.24-liter steel cylinder at 200°C?

SOLUTION:

$$PV = nRT$$

$$P = \frac{nRT}{V} = \frac{26.0 \text{ g}}{\dfrac{4 \text{ g}}{1 \text{ mole}}} \times 0.082 \frac{\text{liters} \times \text{atm}}{\text{mole} \times \text{deg}} \times \frac{473 \text{ deg}}{3.24 \text{ liters}}$$

$$= 77.7 \text{ atm}$$

Note that g, liters, deg, and moles cancel.

7.41 Calculate the weight in grams of the pure H_2S gas contained in a 60.0-liter cylinder at 20°C under a pressure of 2.00 atm.

SOLUTION:

$$PV = nRT$$

$$n = \frac{PV}{RT}$$

$$n = \text{moles of } H_2S = \frac{\text{g of } H_2S}{34.1 \text{ g of } H_2S/\text{mole}}$$

$$\frac{\text{g of } H_2S}{34.1 \text{ g/mole}} = \frac{PV}{RT} = \frac{2.00 \text{ atm} \times 60.0 \text{ liters}}{0.082 \dfrac{\text{liters} \times \text{atm}}{\text{mole} \times \text{deg}} \times 293 \text{ deg}}$$

$$\text{g of } H_2S = \frac{34.1 \text{ g}}{\text{mole}} \times \frac{2.00 \text{ atm} \times 60.0 \text{ liters}}{0.082 \dfrac{\text{liters} \times \text{atm}}{\text{mole} \times \text{deg}} \times 293 \text{ deg}}$$

$$= 170 \text{ g}$$

Note that mole, atm, liters, and deg cancel.

7.42 Calculate the weight in grams of 200 liters of CO_2 gas at 20°C and 746 mm.

7.43 Calculate the volume in liters occupied by 200 g of CO gas at 22°C and 740 mm.*

7.44 A 25.0-liter cylinder contains 14.2 moles of helium gas at 40°C. What is the pressure in atmospheres of the helium gas?

7.45 How many grams of carbon are there in 22.4 liters of CH_4 gas at 2 atm and 546°K?*

7.46 A cylinder containing 85 g of steam at 200°C shows a pressure of 4 atm. What is the volume of the cylinder in liters?

7.47 A storage tank contains 20.0 liters of dry oxygen gas at 27°C and 60.0 atm pressure. Calculate the weight in kilograms of the oxygen gas in the tank.*

7.48 A volume of 22.40 liters of H_2S gas measured at 273°C and 4.000 atm will contain how many molecules of H_2S?

7.49 A volume of 120 cc of a dry gaseous compound, measured at 22°C and 742 mm, weighed 0.820 g. Calculate the approximate molecular weight of the gas.*

7.50 A rigid 40-liter container is filled with N_2 gas at a pressure of 2.5 atm at 27°C. If a valve on the container is opened when the barometer reads 570 mm, how many grams of N_2 gas will escape into the open air? (T remains constant at 27°C; no air diffuses into the container.) What volume will this N_2 gas occupy in the air?

Densities of Gases

The weight of a definite volume of gas is referred to as the *density* of the gas. The definite volume that is commonly used in expressing the density of a gas is either 22.4 liters or 1 liter. In the first instance the density of any gas is the weight in grams of 22.4 liters of that gas; it is expressed as so many grams per 22.4 liters. But the weight in grams of 22.4 liters at STP is the gram-molecular weight of the gas. It follows, therefore, that the density of a gas at STP in grams per 22.4 liters is equal numerically to its gram-molecular weight. Since the density of any gas at STP is equal, numerically, to its molecular weight, it follows that *the densities of two gases at the same temperature and pressure are to each other as their molecular weights.*

The density of a gas in grams per liter at STP is obtained very simply by dividing the gram-molecular weight by 22.4 liters.

The density of a gas can also be expressed in units of moles per liter.

Problems

7.51 What is the density of C_2H_2 gas at STP?

SOLUTION: The density of a gas is the weight of a unit volume of the gas. The volume normally selected is either the molar volume, 22.4 liters, or 1 liter. One mole of C_2H_2 weighs 26.0 g and occupies 22.4 liters. Therefore, the density is 26.0 g per 22.4 liters or 1.16 g/liter.

7.52 Calculate the density of CO gas at STP in g/liter.*

7.53 Calculate the density of SO_2 gas at 40°C and 730 mm.

SOLUTION: Density of a gas is commonly expressed in units of g/liter. Therefore, to find the density of SO_2, we will find the weight in grams of 1 liter at 40°C and 730 mm. We will first find how many moles there are in 1 liter of SO_2 at 40°C and 730 mm by using the formula

$$n = \frac{PV}{RT}$$

To find grams of SO_2 we will then multiply n moles by 64 g/mole (the gram-molecular weight of SO_2).

Since g of $SO_2 = n$ moles × 64 g/mole,

$$\text{g of } SO_2 = \frac{PV}{RT} \times \frac{64 \text{ g of } SO_2}{1 \text{ mole}}$$

Substituting:

$$\text{g of } SO_2 = \frac{730 \text{ mm} \times 1 \text{ liter}}{62.4 \dfrac{\text{liters} \times \text{mm}}{\text{mole} \times \text{deg}} \times 313 \text{ deg}} \times \frac{64.0 \text{ g of } SO_2}{1 \text{ mole}} = 2.39 \text{ g}$$

The density is 2.39 g/liter.

7.54 Calculate the density of CH_4 gas at 120°C and 0.600 atm.

7.55 At a given temperature and pressure, which is heavier, 20.0 liters of C_2H_6 or 20.0 liters of O_2? How many times as heavy?*

7.56 If the density of He gas is 0.026 g/liter at a certain temperature, what is the density of Ne gas at the same temperature and pressure?

Partial Pressure: Dalton's Law of Partial Pressures

The reason why a gas can occupy space and exert pressure is that the molecules are in motion. We have learned that one mole of any gaseous substance contains 6.023×10^{23} molecules. Since one mole of any gas occupies a volume of 22.4 liters at 0°C and 760 mm pressure, it follows that when 6.023×10^{23} molecules of a gas are confined to a volume of 22.4 liters at 0°C they will exert a total pressure of 760 mm. Now if only half that many molecules are placed in a 22.4-liter container at 0°C, they will exert only half that pressure, or 380 mm.

Suppose we place one half a mole of CH_4 gas and one half a mole of CO_2 gas together in a 22.4-liter container at 0°C. (CO_2 and CH_4 do not react with each other.) The half mole (3.011×10^{23} molecules) of CH_4 will exert a pressure of 380 mm and the half mole of CO_2 gas will also exert a pressure of 380 mm. The two gases together will exert a pressure of 760 mm.

The pressure of 380 mm exerted by the half mole of CH_4 is referred to as the *partial pressure* of the CH_4, and the pressure of 380 mm exerted by the CO_2 is the *partial pressure* of the CO_2. One half, or 50 mole per cent of the molecules are CH_4 molecules and one half, or 50 mole per cent, are CO_2 molecules. CH_4 provides half the molecules and exerts half the pressure; CO_2 provides the other half of the molecules and exerts the other half of the pressure.

In a mixture of CH_4 and CO_2 in which half the molecules are CH_4 and half are CO_2 the *mole fraction* of the CH_4 is 0.5 and the mole fraction of the CO_2 is also 0.5. *Mole fraction* is, therefore, the decimal equivalent of mole per cent. That is

$$\text{mole fraction of A} = \frac{\text{moles of A}}{\text{total moles}}$$

In a mixture of 2 moles of CH_4 and 3 moles of CO_2 the mole fraction of CH_4 is 0.4 and the mole fraction of CO_2 is 0.6. If the total pressure of a mixture of 2 moles of CH_4 and 3 moles of CO_2 is 800 mm the partial pressure of the CH_4 (P_{CH_4}) is found to be 320 mm and the partial pressure of the CO_2 (P_{CO_2}) is 480 mm. That means that *in a mixture of gases, the partial pressure of a gas is equal to its mole fraction times the total pressure.*

$$P_A = \text{mole fraction of A} \times P_{total}$$

From what has been stated above we can conclude that *the partial pressure of a gas is directly proportional to its mole fraction.*

$$\frac{P_A}{P_B} = \frac{\text{mole fraction of A}}{\text{mole fraction of B}}$$

This is *Dalton's Law of Partial Pressures*.

We can conclude that in a mixture of non-reacting gases, for any one of the gases:

mole fraction = pressure fraction

and

mole per cent = pressure per cent

This means that the relative number of moles of a gas in a mixture is equal to its relative partial pressure. Thus, if, in a mixture of 0.2 mole of CH_4 and X moles of CO_2, the partial pressure of the CH_4 is 18 mm and of the CO_2 is 45 mm, there must be $45/18 \times 0.2$ mole or 0.5 mole of CO_2.

It should be emphasized that, in a mixture of non-reacting gases, each gas behaves exactly as it would if it alone were present. The other gases have no effect on its behavior. Its partial pressure is the pressure that it would exert if it alone occupied the volume.

Vapor Pressure of Water

When a dry gas, hydrogen for example, is collected over water at a given temperature, water evaporates and the molecules of water vapor (gaseous H_2O) *diffuse* into the space occupied by the hydrogen. This evaporation continues until the rate at which water molecules evaporate equals the rate at which they condense. The hydrogen gas is then said to be *saturated* with water vapor. The pressure exerted by this saturated water vapor is its *vapor pressure* at the given temperature. The vessel in which the hydrogen was collected now contains a mixture of hydrogen and water vapor, and each gas (hydrogen and water vapor) exerts its own partial pressure. The total pressure is the sum of the two partial pressures. It follows, therefore, that when a gas is collected over water only a part of the total pressure is being exerted by the gas itself; some of the pressure is being exerted by the water vapor. Since the outside pressure which is exerted on a confined mixture of gases counterbalances the sum of the pressures exerted by each gas, it follows that when a gas is collected over water, the actual pressure on the gas itself is the total outside pressure *minus* the vapor pressure of water at the particular temperature. That means that when Boyle's law is used in the calculation of the volume of a gas which is collected over water, the partial pressure of the water vapor must be subtracted from the total pressure under which the gas is collected to give the actual pressure on the gas itself. Table 1 in the Appendix gives the pressure of water vapor at various temperatures.

Relative Humidity

Air which contains a high concentration of water vapor is said to be *humid*. *Humidity* refers, therefore, to the water vapor content of a gas. If air is saturated with water vapor at a given temperature its *relative humidity* is 100%; that is, it contains all (100%) the water vapor it can hold. If it contains only half the water vapor it can hold (is 50% saturated), its relative humidity is 50%. *Relative humidity* is, therefore, the ratio between the concentration of water vapor actually present and the concentration that would be present if the gas was saturated with water vapor. The simplest way to express the moisture content of a gas is in terms of the water vapor pressure; the relative humidity is then the ratio between the partial pressure of the water vapor and the equilibrium (saturated) vapor pressure at that temperature.

Problems

7.57 The volume of a dry gas is 600 cc at 25°C and 750 mm. What volume would this gas occupy if collected over water at 746 mm and 32°C?

SOLUTION: Since the gas is to be collected over water, the vapor pressure of water at 32°C must be subtracted from the barometric pressure of 746 mm.

vapor pressure of water at 32°C = 35.4 mm (See Appendix Table 1)

actual new pressure = 746 − 35.4 = 710.6 mm

Using this pressure of 710.6 mm as the new pressure in place of the 746 mm, we can then solve in the manner shown in problem 6.10.

$$\text{new volume} = 600 \text{ cc} \times \frac{750 \text{ mm}}{710.6 \text{ mm}} \times \frac{305°\text{K}}{298°\text{K}} = 648 \text{ cc}$$

7.58 The volume of a dry gas at 758 mm and 12°C is 100 cu ft. What volume will this gas occupy if stored over water at 22°C and a pressure of 740 mm?

7.59 A sample of 100 ml of dry gas, measured at 20°C and 750 mm, occupied a volume of 105 ml when collected over water at 25°C and 750 mm. Calculate the vapor pressure of water at 25°C.*

7.60 The volume of a gas, collected over water at 25°C and 740 mm, was 600 cc. The gas was dried and stored at 20°C and 750 mm. What was its volume in cc?

7.61 What volume in liters will 300 g of oxygen occupy when collected over water at 20°C and 735 mm?*

7.62 How many grams of carbon are there in 20 liters of CO gas measured over water at 26°C and 750 mm?

7.63 In a gaseous mixture of equal grams of CH_4 and CO what is the ratio of moles of CH_4 to CO? What is the mole fraction of CH_4?*

7.64 In a gaseous mixture of CH_4 and C_2H_6 there are twice as many moles of CH_4 as C_2H_6. The partial pressure of the CH_4 is 40 mm. What is the partial pressure of the C_2H_6?

7.65 In a gaseous mixture of CH_4, C_2H_6, and CO_2, the partial pressure of the CH_4 is 50% of the total pressure. What is the mole fraction of the CH_4 in the mixture?*

7.66 In a mixture of gases, A, B, and C, the mole fraction of A is 0.25. What fraction of the total pressure is exerted by gas A?

7.67 A mixture of 50.0 g of oxygen gas and 50.0 g of CH_4 gas is placed in a container under a pressure of 600 mm. What is the partial pressure of the oxygen gas in the mixture?

SOLUTION: The partial pressure of a gas is proportional to its mole fraction. Therefore, we must first find the number of moles of O_2 and CH_4 in the mixture.

$$\text{moles of } O_2 = \frac{50.0 \text{ g}}{32.0 \text{ g/mole}} = 1.56 \text{ moles of } O_2$$

$$\text{moles of } CH_4 = \frac{50.0 \text{ g}}{16.0 \text{ g/mole}} = 3.12 \text{ moles of } CH_4$$

$$\text{total moles} = 1.56 + 3.12 = 4.68 \text{ moles}$$

$$\text{mole fraction of } O_2 = \frac{1.56}{4.68}$$

$$\text{partial pressure of } O_2 = \text{mole fraction of } O_2 \times \text{total pressure}$$

$$= \frac{1.56}{4.68} \times 600 \text{ mm} = 200 \text{ mm}$$

7.68 In a gaseous mixture of equal grams of C_2H_6 and CO_2 the partial pressure of the C_2H_6 is 22 mm. What is the partial pressure of the CO_2?

7.69 In a gaseous mixture of CO_2 and CO the partial pressure of CO_2 is twice the partial pressure of CO. Calculate the ratio of grams of CO_2 to grams of CO.*

7.70 How many grams of pure CO gas would have to be mixed with 40 g of pure CH_4 gas in order to give a mixture in which the partial pressure of the CO is equal to the partial pressure of the CH_4?

7.71 In a mixture of 0.200 moles of CO, 0.300 moles of CH_4, and 0.400 moles of CO_2 at 800 mm, what is the partial pressure of the CO?*

7.72 If the 200 cc of H_2 gas contained in a cylinder under a pressure of 1200 mm are forced into a cylinder whose volume is 400 cc and which already contains 400 cc of CH_4 gas under a pressure of 800 mm, what will be the total pressure exerted by the mixture of H_2 and CH_4 gases in the 400 cc cylinder?

SOLUTION: The total pressure will be the sum of the partial pressures.

7.73 In a mixture of 64 g of CH_4 gas and 56 g of CO gas under a pressure of 1200 mm at 40°C, what is the partial pressure of the CH_4?*

7.74 A mixture of 2.0×10^{23} molecules of N_2 and 8.0×10^{23} molecules of CH_4 exerts a total pressure of 740 mm. What is the partial pressure of the N_2?

7.75 The partial pressures of the four gases contained in a 6-liter cylinder at 1007°C were: $CO_2 = 63.1$ atm; $H_2 = 21.1$ atm; $CO = 84.2$ atm; $H_2O = 31.6$ atm. How many grams of CO_2 gas were there in the cylinder?*

SOLUTION: Since, in a mixture of gases, each gas exerts the pressure that it would exert if it alone occupied the volume, we can ignore the other gases and calculate, by the use of the equation, $PV = nRT$, how many grams of CO_2 gas would exert a pressure of 63.1 atm when placed in a 6-liter cylinder at 1007°C.

7.76 A steel cylinder whose volume is 2 liters is filled with nitrogen gas at 22°C and 740 mm. Two liters of neon gas and 2 liters of helium gas, each volume measured at 22°C and 740 mm, are then forced into the cylinder, the temperature being kept constant at 22°C. What is the pressure of the mixture of gases in the cylinder?

7.77 The vapor pressure of water at 121°C is 2 atm. Some liquid water is injected into a sealed vessel containing air at 1 atm pressure and 121°C and is allowed to come to equilibrium with its vapor. What is the total pressure in the sealed container?*

7.78 The partial pressure of the water vapor in the air in a room is 11.6 mm at 22°C. What is the relative humidity of the air in the room?

SOLUTION: Relative humidity is the ratio between the partial pressure of the water vapor and the equilibrium (saturated) vapor pressure at that temperature. From Table 1 we learn that the vapor pressure of water at 22°C is 19.8 mm

$$\text{relative humidity} = \frac{11.6 \text{ mm}}{19.8 \text{ mm}} \times 100\% = 58.6\%$$

7.79 A weather report gives the temperature as 22.5°C, barometric reading 750 mm, and relative humidity 75%. What is the mole fraction of water vapor in the atmosphere?*

7.80 For the gaseous compound whose true chemical formula is C_3H_8 calculate:

(a) grams in 1.00 mole

(b) moles in 60.0 g

(c) gram atoms of carbon in 6.0 moles

(d) gram atoms of carbon in 75.0 g

(e) grams of carbon in 2.20 moles

(f) grams of carbon in 12.00 g

(g) atoms of hydrogen in 3.00 moles

(h) atoms of carbon in 20.0 g

(i) grams of carbon per g of hydrogen

(j) grams of hydrogen per g of carbon

(k) atoms of hydrogen combined with 60.0 atoms of carbon

(l) atoms of hydrogen combined with 40.0 g of carbon

(m) volume of 3.00 moles at STP

(n) volume of 32.0 g at 18°C and 752 mm

(o) moles in 140 liters of the gas at STP

(p) weight of 100 liters of the gas at 20°C and 700 mm

(q) density of the gas in g/liter at STP

(r) per cent of carbon

(s) partial pressure of C_3H_8 in a gaseous mixture of equal weights of C_3H_8 and CH_4 at 750 mm

(t) density of the gas in g/liter at 80°C and 500 mm

(u) what fraction of the atoms are carbon.

(v) what fraction of the weight of the compound is carbon.

Graham's Law of Diffusion

The rates of diffusion of two gases are inversely proportional to the square roots of their densities. This generalization is known as *Graham's law of diffusion.* The mathematical formula for Graham's law is

$$\frac{\text{the rate of diffusion of gas A}}{\text{the rate of diffusion of gas B}} = \frac{\sqrt{\text{density of B}}}{\sqrt{\text{density of A}}}$$

Problems

7.81 A gas A is nine times as dense as a gas B. In a given diffusion apparatus and at a certain temperature and pressure gas B diffuses 15 cm in 10 sec. In the same apparatus and at the same temperature and pressure, how fast will A diffuse?

SOLUTION:

$$\frac{\text{rate of A}}{\text{rate of B}} = \frac{\sqrt{\text{density of B}}}{\sqrt{\text{density of A}}}$$

Substituting in this formula,

$$\frac{\text{rate of A}}{15 \text{ cm/10 sec}} = \frac{\sqrt{1}}{\sqrt{9}} = \frac{1}{3}$$

$$\text{rate of A} = \frac{15 \text{ cm/10 sec}}{3} = 5 \text{ cm in 10 sec}$$

7.82 The density of CH_4 is 16.0 g per 22.4 liters. The density of HBr is 81.0 g per 22.4 liters. If CH_4 diffuses 2.30 ft in 1 min in a certain diffusion apparatus, how fast will HBr diffuse in the same apparatus at the same temperature and pressure? *

7.83 A gas A is 16 times as dense as a gas B. How do their rates of diffusion compare?*

7.84 A gas A diffuses 3.20 times as fast as a gas B. How do their densities compare?

7.85 How do the rates of diffusion of HBr and SO_2 compare?

SOLUTION: Attention has already been called to the fact that the density of a gas is directly proportional to its molecular weight. That means that the molecular weights of gases can be substituted for densities in the Graham's law formula. That is,

$$\frac{\text{rate of HBr}}{\text{rate of SO}_2} = \frac{\sqrt{\text{molecular weight of SO}_2}}{\sqrt{\text{molecular weight of HBr}}}$$

7.86 In a given diffusion apparatus 15.0 cc of HBr gas were found to diffuse in 1 min. How many cc of CH_4 gas would diffuse in 1 min in the same apparatus at the same temperature?

7.87 An unknown gas diffuses at the rate of 8 cc/sec in a piece of apparatus in which CH_4 gas diffuses 12 cc/sec. Calculate the approximate molecular weight of the gas.*

7.88 s If 0.200 g of H_2 is needed to inflate a balloon a certain size at 20°C, how many grams will be needed to inflate it to the same size at 30°C? Assume elasticity of balloon is the same at 20°C and 30°C.

7.89 s Exactly 1.100 g of carbon dioxide were introduced into a 1-liter flask which contained some pure oxygen. The flask was warmed to 100°C and the pressure was found to be 815 mm. No chemical reaction occurred. Calculate the weight of oxygen in the flask.

7.90 s Three 1-liter flasks, all at 27°C, are interconnected with stopcocks which are initially closed. The first flask contains 1 g of H_2O (liquid and vapor). The second flask contains O_2 at a pressure of 1 atm. The third flask contains 1 g of N_2.

(a) The temperature is kept constant at 27°C. At this temperature the vapor pressure of water is .0380 atm. The stopcocks are all opened. When equilibrium is reached, what is the pressure in the flasks?

(b) If the temperature of the whole system is raised to 100°C, what is the pressure?

7.91 s 10.0 liters of a mixture of neon isotopes is under a pressure of 3.00 atm at 27°C. The partial pressure of ^{18}Ne (atomic mass 18.01) is 570 mm, of ^{20}Ne (atomic mass 19.99) is 600 mm and of ^{24}Ne (atomic mass 24.01) is 1110 mm. What is the average atomic weight of the neon in the mixture?

7.92 s A reaction vessel contained 5 liters of a mixture of N_2 and O_2 gases at 25°C and 2 atm pressure. The oxygen in the mixture was completely removed by causing it to oxidize an excess of electrically heated zinc wire contained in the vessel to solid ZnO. The vapor pressure of this ZnO is zero. The pressure of the nitrogen gas that remained in the vessel, measured at 25°C, was 1.5 atm. What was the mole per cent of oxygen in the original mixture; the weight per cent?

7.93 s The equilibrium vapor pressure of hydrated copper sulfate $(CuSO_4 \cdot H_2O)$ is 4.4 mm at 50°C. What weight of water vapor must be present in a 3.0 liter flask at 50°C if no change in the composition of a small amount of $CuSO_4 \cdot H_2O$ takes place when it is placed in the flask at 50°C? The volume occupied by the solid $CuSO_4 \cdot H_2O$ can be neglected.

7.94 s A gas A has a molecular weight of 300. The vapor pressure of A at 27°C is 300 mm. The critical temperature of A is 95°C. A cylinder whose volume is 1.87 liters contains 10 g of pure A at 100°C. How many grams of A will condense when the cylinder is cooled to 27°C?

7.95 s At 37°C substance A has a vapor pressure of 58.4 mm and substance B a vapor pressure of 73.6 mm. To a sealed, evacuated container of volume 100 liters maintained at 37°C are added 0.20 mole of A and 0.50 mole of B.

(a) What is the total pressure in the container?

(b) Has any A condensed to a liquid? If so, how many moles of A condensed?

(c) Has any B condensed to a liquid? If so, how many moles of B condensed?

7.96 s The vapor pressure of water at 25°C is 23.5 mm and at 21°C is 18.5 mm. A mixture of air and water vapor is placed in a closed container at 25°C under a total pressure of 750 mm; the volume of the gases (air and water vapor) is 22.4 liters. The relative humidity in the container at 25°C is 54%.

The temperature is lowered to 21°C. The container is kept closed and the volume of gases remains constant at 22.4 liters.

(a) What is the total pressure in the container at 21°C?

(b) What is the mole fraction of the water vapor in the container at 21°C?

(c) What is the relative humidity in the container at 21°C?

7.97 s At 24°C the vapor pressure of H_2O is 22.1 mm of Hg. If the relative humidity in a sealed container is 30% at 24°C and 57% when the temperature is lowered to 13°C, what is the vapor pressure of H_2O at 13°C?

7.98 s At a given temperature 12.0 g of CO gas was placed in one evacuated container and 40.0 g of CH_4 gas was placed in a second evacuated container. The pressure of the CO in its container was 800 mm, of the CH_4 was 600 mm. Calculate the relative volumes of the two containers.

7.99 s At a given temperature a certain number of grams of CH_4, when placed in a 10 liter vessel, exerts a pressure of 0.240 atm. An equal number of grams of gas B, when placed in a 12-liter container at the same temperature, exerts a pressure of 0.145 atm. Calculate the approximate molecular weight of gas B.

7.100s A gas which has a density of 2 moles per liter under a pressure of 44.8 atm will be at what temperature?

7.101s The density of a gas is 3 moles per liter at 273°C. The gas is under what pressure?

7.102s A given mass of helium gas, which occupied a volume of 2 liters at STP, was allowed to expand to a volume of 4 liters by changing the temperature and pressure. What was its density at the new temperature and pressure?

7.103s Sodium iodide vapor has a density of 0.0596 g/liter at 1127°C and a pressure of 0.0300 atm. What is the calculated molecular weight of sodium iodide under the conditions? Account for these data.

7.104s The average kinetic energy of gas molecules is calculated from the formula, $KE = \frac{1}{2} mv^2$, and is directly proportional to the absolute temperature. If H_2 gas molecules move at an average speed of 1.2 km per sec at 300°K, what will their average speed, in km per sec, be at 1200°K?

7.105s In a given piece of apparatus it was found that 2.0 cc of CH_4 gas diffused in 1 sec while 1.4 cc of oxygen diffused in 1 sec. On the basis of these facts, what should the formula for a molecule of oxygen gas be?

7.106s The following gases are allowed to diffuse through the same porous partition at the same temperature and pressure. 4.2 liters of CO_2. 5 liters of HCl. 6 liters of HF. Which will take the least time? Which the longest time?

$$2\,HgO = 2\,Hg + O_2$$

8 Mole Relationships in Chemical Reactions. Stoichiometry.

The equation for a chemical reaction represents (a) the chemical formula for each reactant and each product, and (b) the relative number of moles of each reactant and product in the reaction. The equation is said to be *balanced* when the total number of atoms on the left-hand side equals the total number of atoms on the right. It will always be assumed that when we speak of an equation we mean a *balanced equation*.

The equation, $2\,HgO = 2\,Hg + O_2$, tells us that when mercuric oxide, HgO, is heated, it decomposes to give mercury and oxygen, and it shows that 2 moles of HgO yield 2 moles of Hg and 1 mole of O_2. It tells us that, whether we heat a pinch of HgO or a large amount, the HgO that we heat and the Hg and O_2 that are formed are in the *ratio* of 2 moles of HgO to 2 moles of Hg and 1 mole of O_2. Furthermore, the equation emphasizes the fact that the total weight of the products is equal to the total weight of the reactants; that is, there are 2 g atoms of Hg and 2 g atoms of O on the left and the same number on the right.

We have learned in Chapters 5 and 7 that a mole of a particular substance is a specific weight and, if it is a gas at a definite temperature and pressure, a specific volume of that substance.

Therefore, having determined from the equation for a reaction the *mole relationship* of the substances involved, we can then calculate *weight* and *volume relationships*.

The process by which the balanced chemical equation is used as a basis for making calculations is called *stoichiometry*. In a common use of the term the stoichiometry of a reaction refers to the mole relationships represented by the equation for that reaction.

Problems

8.1 How many moles of O_2 will be obtained by heating 3.50 moles of $KClO_3$?

SOLUTION: The equation for the liberation of O_2 from $KClO_3$ is

$$2 \text{ KClO}_3 = 2 \text{ KCl} + 3 \text{ O}_2$$
$$\text{2 moles} \qquad \text{2 moles} \qquad \text{3 moles}$$

In order to be able to solve this problem at all we must *know* that heating liberates all of the oxygen from $KClO_3$. That is, we must *know the reaction* that occurs.

The equation tells us that 3 moles of O_2 are liberated from 2 moles of $KClO_3$.

That means that 1 mole of $KClO_3$ liberates 1.5 moles of oxygen.

Therefore, 3.50 moles of $KClO_3$ will liberate 3.50×1.5 or 5.25 moles.

It should be pointed out that the equation can be written in the form

$$KClO_3 = KCl + 1\tfrac{1}{2} O_2$$

This tells us, at a glance, that the moles of O_2 liberated is 1.5 times the moles of $KClO_3$ heated, and 1.5 times 3.5 moles is 5.25 moles.

It should be emphasized that, if we know that $KClO_3$ liberates all of its oxygen when it is heated, and if we know that oxygen is a diatomic molecule, O_2, we do not actually need to *write* the equation at all. A glance at the formula will tell us that 1 mole of $KClO_3$ will liberate 1.5 moles of O_2; that is the important thing to know.

The last paragraph is not intended to convey the idea that it is not necessary to know the equation for the reaction on which the problem is based. We must *know* the equation, we must *know what happens*, but it is not always necessary to *write* the equation, particularly in a relatively simple problem.

The simplest, shortest, quickest solution is always desirable.

8.2 When antimony is burned in oxygen the following reaction occurs:

$$4 \text{ Sb} + 3 \text{ O}_2 = 2 \text{ Sb}_2\text{O}_3$$

How many *moles* of oxygen will be needed to burn 18 *moles* of antimony? How many grams of Sb_2O_3 will be formed?

SOLUTION: A glance at the equation tells us that 3 moles of O_2 are needed for every 4 moles of Sb burned. That means that it takes $\frac{3}{4}$ mole of O_2 to burn 1 mole of Sb. Therefore, $18 \times \frac{3}{4}$ mole or 13.5 moles of O_2 will be needed to burn 18 moles of Sb.

To find the number of *grams* of Sb_2O_3 we first find the number of *moles* of Sb_2O_3. The equation tells us that the number of moles of Sb_2O_3 formed is $\frac{1}{2}$ the number of moles of Sb burned. Therefore, 9 moles of Sb_2O_3 will be formed.

$$9 \text{ moles of } Sb_2O_3 \times \frac{291.6 \text{ g of } Sb_2O_3}{1 \text{ mole of } Sb_2O_3} = 2628 \text{ g of } Sb_2O_3$$

8.3 When C_3H_8 is burned in O_2 gas, CO_2 and H_2O are formed as products. If 2.40 moles of C_3H_8 are burned in a plentiful supply of oxygen how many grams of H_2O and how many liters of CO_2, measured at STP, will be formed.

SOLUTION: The formula, C_3H_8, tells us that, since 1 molecule of C_3H_8 contains 3 atoms of C and 8 atoms of H, while 1 molecule of CO_2 contains 1 atom of C and 1 molecule of H_2O contains 2 atoms of H, *1 mole of C_3H_8 will yield 3 moles of CO_2 and 4 moles of H_2O.* Therefore, 2.40 moles of C_3H_8 will yield 2.40×3 or 7.20 moles of CO_2 and 2.40×4 or 9.60 moles of H_2O.

At STP 1 mole of CO_2 occupies a volume of 22.4 liters and 7.20 moles will occupy a volume of 7.20×22.4 liters or 161 liters.

Since the molecular weight of H_2O is 18, 1 mole of H_2O weighs 18 g and 9.60 moles will weigh 173 g.

Each calculation can be carried out in one operation.

$$2.40 \text{ moles of } C_3H_8 \times \frac{3 \text{ moles of } CO_2}{1 \text{ mole of } C_3H_8}$$

$$\times \frac{22.4 \text{ liters of } CO_2}{1 \text{ mole of } CO_2} = 161 \text{ liters of } CO_2$$

$$2.40 \text{ moles of } C_3H_8 \times \frac{4 \text{ moles of } H_2O}{1 \text{ mole of } C_3H_8}$$

$$\times \frac{18.0 \text{ g of } H_2O}{1 \text{ mole of } H_2O} = 173 \text{ g of } H_2O$$

8.4 When C_4H_{10} is burned in excess oxygen the following reaction occurs:

$$2 \, C_4H_{10} + 13 \, O_2 = 8 \, CO_2 + 10 \, H_2O$$

How many *liters* of O_2, measured at STP, will be needed to burn 36.0 *grams* of C_4H_{10}? How many *liters* of CO_2, measured at STP, and how many *grams* of H_2O will be formed?

SOLUTION: The equation tells us that 6.5 moles of O_2 are consumed for every mole of C_4H_{10} burned.

The equation, or the formula, C_4H_{10}, tells us that 1 mole of C_4H_{10} yields 4 moles of CO_2 and 5 moles of H_2O.

One mole of any gas, at STP, occupies a volume of 22.4 liters. The molecular weights of C_4H_{10} and H_2O are 58.0 and 18.0, respectively. With these facts before us we can then make each calculation in one operation.

$$\frac{36.0 \text{ g of } C_4H_{10}}{58.0 \text{ g of } C_4H_{10}/\text{mole of } C_4H_{10}} \times \frac{6.5 \text{ moles of } O_2}{1 \text{ mole of } C_4H_{10}}$$

$$\times \frac{22.4 \text{ liters of } O_2}{1 \text{ mole of } O_2} = 90.4 \text{ liters of } O_2$$

$$\frac{36.0}{58.0} \text{ moles of } C_4H_{10} \times \frac{4 \text{ moles of } CO_2}{1 \text{ mole of } C_4H_{10}}$$

$$\times \frac{22.4 \text{ liters of } CO_2}{1 \text{ mole of } CO_2} = 55.7 \text{ liters of } CO_2$$

$$\frac{36.0}{58.0} \text{ moles of } C_4H_{10} \times \frac{5 \text{ moles of } H_2O}{1 \text{ mole of } C_4H_{10}}$$

$$\times \frac{18.0 \text{ g of } H_2O}{1 \text{ mole of } H_2O} = 55.9 \text{ g of } H_2O$$

Note that in solving this problem we first determined how many *moles* of C_4H_{10} were burned. Then we determined how many *moles* of O_2, CO_2, and H_2O, respectively, were involved. Then we converted moles of O_2, CO_2, and H_2O, respectively, to liters, liters, and grams, respectively.

In general, this is the procedure that should be followed in all stoichiometric calculations. The first questions should be: How many moles of reactant do we have? How many moles of product will be formed per mole of reactant?

Having determined the number of moles we then convert to grams or liters, whatever the case may be.

8.5 How many liters of O_2 gas will be required to burn 50 liters of H_2 gas. The volumes of both gases are measured at STP. The equation for the reaction is, $2 H_2 + O_2 = 2 H_2O$.

SOLUTION: The equation tells us that 1 mole of O_2 reacts with 2 moles of H_2. At STP 1 mole of H_2 is 22.4 liters. Therefore, 50 liters is 50/22.4 moles of H_2.

$$\frac{1}{2} \text{ of } \frac{50}{22.4} \text{ moles, } \quad \text{or} \quad \frac{50}{2 \times 22.4} \text{ moles of } O_2 \text{ will be required}$$

$$\frac{50}{2 \times 22.4} \text{ moles of } O_2 \times \frac{22.4 \text{ liters of } O_2}{1 \text{ mole of } O_2} = 25 \text{ liters of } O_2$$

We see that the volume of O_2 required is $\frac{1}{2}$ the volume of H_2 just as the number of moles of O_2 is $\frac{1}{2}$ the number of moles of H_2. In other words at STP *the volumes of the two gases are to each other as the number of moles.* Since both gases will respond equally to changes of temperature and pressure it follows that, *when measured at the same temperature and pressure, the volumes of gases involved in a reaction are to each other as the number of moles of the gases.* This very important generalization is an obvious consequence of the fact, pointed out in Chapter 7, that, at constant temperature and pressure, the volume occupied by a gas is directly proportional to the number of moles of that gas.

8.6 How many liters of CO_2 gas, measured at 200°C and 1.20 atm pressure, will be formed when 40.0 g of carbon are burned? The equation is, $C + O_2 = CO_2$.

SOLUTION: moles of CO_2 formed = moles of C burned.

$$\frac{40.0 \text{ g of C}}{12.0 \text{ g/mole}} = \frac{40.0}{12.0} \text{ moles of C burned}$$

Therefore, 40.0/12.0 moles of CO_2 will be formed.
To find the volume occupied by 40.0/12.0 moles of CO_2 at 200°C and 1.2 atm we will use the ideal gas equation, $PV = nRT$.

$$V = \frac{nRT}{P} = \frac{40.0}{12.0} \text{ moles} \times 0.082 \frac{\text{liters} \times \text{atm}}{\text{mole} \times \text{deg}}$$

$$\times \frac{473 \text{ deg}}{1.20 \text{ atm}} = 108 \text{ liters}$$

The entire calculation, in one operation, is

$$\frac{40.0 \text{ g of C}}{12.0 \text{ g of C/mole of C}} \times \frac{1 \text{ mole of } CO_2}{1 \text{ mole of C}} \times 0.082 \frac{\text{liters} \times \text{atm}}{\text{mole} \times \text{deg}}$$

$$\times \frac{473 \text{ deg}}{1.20 \text{ atm}} = 108 \text{ liters}$$

8.7 How many grams of copper will be formed when the hydrogen gas, liberated when 41.6 g of aluminum is treated with excess HCl, is passed over excess CuO?

SOLUTION: The reactions that occur are:

$$2 \text{ Al} + 6 \text{ HCl} = 3 \text{ H}_2 + 2 \text{ AlCl}_3$$

$$\text{H}_2 + \text{CuO} = \text{Cu} + \text{H}_2\text{O}$$

We note that 2 moles of Al liberate 3 moles of H_2; that means that 1 mole of Al liberates 1.5 moles of H_2.

One mole of H_2, when it reacts with CuO, will produce 1 mole of Cu. That means that the 1.5 moles of H_2 that are liberated by 1 mole of Al will produce 1.5 moles of Cu.

In short, 1 mole of Al will liberate enough hydrogen to produce 1.5 moles of Cu. The Al that reacts and the Cu that is produced are in the *ratio* of 1 mole of Al to 1.5 moles of Cu. The 41.6 g of Al is 41.6/27.0 moles.

Therefore, $1.5 \times 41.6/27.0$ moles of Cu will be produced.

$$\frac{1.5 \times 41.6}{27.0} \text{ moles of Cu} \times \frac{63.5 \text{ g of Cu}}{1 \text{ mole of Cu}} = 147 \text{ g of Cu}$$

8.8 When C_2H_6 is burned in excess oxygen the following reaction occurs:

$$2 \text{ C}_2\text{H}_6 + 7 \text{ O}_2 = 4 \text{ CO}_2 + 6 \text{ H}_2\text{O}$$

How many moles of oxygen will be consumed when 1.20 moles of C_2H_6 are burned? How many moles of CO_2 and how many moles of H_2O will be produced?

8.9 An amount of 0.262 moles of the compound, As_2S_5, was subjected to a series of treatments by which all of the sulfur in the As_2S_5 was converted to BaSO_4 and all of the arsenic was converted to Ag_3AsO_4. How many moles of BaSO_4 and Ag_3AsO_4, respectively, were formed?*

8.10 An amount of 3.16 moles of KClO_3 was heated until all of the oxygen was liberated. This oxygen was then all used to oxidize arsenic to As_2O_5. How many moles of As_2O_5 were formed?

8.11 A quantity of FeCl_3 was completely oxidized, all of the chlorine being liberated as Cl_2 gas. This Cl_2 gas was all used to convert Si to SiCl_4. A total of 6.36 moles of SiCl_4 were produced. How many moles of FeCl_3 were oxidized?*

8.12 How many moles of Cl_2 will be required to liberate all of the bromine from 8.0 moles of $CrBr_3$? The reaction is

$$3 \ Cl_2 + 2 \ CrBr_3 = 3 \ Br_2 + 2 \ CrCl_3$$

8.13 A volume of 65.0 liters of C_3H_8 gas, measured at STP, was completely burned to CO_2 and H_2O. How many moles of CO_2 were formed?*

8.14 An amount of 140 g of phosphorus was burned in excess oxygen. How many moles of P_4O_{10} were produced?

8.15 When C_4H_{10} was burned in excess oxygen, 162 g of CO_2 were produced. How many moles of C_4H_{10} were burned?*

8.16 How many moles of H_2 will be liberated by the action of 60.0 g of Mg on excess hydrochloric acid?

8.17 How many grams of oxygen will be required to prepare 200 g of P_4O_{10} from elemental phosphorus?*

8.18 How many grams of pure zinc must be treated with an excess of dilute sulfuric acid in order to liberate 5.00 g of hydrogen?

8.19 How many liters of oxygen gas, measured at STP, will be required for the preparation of 100 g of P_4O_{10} from elemental phosphorus?*

8.20 How many liters of dry H_2 gas, measured at STP, will be evolved by the action of an excess of HCl on 60.0 g of aluminum?

8.21 How many grams of tin would be formed if an excess of pure SnO were reduced with 1500 cc of dry hydrogen gas measured at 300°C and 740 mm?*

8.22 How many liters of dry H_2 gas, measured at 20°C and 740 mm, will be evolved by the action of excess dilute H_2SO_4 on 100 g of pure zinc?

8.23 When 100 g of aluminum were treated with HCl until all of the metal was dissolved, the hydrogen gas evolved was collected over water at a temperature of 22°C and a barometric pressure of 742 mm. What volume in liters did it occupy?*

8.24 Ammonia gas is oxidized by oxygen gas in the presence of a catalyst as follows:

$$4 \ NH_3 + 5 \ O_2 = 6 \ H_2O + 4 \ NO$$

How many liters of oxygen will be necessary to oxidize 500 liters of NH_3 gas? How many liters of NO and how many liters of steam will be formed? All gases are measured under the same conditions of temperature and pressure.

8.25 How many cubic feet of oxygen gas will be required for the oxidation of 6000 cu ft of SO_2 gas in the "contact" process? How many cubic feet of SO_3 gas wil be formed? All gases are measured under the same conditions of temperature and pressure.*

8.26 How many cubic feet of dry nitrogen gas, measured at 22°C and 740 mm, will be required to combine with 1200 cu ft of dry hydrogen gas, measured at 30°C and 800 mm? How many cubic feet of ammonia gas, measured at 100°C and 750 mm, will be formed?

8.27 How many grams of potassium chlorate must be heated to give 60.0 g of oxygen?*

8.28 How many pounds of KCl will be formed if 50.0 lb of $KClO_3$ are decomposed by heating?

SOLUTION:

$$2 \; KClO_3 = 2 \; KCl + 3 \; O_2$$

1 lb mole of $KClO_3$ will yield 1 lb mole of KCl.

1 lb mole of $KClO_3$ is 122.6 lb.

1 lb mole of KCl is 74.6 lb.

$$\frac{50.0 \text{ lb of } KClO_3}{122.6 \text{ lb/lb mole}} = \frac{50.0}{122.6} \text{ lb mole of } KClO_3 = \frac{50.0}{122.6} \text{ lb mole of KCl}$$

$$\frac{50.0}{122.6} \text{ lb mole of KCl} \times \frac{74.6 \text{ lb of KCl}}{1 \text{ lb mole of KCl}} = 30.4 \text{ lb of KCl}$$

8.29 How many tons of sulfur must be burned to produce 12 tons of SO_2 gas?

SOLUTION:

$$S + O_2 = SO_2$$

moles of SO_2 = moles of S.

$$\frac{12 \text{ tons of } SO_2}{64 \text{ tons/ton mole of } SO_2} = \frac{12}{64} \text{ ton moles of } SO_2$$

Therefore, 12/64 ton moles of S must be burned.

$$\frac{12}{64} \text{ ton moles of S} \times \frac{32 \text{ tons of S}}{\text{ton mole of S}} = 6 \text{ tons of S}$$

The solution, in one operation, is

$$\frac{12 \text{ tons of } SO_2}{64 \text{ tons of } SO_2/\text{ton mole of } SO_2} \times \frac{1 \text{ ton mole of } S}{1 \text{ ton mole of } SO_2}$$

$$\times \frac{32 \text{ tons of } S}{1 \text{ ton mole of } S} = 6 \text{ tons of } S$$

Note, in Problems 8.27, 8.28, and 8.29, that the solution is the same regardless of the units in which weight is expressed.

8.30 How many tons of $KClO_3$ will be required to liberate 40.0 tons of oxygen?

8.31 How many pounds of ZnO will be formed by the complete oxidation of 100 lb of pure Zn?*

8.32 How many tons of CO_2 gas will be formed when 15 tons of pure C are burned in air?

8.33 How many grams of copper oxide (CuO) can be formed by the oxygen liberated when 160 g of silver oxide are decomposed?*

8.34 How many grams of aluminum must be treated with excess H_2SO_4 in order to generate enough hydrogen gas to reduce 100 g of copper oxide (CuO) to Cu?

8.35 A sample of pure MgO was first dissolved in hydrochloric acid to give a solution of $MgCl_2$ and was then converted to a precipitate of pure dry $Mg_2P_2O_7$ weighing 6.00 g. Calculate the weight in grams of the sample of MgO.*

8.36 A sample of pure Na_3PO_4 was converted, by a series of reactions, into pure P_4O_{10}. Twelve g of P_4O_{10} were obtained. How many grams of Na_3PO_4 were there in the sample?

8.37 The formula weight of P_4S_3 is 220. The formula weight of Ag_3PO_4 is 419. A 13.2-g sample of P_4S_3 was first boiled with excess HNO_3 and, eventually, treated with excess $AgNO_3$. In the process all of the phosphorus in the P_4S_3 was converted to insoluble Ag_3PO_4. How many grams of Ag_3PO_4 were formed?*

8.38 A sample of impure copper weighing 1.25 g was dissolved in nitric acid to yield $Cu(NO_3)_2$. It was subsequently converted, first to $Cu(OH)_2$, then to CuO, then to $CuCl_2$, and finally to $Cu_3(PO_4)_2$. There was no loss of copper in any step. The pure dry $Cu_3(PO_4)_2$

that was recovered weighed 2.00 g. Calculate the per cent of pure copper in the impure sample.

8.39 A sample of 1.20 g of crude siderite iron ore containing $FeCO_3$ as the iron mineral yielded 0.400 g of Fe_2O_3. Calculate the per cent of $FeCO_3$ in the ore.*

8.40 If 1.0 g of crude sulfur gave, on complete combustion, 448 cc of SO_2 gas measured at standard conditions, calculate the per cent of sulfur in the crude material.

8.41 A 200-g sample of a crude FeS_2 ore containing SiO_2 as the only impurity was roasted until all of the sulfur was converted to SO_2. A total of 36.0 liters of dry SO_2 gas, collected and measured at 40°C and 740 mm was obtained. Calculate the per cent of FeS_2 in the crude ore.*

8.42 A crude Sb_2S_3 ore was found to contain 40.0% Sb_2S_3; no other sulfur compounds were present in the ore. A 140-g sample of this ore was roasted until all of the sulfur was converted to SO_2. How many liters of dry SO_2 gas measured at 27°C and 600 mm were obtained?

8.43 A 1.000-g sample of crude sulfide ore in which all sulfur was present as ZnS was analyzed as follows: The sample was digested with hot concentrated HNO_3 until all sulfur was converted to sulfuric acid. The sulfate was then completely precipitated as $BaSO_4$. The insoluble $BaSO_4$ was filtered off, washed, dried, and weighed. This yielded 1.167 g of $BaSO_4$. Calculate the per cent of ZnS in the crude ore.*

8.44 A 5.00-g sample of a crude sulfide ore in which all the sulfur was present as As_2S_5 was analyzed as follows: The sample was digested with concentrated HNO_3 until all the sulfur was converted to sulfuric acid. The sulfate was then completely precipitated as $BaSO_4$. The recovered $BaSO_4$ weighed 0.752 g. Calculate the per cent of As_2S_5 in the crude ore.

8.45 How many tons of lead will be obtained from 2000 tons of ore containing 21.0% PbS, the yield of lead being 94.0% of the theoretical amount?*

8.46 How many tons of crude cassiterite ore containing 70% by weight of SnO_2 will be required for the preparation of 12 tons of tin in a process in which the yield of tin is 96% of the theoretical amount?

8.47 A pure compound containing 63.3% manganese and 36.7% oxygen was heated until no more reaction took place, oxygen gas having been evolved. The solid product was a pure compound containing 72% manganese and 28% oxygen. Write a chemical equation to represent the reaction which took place.*

8.48 After complete reduction of 0.800 g of a pure oxide of lead with excess hydrogen gas, there remained 0.725 g of lead. Write the chemical equation for the reaction that took place.

8.49 A compound contained 27.1% sodium, 16.5% nitrogen, and 56.4% oxygen. Five g of this compound were heated until no more reaction took place. A weight of 0.942 g of oxygen was given off. A pure chemical compound remained as a solid product. Write a chemical equation to represent the reaction which took place.*

8.50 A compound is either zinc bromide ($ZnBr_2$) or zinc iodide (ZnI_2). An 8.00-g sample yielded 1.64 g of zinc. What is the compound?

8.51 A mixture of 12.2 g of potassium and 22.2 g of bromine was heated until the reaction was completed. How many grams of KBr were formed?

SOLUTION: From the formula, KBr, and the equation,

$$2\,K + Br_2 = 2\,KBr$$

we see that potassium and bromine combine in the ratio of 1 mole of K to 1 mole of Br to form 1 mole of KBr. The quantity 12.2 g of K is 12.2/39.1 or 0.312 mole of K; 22.2 g of Br is 22.2/79.9 or 0.278 mole of Br. That means that there is an excess of potassium; the quantity of KBr that will be formed will be the amount produced by 0.278 mole of Br. Therefore, 0.278 mole of KBr will be formed.

0.278 mole $\times$ 119 g of KBr per mole = 33.1 g of KBr

8.52 What weight in grams of silver chloride will be formed when 35.4 g of NaCl and 99.8 g of $AgNO_3$ are mixed in water solution?

8.53 The nitrogen in $NaNO_3$ and $(NH_4)_2SO_4$ is all available to plants as fertilizer. Which is the more economical source of nitrogen, a fertilizer containing 30% $NaNO_3$ and costing $3.00 per 100 lb or one containing 20% $(NH_4)_2SO_4$ and costing $2.70 per 100 lb?*

8.54 s Exactly 3.00 moles of chromium are reacted with excess of element Q; all of the Cr is converted to Cr_2Q_3. The Cr_2Q_3 is then treated with excess of strontium metal; all of the Q in the Cr_2Q_3 is converted to SrQ. The SrQ is then reacted with excess of sodium metal; all of the SrQ is converted to Na_2Q; 782 g of Na_2Q are formed. What is the atomic weight of element Q?

8.55 s Some dry hydrogen gas was prepared by treating a definite weight of aluminum metal with excess hydrochloric acid. The only receptacle available for collecting the dry hydrogen gas was a 44.8-liter storage tank filled with CH_4 gas at 0°C and 1 atm pressure. After the hydrogen gas was introduced into the tank containing the CH_4 it was observed that the partial pressure of the hydrogen in the gas mixture was the same as the partial pressure of the CH_4 in the mixture. The temperature of the tank at the time this observation was made was 20°C. How many grams of aluminum were treated with HCl?

8.56 s A sample of pure CuO was reduced with H_2 gas and the H_2O that was formed was all collected in a 44.8-liter tank containing dry N_2 gas. At 26°C the total pressure in the tank containing N_2 and H_2O was 1 atm and the relative humidity in the tank was 80%. The vapor pressure of H_2O at 26°C is 25 mm. How many grams of CuO were reduced?

8.57 s Equal volumes of hydrogen and oxygen, both at room temperature and atmospheric pressure, were introduced into a completely evacuated reaction bomb. The bomb was sealed and was heated to 120°C; the pressure of the mixture of gases in the bomb was found to be 100 mm at 120°C. An electric arc inside the container was turned on, which caused the reaction, $2 H_2 + O_2 = 2 H_2O$, to take place. When the reaction was over the bomb was cooled until the temperature was again 120°C. An examination revealed that there was no liquid water in the bomb. What was the new pressure inside the bomb?

8.58 s A 20-liter vessel contains a mixture of 1 mole of H_2 and 1 mole of O_2 at 27°C. When the mixture is ignited with a spark the reaction, $2 H_2 + O_2 = 2 H_2O$, proceeds to completion. The system is then cooled to 27°C. What is the final pressure in the vessel at 27°C?

8.59 s A gaseous compound which contains only C and H has a density of 1.763 g/liter at 22°C and 740 mm. When it is burned in an atmosphere of O_2 gas, CO_2 gas and steam are formed as products;

the volume of O_2 gas required is 5 times the volume of compound burned, these volumes being measured at the same temperature and pressure. Calculate the chemical formula of the compound.

8.60 s One volume of gaseous tetraethyl lead, $Pb(C_2H_5)_4$, and 24 volumes of oxygen gas, both measured at the same temperature and pressure, were placed in an evacuated reaction bomb. The bomb was sealed and heated to 180°C. The pressure of the mixture of gases in the bomb at 180°C was found to be 100 mm. When the gas mixture was ignited by an electric spark the reaction represented by the following unbalanced equation took place:

$$Pb(C_2H_5)_4 + O_2 = PbO + CO_2 + H_2O$$

When the reaction was over the bomb was cooled to the original temperature, 180°C. An examination revealed that there was some solid PbO in the bomb but no liquid of any kind. The vapor pressure of solid PbO at 180°C is zero. What was the total pressure inside the bomb at the end of the experiment?

8.61 s A sample of a gaseous hydrocarbon is burned in oxygen. At the same temperature and pressure the volume of the CO_2 gas produced is three times the volume of the hydrocarbon taken. The weight of the CO_2 produced is three times the weight of the hydrocarbon taken. What is the chemical formula of the hydrocarbon?

8.62 s When a compound X, which contains only S, C, and H, is burned in oxygen, one volume of X yields 1 volume of SO_2, 3 volumes of CO_2 and 4 volumes of steam (all volumes measured at the same temperature and pressure). What is the formula of X?

8.63 s A certain hydrocarbon gas was mixed with the exact volume of oxygen gas required to burn it completely to CO_2 and H_2O; the volume of the mixture of O_2 and hydrocarbon, measured at a certain temperature and pressure, was 750 ml. The mixture was ignited with a spark and complete combustion to CO_2 and steam occurred. When the mixture was brought back to the original temperature and pressure the volume was 900 ml and the partial pressure of the steam was 1.25 times the partial pressure of the CO_2. There was no liquid present. What is the formula of the hydrocarbon?

8.64 s A mixture of C_6H_{14} gas and oxygen gas, when placed in an evacuated steel bomb at 227°C, was found to exert a pressure of 425 mm.

When the mixture was ignited by a spark all of the C_6H_{14} reacted with all of the oxygen to form a mixture of CO gas, CO_2 gas, and steam (H_2O). The total pressure exerted by the mixture of gases formed in the bomb was 650 mm at 227°C. Write the equation for the reaction that took place in this particular experiment.

8.65 s A quantity of C_2H_4, when burned to CO_2 and H_2O, yielded 120 liters of CO_2 measured at a certain temperature and pressure. Measured at the same temperature and pressure a quantity of C_5H_{12}, when burned to CO_2 and H_2O yielded 50.0 liters of CO_2. Calculate the ratio of the weights, in grams, of the C_2H_4 and C_5H_{12} that were burned.

8.66 s A hydrocarbon contains 85.71% carbon. A volume of 180 ml of this hydrocarbon vapor, measured at 327°C and a pressure of 692.64 mm, when mixed with a quantity of oxygen and heated to a higher temperature, was completely converted to 1.0989 g of CO_2, 0.4195 g of H_2O and an unknown quantity of CH_4. What fraction of the carbon in the hydrocarbon was converted to CO_2 and what fraction to CH_4?

8.67 s At a very high temperature 2 volumes of H_2S gas decomposed completely to give 3 volumes of a mixture of H_2 gas and sulfur vapor. Write the equation for the reaction.

8.68 s When CO_2 gas, in a steel bomb at 427°C and a pressure of 10 atm, is heated to 1127°C the pressure rises to 22.5 atm. The following reaction occurs: $2 CO_2 = 2 CO + O_2$. Calculate the mole per cent of CO_2 decomposed.

8.69 s When a sample of acetylene, C_2H_2, is treated with a catalyst, some of it is converted to benzene, C_6H_6, according to the equation, $3 C_2H_2 = C_6H_6$. The density of the gaseous mixture of C_2H_2 and C_6H_6 at 27°C and a pressure of 0.44 atm is 0.760 g/liter. What fraction of the C_2H_2 originally present has changed to C_6H_6?

8.70 s A compound, X, is known to contain C, H, and O. A quantity of gaseous X was mixed with oxygen gas and placed in an evacuated steel reaction vessel at 127°C. When a spark was passed through the mixture all of the X was converted to CO_2 and H_2O (steam). In the reaction all of the O_2 gas was consumed. The pressure of the mixture of CO_2 and steam (no liquid water present) in the steel vessel, measured at 127°C, was 1.2 times as great as the pressure of the mixture of X and O_2 before sparking and the partial pressure of the steam was twice as great as that of the CO_2. Calculate the formula of compound X.

8.71 s A mixture of CS_2 gas and excess O_2 gas in a 10-liter reaction vessel at 127°C is under a pressure of 3.28 atm. When the mixture is ignited by a spark all of the CS_2 is oxidized to CO_2 and SO_2. The pressure of the mixture of CO_2, SO_2, and O_2 gases in the reaction vessel at 127°C is 2.62 atm. Calculate the number of grams of CS_2 in the original mixture.

8.72 s A mixture of O_2 and N_2 contains 30.0 mole per cent oxygen. To this mixture of gases is added just enough carbon so that, on heating, all the oxygen and all of the carbon are consumed and, in the reaction, half of the carbon is converted to CO and half to CO_2. What is the average molecular weight of the resulting mixture of CO, CO_2, and N_2?

8.73 s A sample of air in a 20.0-liter reaction vessel consists of 20.0% by volume oxygen and 80.0% by volume nitrogen. A quantity of sulfur is added to the vessel and the temperature is raised to 327°C. In the reaction that occurs all of the sulfur and oxygen are used up. One-half of the sulfur is oxidized to SO_2 gas and one-half to SO_3 gas. The pressure in the reaction vessel, at 327°C, when the reaction is completed, is 4.72 atm. How many moles of S were added to the vessel?

8.74 s When solid $CrCl_3$ is heated with H_2 gas reduction occurs; HCl is the only gaseous product, the other possible products ($CrCl_2$, CrCl, and Cr) being non-volatile solids. A liter reaction bomb contained 0.2000 g of anhydrous $CrCl_3$ and hydrogen gas at 27°C and a pressure of 3.000 atm. When the temperature was raised to 327°C, a reduction reaction took place. The pressure in the bomb, when the reaction was completed at 327°C, was 6.094 atm. Write the equation for the reaction that took place.

8.75 s The decomposition of 13.14 g of strontium iodate, $Sr(IO_3)_2$, results in the production of SrI_2 and 4.032 liters of O_2, measured at 136.5°C and 570 mm. The SrI_2 thus produced is quantitatively converted to $SrCl_2$, of which 4.77 g are obtained. The atomic weight of Cl is 35.5 and of O is 16.0. Calculate the atomic weights of Sr and I.

8.76 s Exactly 2.000 g of NH_3 were neutralized by HCl, NH_4Cl being formed as a product. In a separate experiment exactly 20.000 g of $AgNO_3$ were formed by the action of excess HNO_3 on 12.70 g of silver. All of the NH_4Cl formed in the first experiment was exactly sufficient to react with all of the $AgNO_3$ formed in the second experiment. Knowing that the atomic weight of H is 1.008 and of O is 15.999, calculate the atomic weights of N and Ag.

8.77 s When 1.82 g of zirconium metal (at. wt 91.22) reacts with excess HCl 1.04 liters of dry H_2 gas, measured at 27°C and 720 mm, are liberated. Write a balanced equation for the reaction that occurs when Zr is treated with HCl.

8.78 s An amount of 6.00 g of Mg is treated with a halogen, X_2, in excess. All the product of this reaction (i.e., MgX_2) is then treated with excess $AgNO_3$, and 117.5 g AgX are formed. What is the halogen X?

8.79 s When SiH_4 gas is heated with certain oxides it reacts with them according to the equation

$$SiH_4 \text{ (gas)} + 4 \text{ (O) (oxygen from the oxide)}$$
$$= SiO_2 \text{ (solid)} + 2 H_2O \text{ (gas)}$$

An element M forms a series of oxides, one of which is M_2O_5. Exactly 1 mole of solid M_2O_5 is mixed with excess SiH_4 gas in a 20-liter reaction vessel at 27°C. The total pressure in the vessel at 27°C is 8 atm; the volume occupied by the solid M_2O_5 is negligible. When the temperature is raised to 327°C a reaction occurs. When the reaction is completed the vessel contains SiH_4 gas, steam (no liquid water), solid SiO_2 and *one* other pure, homogeneous, non-volatile solid substance; the pressure in the 20-liter vessel when reaction is completed at 327°C is 16.615 atm. Write the equation for the reaction that occurs.

8.80 s To burn 2 volumes of a gaseous hydrocarbon to CO_2 and H_2O (steam) required 9 volumes of pure oxygen gas, both volumes being measured at the same temperature and pressure. Complete combustion of a sample of the hydrocarbon yielded 0.135 g of H_2O and 0.330 g of CO_2. Calculate the molecular weight of the hydrocarbon.

Stoichiometry
of Mixtures

The mole relationships that were used in solving the types of problems illustrated in Chapter 8 can also be employed when it is necessary to determine the relative or absolute amounts of two (or more) substances in a mixture. In order to be able to solve for the quantity of each substance in a mixture of two substances there must be at least two mathematical relationships involving these substances. This is in line with the mathematical principle that there must be as many equations as there are unknowns.

Problems

9.1 A mixture of C and S, when burned, yielded a mixture of CO_2 and SO_2 in which the partial pressures of the two gases were equal Calculate the mole per cent of C in the original mixture.

SOLUTION:

$$C + O_2 = CO_2$$
$$S + O_2 = SO_2$$

The mathematical relationships involving the C and S are:

(1)   moles of CO_2 formed = moles of C burned

(2)   moles of SO_2 formed $=$ moles of S burned

(3) $P_{CO_2} = P_{SO_2}$

(4)   In a mixture of gases the partial pressure of a gas is directly proportional to the number of moles of that gas.

Since $P_{CO_2} = P_{SO_2}$, then the number of moles of CO_2 must equal the number of moles of SO_2.

Since moles of C $=$ moles of CO_2 and moles of S $=$ moles of SO_2, and since moles of $CO_2 =$ moles of SO_2, it follows that moles of C $=$ moles of S.

That is the mixture consists of 50 mole per cent C and 50 mole per cent S.

9.2   A mixture of H_2S and CH_4, when burned, yielded a mixture of SO_2, CO_2, and H_2O (steam) in which the partial pressures of the SO_2 and CO_2 were equal. Calculate the mole per cent of H_2S in the original mixture.

SOLUTION:
$$2\,H_2S + 3\,O_2 = 2\,SO_2 + 2\,H_2O$$
$$CH_4 + 2\,O_2 = CO_2 + 2\,H_2O$$

We note that:

(1)   moles of $SO_2 =$ moles of H_2S burned

(2)   moles of $CO_2 =$ moles of CH_4 burned

(3)   In a mixture of gases the number of moles of a gas is directly proportional to its partial pressure.

Since $P_{CO_2} = P_{SO_2}$ moles of CO_2 must equal moles of SO_2. And since moles of $CO_2 =$ moles of CH_4 and moles of $SO_2 =$ moles of H_2S, moles of CH_4 must have been equal to moles of H_2S. That is, there was 50 mole per cent of H_2S in the original mixture.

9.3   A 12-g mixture of carbon and sulfur, when burned in air, yielded a mixture of CO_2 and SO_2 in which the partial pressure of the CO_2 was one half the partial pressure of the SO_2. How many grams of carbon were there in the mixture?

SOLUTION: Let $X = $ g of C. Then, $12 - X = $ g of S.
$$C + O_2 = CO_2$$
$$S + O_2 = SO_2$$

We note that:

(1) moles of CO_2 = moles of C burned

(2) moles of SO_2 = moles of S burned

(3) $X/12$ = moles of C = moles of CO_2

(4) $(12 - X)/32$ = moles of S = moles of SO_2

(5) In a mixture of gases the number of moles of a gas is directly proportional to its partial pressure.

Since $P_{CO_2} = \frac{1}{2} P_{SO_2}$, moles of $CO_2 = \frac{1}{2}$ moles of SO_2.
That is,

$$\frac{X}{12} = \frac{1}{2}\left(\frac{12 - X}{32}\right)$$

Solving, $X = 1.9$ g of carbon.

9.4 A sample of C was burned to CO_2 and a sample of S was burned to SO_2. The combined weight of the C and S was 10.0 g. The volumes of the CO_2 and SO_2, measured at the same temperature and pressure, were equal. How many grams of carbon were burned?

9.5 A sample of C was burned to CO_2 and a sample of S was burned to SO_2. When measured at the same temperature and pressure the volume of the CO_2 was twice the volume of the SO_2. The carbon was what per cent by weight of the total C and S burned?*

9.6 A mixture consisting of an equal number of grams of carbon and sulfur yielded 67.2 liters of a mixture of CO_2 and SO_2 measured at STP. How many grams of each element were present in the original mixture?

9.7 A 10-g mixture of H_2S and CS_2 was burned in oxygen to form a mixture of H_2O, SO_2, and CO_2. The dried mixture, on being separated into its pure components at a given temperature and pressure, yielded 5.34 liters of SO_2 and 1.50 liters of CO_2. How many grams of H_2S were there in the original mixture?*

9.8 A mixture of CS_2 and CH_4 was burned to a mixture of CO_2, SO_2, and H_2O at 450°C. The partial pressures of the CO_2, SO_2, and H_2O in the mixture were 175 mm, 200 mm, and 150 mm, respectively. What was the weight per cent of CH_4 in the original mixture?

9.9 A mixture contains solid carbon, gaseous CS_2, and gaseous CH_4. The mixture is oxidized completely to give a gaseous mixture of

CO_2, SO_2, and steam (H_2O). The ratio of the partial pressures of the CO_2, H_2O, and SO_2 in this gaseous mixture is 5.00 for the CO_2 to 2.00 for the H_2O to 1.00 for the SO_2. What was the per cent by weight of solid carbon in the original mixture?*

9.10 A 10.0-g sample of a mixture of $CuSO_4 \cdot 5\ H_2O$ and $CaCO_3$ was heated, decomposing the carbonate and dehydrating the hydrate. If 5.00 cc of water vapor (steam) were produced for every 2.00 cc of CO_2, both volumes being measured at the same T and P, calculate the per cent by weight of $CaCO_3$ in the original mixture.

9.11 A mixture of sulfur and carbon weighing 2.0 g when burned gave a mixture of SO_2 and CO_2 weighing 6.0 g. How many grams of carbon were there in the original mixture?

SOLUTION: In the first 10 problems in this chapter the facts have permitted mole relationships to be determined from the *volumes* or *pressures* of gaseous substances. In cases where *weights* of substances are primarily involved these weights will be related to the relative molecular *weights* of the substances involved.

In solving this particular problem we should first note that each of the following is true:

(1) $X = $ g of C

(2) $2.0 - X = $ g of S

(3) $C + O_2 = CO_2$

(4) $S + O_2 = SO_2$

(5) moles of $CO_2 = $ moles of C

(6) moles of $SO_2 = $ moles of S

(7) moles of C + moles of S = moles of O_2

(8) moles of C $= \dfrac{X}{12}$

(9) moles of S $= \dfrac{2.0 - X}{32}$

(10) moles of $CO_2 = \dfrac{X}{12}$

(11) moles of $SO_2 = \dfrac{2.0 - X}{32}$

(12) grams of CO_2 + grams of $SO_2 = 6.0$ g

(13) g of $(CO_2 + SO_2)$ − g of $(C + S)$ = g of O_2 = 4.0 g

(14) moles of $O_2 = \dfrac{4.0}{32}$

(15) g of CO_2 = moles of $CO_2 \times \dfrac{\text{g of } CO_2}{\text{mole of } CO_2} = \dfrac{X}{12} \times 44$

(16) g of SO_2 = moles of $SO_2 \times \dfrac{\text{g of } SO_2}{\text{mole of } SO_2} = \dfrac{2.0 - X}{32} \times 64$

(17) g of O_2 in CO_2 + g of O_2 in SO_2 = 4.0 g

(18) g of O_2 in $CO_2 = \dfrac{32}{12} \times$ g of C $= \dfrac{32}{12}X$

Since 1 mole of CO_2 contains 1 mole of C and 1 mole of O_2 it follows that

$$\frac{\text{weight of the } O_2}{\text{weight of the C}} = \frac{\text{mol weight of } O_2}{\text{mol weight of C}} = \frac{32}{12}$$

Therefore,

$$\text{weight of the } O_2 = \frac{32}{12} \times \text{weight of the C}$$

(19) g of O_2 in $SO_2 = \dfrac{32}{32} \times$ g of S $= \dfrac{32}{32} \times (2 - X)$

(20) g of $CO_2 = \dfrac{44}{12} \times$ g of C $= \dfrac{44}{12}X$

Since 1 mole of CO_2 contains 1 mole of C it follows that

$$\frac{\text{weight of the } CO_2}{\text{weight of the C}} = \frac{\text{mol weight of } CO_2}{\text{mol weight of C}} = \frac{44}{12}$$

Therefore,

$$\text{weight of the } CO_2 = \frac{44}{12} \times \text{weight of the C}$$

(21) g of $SO_2 = \dfrac{64}{32} \times$ g of S $= \dfrac{64}{32}(2.0 - X)$

From among these 21 relationships the following combinations will give us the following equations, each of which can be solved for the value of X:

SOLUTION 1: From Equations (7), (8), (9), and (14).

(7)   moles of C + moles of S = moles of O_2

$$\frac{X}{12} + \frac{2.0 - X}{32} = \frac{4.0}{32} \qquad (X = 1.2)$$

SOLUTION 2: From Equations (12), (15), and (16).

(12) g of CO_2 + g of SO_2 = 6.0 g

$$\frac{X}{12} \times 44 + \frac{2.0 - X}{32} \times 64 = 6.0 \text{ g} \qquad (X = 1.2)$$

SOLUTION 3: From Equations (17), (18), and (19).

(17) g of O_2 in CO_2 + g of O_2 in SO_2 = 4.0 g

$$\frac{32}{12} X + \frac{32}{32} (2.0 - X) = 4.0 \text{ g} \qquad (X = 1.2)$$

SOLUTION 4: From Equations (12), (20), and (21).

(12) g of CO_2 + g of SO_2 = 6.0 g

$$\frac{44}{12} X + \frac{64}{32} (2.0 - X) = 6.0 \text{ g} \qquad (X = 1.2)$$

Note that, although Solutions 2 and 4 involve the same terms, they represent different approaches to the problem.

In most mixture problems more than one method of solution is possible. It is, of course, not necessary to probe all of the methods, as has been done in this problem. The simplest, shortest, and most obvious method should be selected.

9.12 A mixture of Mg and Zn weighing 1.000 g, when burned in oxygen, gave a mixture of MgO and ZnO which weighed 1.409 g. How much Zn was there in the original mixture?

SOLUTION: X = g of Zn.   1.000 − X = g of Mg.

By examining the formulas, MgO and ZnO, we see that 1 mole of Mg will yield 1 mole of MgO and 1 mole of Zn will yield 1 mole of ZnO. Since the atomic weights of Mg and Zn are 24.3 and 61.4, respectively, and the molecular weights of MgO and ZnO are 40.3 and 81.4, respectively, it is true that

$$\frac{\text{weight of the MgO}}{\text{weight of the Mg}} = \frac{\text{mol weight of MgO}}{\text{mol weight of Mg}} = \frac{40.3}{24.3}$$

Therefore,

$$\text{weight of MgO} = \frac{40.3}{24.3} \times \text{weight of the Mg burned}$$

Likewise,

$$\text{weight of the ZnO} = \frac{81.4}{65.4} \times \text{weight of the Zn burned}$$

But,
$$g \text{ of ZnO} + g \text{ of MgO} = 1.409 \text{ g}$$
and
$$g \text{ of Zn} = X \quad \text{and} \quad g \text{ of Mg} = 1.000 - X$$
Therefore,
$$\frac{81.4}{65.4} X + \frac{40.3}{24.3} (1.000 - X) = 1.409 \text{ g} \qquad (X = 0.569 \text{ g of Zn})$$

9.13 A mixture of NaBr and NaI weighs 1.620 g. When treated with excess $AgNO_3$ it yields a mixture of AgBr and AgI which weighs 2.822 g. How many grams of NaI were there in the original mixture?

SOLUTION: $X = $ g of NaI; $1.620 - X = $ g of NaBr. The formula weights are:

$$\text{NaBr} = 102.9; \text{NaI} = 149.9; \text{AgBr} = 187.8; \text{AgI} = 234.8$$

Since 1 mole of NaBr and 1 mole of AgBr each contain 1 mole of Br and since 1 mole of NaI and 1 mole of AgI each contain 1 mole of I, 1 mole of NaBr will yield 1 mole of AgBr and 1 mole of NaI will yield 1 mole of AgI.
It follows, therefore, that

$$\frac{\text{weight of the AgBr}}{\text{weight of the NaBr}} = \frac{\text{mol weight of AgBr}}{\text{mol weight of NaBr}} = \frac{187.8}{102.9}$$

$$\text{weight of AgBr} = \frac{187.8}{102.9} \times \text{weight of NaBr}$$

Likewise,

$$\text{weight of AgI} = \frac{234.8}{149.9} \times \text{weight of NaI}$$

$$g \text{ of AgI} = \frac{234.8}{149.9} \times g \text{ of NaI} = \frac{234.8}{149.9} X$$

$$g \text{ of AgBr} = \frac{187.8}{102.9} \times g \text{ of NaBr} = \frac{187.8}{102.9} (1.620 - X)$$

$$g \text{ of AgI} + g \text{ of AgBr} = 2.822 \text{ g}$$

$$\frac{234.8}{149.9} X + \frac{187.8}{102.9} (1.620 - X) = 2.822 \text{ g} \qquad (X = 0.520 \text{ g of NaI})$$

9.14 A mixture of CO_2 and SO_2 weighs 2.952 g and contains a total of 5.300×10^{-2} moles. How many moles of CO_2 are there in the mixture?
Molecular weights: $CO_2 = 44.01$, $SO_2 = 64.06$.

SOLUTION: X = moles of CO_2. $5.300 \times 10^{-2} - X$ = moles of SO_2.

$$44.01 \, X + 64.06 \, (5.300 \times 10^{-2} - X) = 2.952 \text{ g}$$
$$(X = 2.200 \times 10^{-2} \text{ moles of } CO_2)$$

9.15 A mixture of pure AgCl and pure AgBr contains 66.35% silver. What is the weight per cent of bromine in the mixture?*

SOLUTION: We will assume that we have 100 g of mixture. The answer, in grams, will then equal, numerically, the weight per cent. Let X = g of Br.

Each of the following relationships will be true:

(1) g of AgCl + g of AgBr = 100 g

(2) g of Ag = 66.35 g

(3) g of Cl + g of Br = 33.65 g

(4) moles of Cl = moles of AgCl

(5) moles of Br = moles of AgBr

(6) moles of Cl + moles of Br = moles of Ag

(7) moles of AgCl + moles of AgBr = moles of Ag

(8) $\text{g of AgBr} = \dfrac{187.8}{79.9} \times \text{g of Br} = \dfrac{187.8}{79.9} X$

(9) $\text{g of AgCl} = \dfrac{143.4}{35.5} \times \text{g of Cl} = \dfrac{143.4}{35.5}(33.65 - X)$

(10) $\text{g of Ag in AgBr} = \dfrac{107.9}{79.9} \times \text{g of Br} = \dfrac{107.9}{35.5} X$

(11) $\text{g of Ag in AgCl} = \dfrac{107.9}{35.5} \times \text{g of Cl} = \dfrac{107.9}{35.5}(33.65 - X)$

(12) $\text{moles of Br} = \dfrac{X}{79.9}$

(13) $\text{moles of Cl} = \dfrac{33.65 - X}{35.5}$

(14) $\text{moles of Ag} = \dfrac{66.35}{107.9}$

From these relationships an equation can be set up which, when solved, will give the value of X, that is, the weight per cent of bromine.

9.16 A mixture of $BaCl_2$ and $CaCl_2$ contains 43.1% chlorine. Calculate the per cent of barium in the mixture.

9.17 A mixture of pure Na_2SO_4 and Na_2CO_3 weighs 1.200 g and yields a mixture of $BaSO_4$ and $BaCO_3$ weighing 2.077 g. Calculate the per cent of Na_2SO_4 in the original mixture.*

9.18 A mixture of CO_2 and CS_2 contains 20.0% carbon. How many grams of SO_2 will be formed by the complete oxidation of 10.0 g of the mixture to CS_2 and SO_2?

9.19 A mixture of NaCl and NaBr contains twice as many grams of NaCl as NaBr. When treated with excess $AgNO_3$ this mixture yields 100 g of a mixture of AgCl and AgBr. How many grams of NaCl were there in the original mixture?*

9.20 A 10-g mixture of Na_2CO_3 and Na_2SO_4, when treated with excess $BaCl_2$ solution, yielded a mixture of $BaSO_4$ and $BaCO_3$ containing twice as many grams of $BaSO_4$ as $BaCO_3$. Calculate the mole per cent of Na_2CO_3 in the original mixture.

9.21 A 10-g mixture of ZnS and MgS, when oxidized completely to ZnO, MgO, and SO_2, yielded 3.27 liters of SO_2 measured at 0°C and 760 mm. How many grams of MgO were formed?*

9.22 A mixture of As_2S_3 and CuS weighing 8 g was roasted in air until completely oxidized to SO_2, As_2O_3, and CuO. The SO_2 gas was oxidized to sulfate which was then completely precipitated as $BaSO_4$; 21.5 g of $BaSO_4$ were formed. Calculate the number of grams of Cu in the mixture.

9.23 When 50.0 g of mercury and 50.0 g of iodine are heated together they are completely converted into a mixture of Hg_2I_2 and HgI_2. How many grams of Hg_2I_2 are there in the mixture?*

9.24 s When a mixture of H_2S and CS_2 was burned in oxygen to give H_2O, CO_2, and SO_2 the weight in grams of the SO_2 that was formed was four times the weight of the CO_2. Calculate the weight per cent of CS_2 in the mixture of H_2S and CS_2.

9.25 s A gaseous mixture of equal grams of CH_4 and C_2H_6 plus excess O_2 was contained in a reaction vessel at 300°C. The partial pressure of the CH_4 in this mixture was 15 mm. The mixture was ignited, resulting in all of the CH_4 and C_2H_6 being completely oxidized, yielding a gaseous mixture of CO_2, H_2O (steam), and O_2 (no liquid water). The mole fraction of the CO_2 in this gaseous mixture was

0.20. What was the partial pressure of the oxygen gas in the original mixture?

9.26 s A gaseous mixture contained in a 1-liter reaction vessel at 127°C and 10 atm pressure consisted of an excess of oxygen and an equal number of grams of CS_2 and CH_4. The mixture was ignited by a spark and complete oxidation to CO_2, SO_2, and H_2O (steam) occurred. After the reaction had occurred the pressure in the 1-liter vessel, measured at 527°C, was 17.1 atm. How many grams of CS_2 were in the mixture?

9.27 s A mixture of methane (CH_4), ethylene (C_2H_4), and acetylene (C_2H_2) contained in a 10-liter flask at 27°C is under a pressure of 7.39 atm. This mixture is burned completely to CO_2 and H_2O, the resulting gases being passed through an absorbtion train, where the H_2O is absorbed by $CaCl_2$ and the CO_2 is absorbed by NaOH. The $CaCl_2$ tube increases in weight by 88.2 g and the NaOH tube increases by 198 g. How many moles of each gas were present in the original mixture?

9.28 s A mixture of Cl_2 and Br_2 gases was contained in a cylinder at a pressure of 2 atm. When combined with H_2, the Cl_2 and Br_2 yielded 55.84 g of a mixture of HCl and HBr gases; this mixture of HCl and HBr gases was stored in a 10-liter tank at 123°C and a pressure of 2.62 atm. Calculate the partial pressure of the Br_2 in the original mixture of Cl_2 and Br_2.

9.29 s A sample of water contains natural oxygen and a mixture of 2 hydrogen isotopes, H and T (tritium). Exactly 1 gram of this water is completely electrolyzed, giving 0.792 g of oxygen. Calculate the mole fraction of T_2O in the sample of water.

9.30 s A solid mixture of $CaCO_3$, $NaHCO_3$, and Na_2CO_3 contains 40% Na_2CO_3. The mixture is heated until all reaction ceases, and the resulting dry solid is found to contain 62.3% Na_2CO_3. Calculate the composition of the original mixture.

9.31 s A mixture of Al and Mg contained 3 times as many grams of Al as Mg. When the mixture was treated with excess HCl the hydrogen that was liberated reduced 119.25 g of CuO to Cu. How many grams of Al were in the mixture?

9.32 s A certain symmetrical ether is known to contain the same alkyl groups as a certain alkane. An equimolar mixture of this ether and this alkane weighs 460 g. When the mixture is oxidized completely to CO_2 and H_2O 64 moles of products are obtained. Calculate the formula of the ether and of the alkane.

9.33 s A mixture of an alkyne and a saturated alcohol weighed 37.20 g., contained 74.19% C and 12.90% H, and, in the gaseous state, occupied a volume of 41.0 liters at 227°C and a pressure of 0.500 atm. When the mixture was oxidized completely to CO_2 and H_2O the weight of the CO_2 formed from the alkyne was 24.37% of the total weight of CO_2 plus H_2O formed. Calculate the formula of the alkyne and of the alcohol.

10

Heat of Reaction. Heat of Formation.
Heat of Combustion. Specific Heat. The Calorie.

Most chemical reactions are accompanied by the evolution or absorption of heat energy. This heat energy is referred to as the *heat of reaction*. A reaction that evolves heat is *exothermic*; one that absorbs heat is *endothermic*. When the chemical reaction proceeds at such a rate that heat and light are evolved, the process is called *combustion*, and the heat that is given off is called *heat of combustion*. The heat energy that is evolved, or absorbed, when a compound is formed from its constituent elements is called the *heat of formation* of the compound. Heat of reaction, heat of combustion, and heat of formation are commonly expressed in units of *calories per gram, calories per mole*, or *kilocalories per mole. A calorie is the quantity of heat required to raise the temperature of one gram of water one degree centigrade*. The *specific heat* of a substance refers to the number of calories of heat required to raise the temperature of one gram of the substance one degree centigrade. Water has a specific heat of 1 cal/gram × deg (1 cal per g and per deg). Methyl alcohol has a specific heat of 0.600 cal/g × deg, while the specific heat of ethyl alcohol is 0.456 cal/g × deg. The specific heat of a substance is also referred to as its *heat capacity*. The *molar heat capacity* of a substance is the quantity of heat, in calories or kilocalories, required to raise the temperature of one mole one degree C.

Problems

10.1   The specific heat of water is 1 cal/g × deg C. How many calories of heat will be required to raise the temperature of 150 g of water 40°C?

SOLUTION: Since 1 cal is required to raise the temperature of 1 g of water 1°C, 150 cal will be required to raise the temperature of 150 g of water 1°, and 40 × 150 cal or 6000 cal will be required to raise the temperature of 150 g of water 40°.

The calculation, in one operation, is

$$150 \text{ g of water} \times 40° \times \frac{1 \text{ cal}}{1 \text{ g of water} \times 1°} = 6000 \text{ cal}$$

Note that "grams of water" and "degrees" will cancel. The answer will then be in calories.

10.2   The specific heat of water is 1 cal/g × deg. How many grams of water can be heated from 20 to 60°C by 3200 cal of heat?

10.3   The specific heat of methyl alcohol is 0.600 cal/g × deg. How many calories of heat will be required to raise the temperature of 4000 g of methyl alcohol from 2 to 22°C?

SOLUTION:

$$\text{total calories} = 4000 \text{ g of alcohol} \times 20° \times \frac{0.600 \text{ cal}}{1 \text{ g of alcohol} \times 1°}$$

$$= 48,000 \text{ cal}$$

10.4   The heat of combustion of a sample of coal is 6000 cal/g. How many grams of this coal would have to be burned in order to generate enough heat to raise the temperature of 1000 g of water from 10 to 34°C? The specific heat of water is 1 cal/g × deg.

SOLUTION:

$$\frac{\text{calories required to heat the water}}{\text{calories evolved per g of coal burned}} = \text{g of coal burned}$$

$$\frac{1000 \text{ g of H}_2\text{O} \times 24° \times \dfrac{1 \text{ cal}}{1 \text{ g of H}_2\text{O} \times 1°}}{\dfrac{6000 \text{ cal}}{1 \text{ g of coal}}} = 4 \text{ g of coal}$$

10.5   A sample of 12 g of a certain grade of coal gave off enough heat to raise the temperature of 4000 g of water from 12 to 30°C. Calculate the heat of combustion of the coal in calories per gram. The specific heat of water is 1 cal/g × deg.*

10.6 The heat of combustion of magnesium is 6075 cal/g. The specific heat of kerosene is 0.557 cal/g × deg. How many grams of magnesium must be burned in order to generate enough heat to raise the temperature of 1.00 kg of kerosene from 22 to 140°C?

10.7 The heat of combustion of a sample of coal was 5000 cal/g. When burned, 1.0 g of this coal gave off enough heat to raise the temperature of 8478 g of silver from 20 to 30°C. Calculate the specific heat of the silver.*

10.8 A sample of 2.5 g of sulfur, when burned to SO_2, raised the temperature of 1080 g of water from 22.5 to 27.5°C. Calculate the heat of formation of SO_2 in kilocalories per mole.

SOLUTION: To form 1 mole of SO_2 one must burn 1 mole of S. Therefore, the heat of formation of SO_2 is the same as the heat of combustion of S.

10.9 The heat of formation of SO_2 is 69.12 kcal/mole. How many grams of sulfur would have to be burned to furnish enough heat to raise the temperature of a piece of iron weighing 5000 g from 15 to 35°C? The specific heat of iron is 0.113 cal/g × deg.*

10.10 When burned in oxygen, 10.00 g of phosphorus generated enough heat to raise the temperature of 2950 g of water from 18 to 38°C. Calculate the heat of formation of P_4O_{10} in kilocalories per mole.

10.11 The specific heat of ethyl alcohol is 0.456 cal/g × deg. The heat of combustion of Mg is 145.8 kcal/mole. The density of ethyl alcohol at 12°C is 0.80 g/cc. How many grams of magnesium must be burned to generate enough heat to raise the temperature of 12,500 cc of ethyl alcohol from 12 to 22°C?*

10.12 The heat of fusion of ice is 79.7 cal/g. The heat of combustion of methyl alcohol is 170,900 cal/mole. The density of ice at 0°C is 0.920 g/cc. How many grams of methyl alcohol, CH_3OH, must be burned in order to generate enough heat to melt a cube of ice 100 cm on each edge?

10.13 Elemental phosphorus is prepared commercially by reduction of rock phosphate, $Ca_3(PO_4)_2$, with coke and sand in an electric furnace at about 2000°C. A 140-g sample of crude rock phosphate containing 87% by weight of $Ca_3(PO_4)_2$ was reduced to pure elemental phosphorus in the manner described above. This phosphorus was then completely oxidized to P_4O_{10} by burning it in an atmosphere of oxygen. The heat that was given off in the latter reaction raised the temperature of 4070 g of methanol from -10 to $35°C$. What per cent of the total amount of heat evolved by the burning phosphorus was actually used to heat the methanol? Heat of formation of P_4O_{10} is 732 kcal per mole. The specific heat of methanol is 0.600 cal/g $\times$ deg.*

10.14 A vessel partly filled with water is cooled to $0°C$ (no ice formed) and then connected to a vacuum pump. The vessel is insulated perfectly from the surroundings and the cooling coil is disconnected. When the vacuum becomes high enough the water begins to boil. If 10 g of ice formed, how much steam was given off?

$$\text{heat of fusion of } H_2O = 80 \text{ cal/g}$$

$$\text{heat of vaporization of } H_2O = 540 \text{ cal/g}$$

10.15 s At $920°C$ the reaction of carbon with oxygen evolves heat according to the equation, $2 C (s) + O_2 (g) = 2 CO (g) + 57.3$ kcal, and the reaction of carbon with carbon dioxide absorbs heat according to the equation, $C (s) + CO_2 (g) = 2 CO (g) - 28.8$ kcal. How many moles of CO_2 per mole of O_2 must be present in order that there shall be no heat change when the gas mixture reacts with C at $920°C$?

SOLUTION: When including the heat evolved or absorbed in the equation for a reaction we will follow the practice of representing evolved heat as a positive quantity and absorbed heat as a negative quantity. Thus, the equation

$$C (s) + O_2 (g) = CO_2 (g) + 94 \text{ kcal/mole}$$

tells us that, when solid carbon reacts with O_2 gas to form CO_2 gas, 94 kcal of heat are *evolved* for each mole of CO_2 formed. The heat that is evolved is *lost* by the C and O_2 when they combine to form CO_2.

The reaction of C (s) with CO_2 (g) to form CO (g) is an endothermic reaction; 14.4 kcal of heat are *absorbed* per mole of CO formed. This fact is shown by representing the heat of reaction as a negative quantity in the equation,

$$C (s) + CO_2 (g) = 2 CO (g) - 28.8 \text{ kcal}$$

10.16 s The heat of formation of HCl from the elements is 22,000 cal evolved per mole of HCl. The heat of formation of N_2O from the elements is 17,000 cal absorbed per mole. The heat liberated when 2.0 moles of hydrogen gas are reacted with excess chlorine is used, with 100% efficiency, for the conversion of a mixture of excess N_2 and excess O_2 into N_2O. How many grams of N_2O are formed?

10.17 s *Hess' Law of Heat Summation* states that the energy liberated in the formation of a substance is independent of the path that is followed and is the algebraic sum of the heat changes in the steps in the reaction. Calculate the energy change for the reaction,

$$H_2 \text{ (g)} + \tfrac{1}{2} O_2 \text{ (g)} = H_2O \text{ (liquid)}$$

from the following data:*

$C \text{ (s)} + 2 H_2O \text{ (g)} = CO_2 \text{ (g)} + 2 H_2 \text{ (g)} - 39,000 \text{ cal}$

$C \text{ (s)} + \tfrac{1}{2} O_2 \text{ (g)} = CO \text{ (g)} + 29,000 \text{ cal}$

$H_2O \text{ (g)} = H_2O \text{ (l)} + 9700 \text{ cal}$

$CO \text{ (g)} + \tfrac{1}{2} O_2 \text{ (g)} = CO_2 \text{ (g)} + 67,700 \text{ cal}$

10.18 s How many grams of ethanol (C_2H_5OH) will be changed from solid at $-124°C$ to liquid at $-104°C$ by the heat generated when 5 moles of butanol (C_4H_9OH) are burned?

heat of combustion of C_4H_9OH = 65,000 calories evolved per mole

specific heat of solid ethanol = 0.30 cal/deg × g

specific heat of liquid ethanol = 0.50 cal/deg × g

heat of fusion of ethanol = 25 cal/g

melting point of ethanol = $-114°C$

molecular weights: C_2H_5OH = 46; C_4H_9OH = 74

10.19 s The molar heats of formation of CO and CO_2 from C and O_2 are +28.2 kcal and +94.4 kcal, respectively. Calculate the heat of the reaction,*

$$CO \text{ (g)} + \tfrac{1}{2} O_2 \text{ (g)} = CO_2 \text{ (s)}$$

SOLUTION: Heat of reaction = heat of formation of products − heat of formation of reactants.

10.20 s Given the equations:

$$SO_2 \text{ (g)} + \tfrac{1}{2} O_2 \text{ (g)} = SO_3 \text{ (g)} - 21.4 \text{ kcal/mole}$$

$$S \text{ (s)} + 1\tfrac{1}{2} O_2 \text{ (g)} = SO_3 \text{ (g)} + 48.8 \text{ kcal/mole}$$

Calculate the heat of formation of SO_2 (g) from S (s) and O_2 (g).

11 Nuclear Reactions

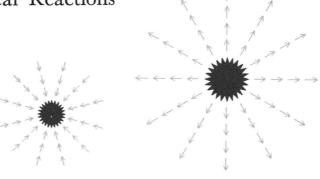

When a radioactive atom decays its nucleus loses either an alpha particle or a beta particle. An alpha particle has a mass of 4 atomic weight units and carries 2 positive charges. A beta particle has the negligible mass of an electron and carries 1 negative charge. It follows, therefore, that when an alpha particle is emitted, the mass number (atomic mass) of the atom decreases by 4 and the atomic number (the charge on the nucleus) decreases by 2. The loss of a beta particle (an electron) involves no change in the mass number of an atom but an increase of 1 in its atomic number. The increase in the atomic number when a beta particle is expelled is accounted for as follows: The beta particle (electron) which is expelled is formed from a neutron by the following change: neutron = proton + electron. Therefore, when a beta particle is emitted a new proton is created. Since a proton has 1 positive charge, the creation of this new proton increases the atomic number by 1.

The mass numbers and atomic numbers of elements are represented by the notation $^{238}_{92}U$ in which the number above and to the left of the symbol represents the mass number and the number below and to the left represents the atomic number. Since an alpha particle has the same mass as the helium atom, it is usually represented as ^4_2He. The beta particle, since it is an electron, is represented as $^0_{-1}e$; the -1 indicates that it has a single negative charge.

The reaction that takes place when an atom undergoes radioactive decay may be represented by an equation of the following type:

$$^{226}_{88}\text{Ra} = {}^{222}_{86}\text{Rn} + {}^{4}_{2}\text{He}$$

This reaction tells us that when radium decays, an alpha particle ($^{4}_{2}\text{He}$) is emitted and radon, with a mass number of 222 and an atomic number of 86, is formed.

The reaction

$$^{239}_{92}\text{U} = {}^{239}_{93}\text{Np} + {}_{-1}^{0}\text{e}$$

tells us that the uranium isotope with a mass number of 239 and an atomic number of 92 emits a beta particle ($_{-1}^{0}\text{e}$) and is converted to neptunium, whose mass number is 239 and atomic number is 93. It should be noted that, in this reaction as in all decay and transmutation reactions, mass number and charge are both conserved. Thus,

$$239 = 239 + 0 \quad \text{and} \quad 92 = 93 - 1$$

Problems

11.1 A radioactive element A, whose mass number is 220 and atomic number 85, emits an alpha particle and changes to element B. Element B emits a beta particle and is converted to element C. What are the mass numbers and atomic numbers of elements B and C? Of what elements are B and C isotopes?

SOLUTION: When A loses an alpha particle ($^{4}_{2}\text{He}$), its mass number decreases by 4 and its atomic number decreases by 2. Therefore, B has a mass number of 216 and an atomic number of 83. When B emits a beta particle ($_{-1}^{0}\text{e}$), its atomic number increases to 84 but the mass number remains the same, 216. Therefore C has a mass number of 216 and an atomic number of 84. Isotopes have the same atomic numbers but different atomic weights. Therefore, by consulting the table of atomic numbers, we find that B is an isotope of bismuth while C is an isotope of polonium.

11.2 The sodium isotope of mass number 24 is radioactive, a beta particle being emitted during its disintegration. What is the mass number and the atomic number of the element formed as a product of this disintegration and in what periodic group does it fall?

11.3   Actinium, which has a mass number of 227 and an atomic number of 89, undergoes radioactive disintegration as follows: Actinium loses a beta particle and becomes radioactinium. Radioactinium loses an alpha particle and becomes actinium X. Actinium X loses an alpha particle and becomes actinon. For each of the 3 elements formed in the above series of changes, give the mass number, the atomic number, and the symbol of the element of which it is an isotope.*

11.4   Complete the following disintegration equations, supplying in each instance the symbol, mass number, and atomic number of the product element:

(a) $^{232}_{90}\text{Th} = {}^{4}_{2}\text{He} + \text{-----}$

*(b) $^{228}_{89}\text{Ac} = {}^{0}_{-1}\text{e} + \text{-----}$

(c) $^{224}_{88}\text{Ra} = {}^{4}_{2}\text{He} + \text{-----}$

11.5   Complete the following disintegration equations, indicating in each instance whether an alpha or beta particle has been emitted:

(a) $^{227}_{89}\text{Ac} = {}^{227}_{90}\text{Th} + \text{-----}$

*(b) $^{223}_{88}\text{Ra} = {}^{219}_{86}\text{Rn} + \text{-----}$

Nuclear Transmutations

If the nucleus of an atom is bombarded by a certain particle, such as an alpha particle ($^{4}_{2}\text{He}$), a beta particle ($_{-1}^{0}\text{e}$), a neutron ($^{1}_{0}\text{n}$), a proton ($^{1}_{1}\text{H}$), or a deuteron ($^{2}_{1}\text{D}$), the bombarding particle may be captured by the nucleus. As a result, the atom is converted into a new element or an isotope of the original element. The capture of the particle may or may not be accompanied by the expulsion from the nucleus of some other particle. For example, when nitrogen is bombarded by alpha particles, the nitrogen nucleus captures one alpha particle, but, in so doing, it also ejects a proton ($^{1}_{1}\text{H}$). The product is an atom of oxygen. The reaction involved in this transmutation may be represented as follows:

$$^{14}_{7}\text{N} + {}^{4}_{2}\text{He} = {}^{17}_{8}\text{O} + {}^{1}_{1}\text{H}$$

[This is referred to as a (α, p) transmutation, since an alpha particle ($^{4}_{2}\text{He}$) is captured and a proton ($^{1}_{1}\text{H}$) is ejected.]

Problems

11.6 When boron (mass number 11, atomic number 5) is bombarded with alpha particles the following changes take place:

$$B + \text{alpha particle} = \text{new element} + \text{neutron}$$

[This is a (a, n) transmutation.]

What is the mass number and atomic number of the new element and in what group of the periodic table will it fall?

SOLUTION: The alpha particle has 2 positive charges and a mass of 4 awu. A neutron has no charge and a mass of 1 awu. Therefore, the mass number of the new element is 14 $(11 + 4 - 1)$. Since the boron nucleus picks up 2 positive charges, the atomic number, which is the number of protons (positively charged units) in the nucleus, is increased by 2. Therefore, the atomic number of the new element is 7. This means that the new atom has 5 electrons in the valence shell. Therefore, it falls in group 5 of the periodic table.

11.7 When the isotope of boron (mass number 10, atomic number 5) is bombarded with alpha particles, the following reaction takes place:

$$B + \text{alpha particle} = \text{new element} + \text{neutron (ejected)}$$

What is the mass number of the new element? The atomic number? In what periodic group does it fall? Of what element is it an isotope?

11.8 Complete the following transmutation reactions, indicating, in each case, the symbol, mass number, and atomic number of the element formed:

*(a) $^{9}_{4}\text{Be} + ^{4}_{2}\text{He} = \text{-----} + ^{1}_{0}\text{n}$

(b) $^{28}_{14}\text{Si} + ^{2}_{1}\text{D} = \text{-----} + ^{1}_{0}\text{n}$

*(c) $^{27}_{13}\text{Al} + ^{1}_{0}\text{n} = \text{-----} + ^{4}_{2}\text{He}$

11.9 Complete the following transmutation reactions, indicating, in each case, what particle, if any, was ejected:

(a) $^{14}_{7}\text{N} + ^{1}_{0}\text{n} = ^{11}_{5}\text{B} + \text{-----}$

*(b) $^{9}_{4}\text{Be} + ^{2}_{1}\text{D} = ^{10}_{5}\text{B} + \text{-----}$

(c) $^{27}_{13}\text{Al} + ^{4}_{2}\text{He} = ^{30}_{15}\text{P} + \text{-----}$

11.10 Complete the following transmutation reactions, indicating, in each case, what particle was captured by the nucleus of the bombarded atom:

*(a) $^{238}_{92}U$ + _____ = $^{239}_{93}Np$ + $_{-1}^{0}e$

(b) $^{10}_{5}B$ + _____ = $^{13}_{7}N$ + $^{1}_{0}n$

*(c) $^{23}_{11}Na$ + _____ = $^{24}_{11}Na$ + $^{1}_{1}H$

11.11 s In the complete transformation of $^{238}_{92}U$ to $^{206}_{82}Pb$ how many alpha particles and how many beta particles are emitted for each atom of $^{206}_{82}Pb$ formed?

11.12 s In the complete radioactive decay of 1 mole of $^{235}_{92}U$ to form 1 mole of a stable solid element as the end product a total of 156.8 liters of helium gas (measured at STP) will be produced. In the course of this complete decay 4 beta particles will be emitted for each atom of stable element that is formed. Give the symbol, atomic number, and mass number of the end product.

11.13 s An isotope of neptunium, $^{237}_{93}Np$, decays by alpha and beta emission. A 0.0100 mole sample of this isotope, if allowed to decay completely, would form 1.792 liters of helium gas measured at standard conditions. Six beta particles are given off in the radioactive decay for each atom of stable product formed. Write one balanced nuclear equation representing the over-all decay process.

11.14 s The nuclide $^{80}_{35}Br$ decays with a half life of 18 min. How much time will elapse before $\frac{7}{8}$ of a starting sample of the nuclide has decayed?

SOLUTION: The half life of a radioactive nuclide is, by definition, the time required for one half of any given quantity of that nuclide to decay. Since the half life of $^{80}_{35}Br$ is 18 min, at the end of 18 min one half of the sample will have decayed and one half will remain. At the end of another 18-min period one half of the remaining half will have decayed and the other half of the half (or one fourth of the original sample) will remain. At the end of a third 18-min period one half of the remaining one fourth will have decayed and one half of that fourth, or one eighth of the original sample, will remain. That means that, at the end of 54 min, $\frac{7}{8}$ of a starting sample of $^{80}_{35}Br$ will have decayed.

11.15 s When the radioactive element, A, decays to form the stable product, B, it emits an alpha particle. If the half life of A is 64 days and its atomic mass is 210, how many grams of A must you start out with in order to have collected 1.68 liters of helium gas, measured at 0°C and 2 atm pressure, at the end of 192 days?

11.16 s $^{253}_{99}$Es and $^{230}_{92}$U both have 20-day half lives and both decay by alpha emission. In each case the daughters are beta emitters with very long half lives. If 1 g of pure $^{230}_{92}$U and 1 g of pure $^{253}_{99}$Es were placed in an evacuated 22.4 liter flask at 0°C, what would the pressure be at the end of 20 days?

11.17 s The metal M is in Group IIA. A particular isotope of M decays with a 20.0-day half life by alpha emission to form a product, X, whose half life is so large that, for the purposes of this problem, it can be considered to be non-radioactive.

Exactly 1.00 mole of MH_2, with all M initially present as the isotope described above, is placed in an evacuated 22.4-liter heavy-walled glass container maintained at 0°C. Calculate the total pressure in the vessel at the end of 40 days.

11.18 s $^{38}_{17}$Cl decays by beta emission with a half life of 40 min. Four moles of H^{38}_{17}Cl are placed in an evacuated 62.4-liter heavy-walled container. After 80 min the pressure in the container is found to be 1650 mm of mercury. What is the temperature of the container in degrees Kelvin?

11.19 s You are given a sample of pure "ammonia" gas in which all of the hydrogen that is present in the NH_3 molecule is the isotope of hydrogen, tritium (T), with mass 3. The formula of this ammonia can then be written NT_3.

It is a known fact that tritium undergoes radioactive decay according to the reaction:

$$^3_1T = {}^3_2He + {}_{-1}^0e$$

The ^{3}He, like ^{4}He, is a monatomic gas. Write the equation for the chemical reaction that occurs when the T in NT_3 decays.

In a series of precise experiments you observe that when a sample of pure NT_3 gas contained in a 1.00-liter sealed steel tank at 27°C and an unknown initial pressure is allowed to stand until exactly half of the ^{3}T has decayed to ^{3}He the pressure in the tank rises to 2.46 atm. (The temperature is kept constant at 27°C.) Geiger counter readings show that, during the interval from the start of the experiment until the pressure reached a value of 2.46 atm, a total of 4.0×10^{22} beta particles were emitted. Calculate the value of the Avogadro number.

11.20 s A student is given a sample of ammonia gas. He knows it has the formula NH_3, that the nitrogen has atomic weight 14.0 and that the hydrogen is partly the isotope of atomic weight 1.00 (^1H), and partly tritium (^3H or T, atomic weight 3.00). He knows the gas constant R. He is asked to redetermine Avogadro's number and to find the $^3H/^1H$ ratio in the sample.

He knows ^3H undergoes radioactive decay to ^3He.

He observes that a 1.00 liter sample at 1.50 atm pressure at 27°C increases in pressure to 3.75 atm on standing until all the ^3H decays. During this time 7.7×10^{22} disintegrations occur.

What does he calculate for the $^3H/^1H$ atom ratio and for Avogadro's number?

11.21 s When ordinary BF_3 gas is bombarded with neutrons the boron undergoes a (n, α) reaction but the fluorine is not affected. Two moles of BF_3 gas contained in a 62.4-liter flask at 27°C are bombarded with neutrons until half of the BF_3 has reacted. What is the pressure in the container, measured at 27°C, when half of the BF_3 has reacted?

12

Per Cent
Strength
of Solutions.
Density.

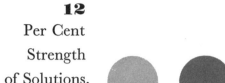

Per cent means parts per hundred: when applied to solutions it *means parts by weight of solute per 100 parts by weight of solution.*

The *density* of a solution is the mass of unit volume of that solution; it is commonly expressed in units of grams per cubic centimeter (g/cc) or grams per milliliter (g/ml).

Problems

12.1 Twelve g of NaCl are dissolved in 68 g of water. Calculate the per cent strength of the solution.

SOLUTION: Per cent strength means grams of solute (NaCl) per 100 g of solution.

We will first find grams of solute per 1 g of solution and then multiply this by 100 g of solution.

Twelve g of NaCl dissolved in 68 g of water yields 80 g of solution.

$$\frac{12 \text{ g of NaCl}}{80 \text{ g of solution}} = \frac{12}{80} \text{ g of NaCl/1 g of solution}$$

(Any fraction, when solved, gives the number of units of numerator per one unit of denominator.)

$$\frac{12}{80} \text{ g of NaCl/1 g of solution} \times 100 \text{ g of solution} = 15 \text{ g} = 15\%$$

The calculation, in one operation, is

$$\frac{12 \text{ g of NaCl}}{80 \text{ g of solution}} \times 100 = 15\%$$

NOTE: The number of grams of solute per 1 g of solution is the *decimal per cent* or *weight fraction*. Thus $12/80 = 0.15$. This is the decimal per cent or weight fraction of NaCl in the solution.

12.2 How many grams of NaCl are there in 60 g of a 15% solution of NaCl in water?

SOLUTION: 15% means that 0.15 of the weight of the solution is NaCl.

$$0.15 \times 60 \text{ g} = 9.0 \text{ g}$$

12.3 How many grams of sugar would have to be dissolved in 60 g of water to yield a 25% solution?

SOLUTION: What we want is a solution in which the weight of the sugar is 0.25 of the weight of the solution.
The weight of the solution is the weight of the sugar plus the weight of the water.
Let X = weight of sugar
$X + 60$ g = weight of the solution

$$X = 0.25 \ (X + 60 \text{ g})$$

Solving, $X = 20$ g of sugar

12.4 How many grams of water and how many grams of salt would you use to prepare 80 g of a 5.0% solution?

SOLUTION: In a 5.0% solution, the weight of the salt is 0.050 of the weight of the solution.

$$0.050 \times 80 \text{ g} = 4.0 \text{ g of salt}$$

The weight of the solution = weight of salt + weight of water.

$$80 \text{ g of solution} - 4.0 \text{ g of salt} = 76 \text{ g of water}$$

12.5 The weight of 15 cc of a solution is 12 g. Calculate the density of the solution.

SOLUTION: Density means grams per cubic centimeter. Therefore, to find the density we will divide the weight in grams by the volume in cc. That is,

$$\text{density} = \frac{\text{g}}{\text{cc}} = \frac{12 \text{ g}}{15 \text{ cc}} = 0.80 \text{ g/cc}$$

12.6   The density of a solution is 1.5. Calculate the weight in grams of 10 cc of the solution.

SOLUTION: To find the weight in grams of a certain volume of solution we must multiply the number of cc by the weight in grams of 1 cc; that is, we must multiply the volume by the density:

$$\text{grams of solution} = \text{cc of solution} \times \frac{g}{cc} = 10 \text{ cc} \times \frac{1.5 \text{ g}}{1 \text{ cc}} = 15 \text{ g}$$

12.7   The density of a solution is 1.80 g/cc. What volume will 360 g of the solution occupy?

SOLUTION: To find the volume in cc occupied by 360 g of a solution we must divide the weight in grams (360 g) by the weight in grams of 1 cc. That is,

$$\frac{g}{g/cc} = cc$$

$$\frac{360 \text{ g}}{1.80 \text{ g/cc}} = 200 \text{ cc}$$

12.8   A 44.0% solution of H_2SO_4 has a density of 1.343 g/ml. How many grams of H_2SO_4 are there in 60 ml of this solution?

SOLUTION: The weight in grams of 60 ml of this solution will be

$$60 \text{ ml of solution} \times 1.343 \text{ g/ml} = 80.58 \text{ g of solution}$$

0.440 g of H_2SO_4 per g of solution
$$\times 80.58 \text{ g of solution} = 35.46 \text{ g of } H_2SO_4$$

The entire calculation, in one operation, is

$$60 \text{ ml} \times 1.343 \text{ g/ml} \times 0.440 \text{ g of } H_2SO_4/g = 35.46 \text{ g of } H_2SO_4$$

12.9   A 44.0% solution of H_2SO_4 has a density of 1.343. A volume of 25.0 cc of 44.0% H_2SO_4 solution was treated with an excess of Zn. What volume did the dry hydrogen gas which was liberated occupy at STP?

SOLUTION: $Zn + H_2SO_4 = ZnSO_4 + H_2$. Therefore, 1 mole of H_2SO_4 will liberate 1 mole of H_2.
We will calculate how many moles of H_2SO_4 are present in the solution.

$$25.0 \text{ cc} \times 1.343 \text{ g/cc} \times 0.440 = 14.8 \text{ g of } H_2SO_4$$

$$\frac{14.8 \text{ g of } H_2SO_4}{98.1 \text{ g/mole}} = 0.151 \text{ mole of } H_2SO_4$$

Therefore, 0.151 mole of H_2 was evolved. One mole of H_2 occupies a volume of 22.4 liters at STP. Therefore,

$$0.151 \text{ mole} \times \frac{22.4 \text{ liters}}{1 \text{ mole}} = 3.38 \text{ liters of } H_2$$

The entire calculation, in one operation, is

$$\frac{25.0 \text{ cc} \times 1.343 \text{ g/cc} \times 0.440 \text{ g of } H_2SO_4/g}{98.1 \text{ g of } H_2SO_4/\text{mole of } H_2SO_4} \times \frac{1 \text{ mole of } H_2}{1 \text{ mole of } H_2SO_4}$$

$$\times \frac{22.4 \text{ liters of } H_2}{1 \text{ mole of } H_2} = 3.38 \text{ liters of } H_2$$

12.10 How many liters of dry HCl gas, measured at 25°C and 740 mm, can be prepared by combining chlorine gas with the hydrogen which will be liberated when 100 cc of a 20.0% solution of H_2SO_4 of density 1.14 is treated with an excess of aluminum?

SOLUTION: The analysis of this problem could run something like this: From the equation,

$$2 \text{ Al} + 3 \text{ H}_2SO_4 = 3 \text{ H}_2 + \text{Al}_2(SO_4)_3$$
$$\text{H}_2 + \text{Cl}_2 = 2 \text{ HCl}$$

or, more simply, by comparing the formulas, H_2SO_4 and HCl, we can see that 1 mole of H_2SO_4 will yield 2 moles of HCl. If we knew how many *moles* of H_2SO_4 there were in 100 cc of 20.0% sulfuric acid of density 1.14, we would then know that twice that many moles of HCl gas would be formed. Since 1 mole of HCl gas occupies a volume of 22.4 liters at STP, we could then calculate what volume the calculated number of moles of dry HCl would occupy at 25°C and 740 mm.

12.11 How many cubic centimeters of hydrochloric acid of density 1.12 and containing 40.0% by weight of HCl are required to produce 200 cc of dry hydrogen gas when mixed with excess Mn at STP?*

12.12 A 44.2-cc sample of a 70% solution of sulfuric acid of density 1.61 was first diluted with 3 volumes of water and was then treated with an excess of Mg. All of the H_2SO_4 reacted with Mg. The evolved hydrogen gas was used to reduce heated CuO. Ten per cent of the evolved H_2 was lost. The remaining 90% reacted with the heated CuO. How many grams of copper were formed?

12.13 A sample of 130 cc of a 15% solution of HCl of density 1.08 was treated with 26.2 g of zinc. How many liters of hydrogen gas, collected and measured over water at 740 mm and 27°C, were obtained?*

12.14 Ten g of NH_4Cl are dissolved in 100 g of a 10% solution of NH_4Cl in water. Calculate the per cent strength of the resulting solution.

12.15 You are given 100 g of a 10.0% solution of $NaNO_3$ in water. How many more grams of $NaNO_3$ would you have to dissolve in the 100 g of 10.0% solution to change it to a 20.0% solution?*

12.16 Sixty g of a 12% solution of NaCl in water were mixed with 40 g of a 7.0% solution of NaCl in water. What was the per cent strength of the resulting solution?

12.17 How many tons of 95% H_2SO_4 could be prepared from 1.10 tons of pyrites ore containing 90% FeS_2, assuming all the sulfur to be converted into the acid?*

$$\text{Molarity} = \frac{\text{moles of solute}}{\text{liters of solution}}$$

13

Molarity of Solutions

Concentrations of solutions are commonly designated by the term "molarity." *The molarity of a solution represents the number of moles of solute contained in one liter of solution or the number of millimoles of solute in one milliliter of solution.* ("Milli-" means a thousandth part of something.) Molarity is represented by the letter M. A 1 M solution of KCl contains 1 mole of KCl dissolved in enough water to make a liter of solution. A 0.1 M solution of NaCl contains one tenth of a mole of NaCl dissolved in enough water to make a liter of solution. Likewise, 0.2 M Na_2CO_3 contains 0.2 of a millimole of Na_2CO_3 dissolved in enough water to make a milliliter of solution. Expressed as a formula,

$$\text{molarity} = \frac{\text{moles of solute}}{1000 \text{ ml of solution}}$$

$$= \frac{\text{moles of solute}}{1 \text{ liter of solution}}$$

$$= \frac{\text{millimoles of solute}}{\text{milliliter of solution}}$$

It should be emphasized that, in problems dealing with reactions that occur in solution, the *mole relationships are treated exactly as they were treated in the chapter on stoichiometry* (Chapter 8). The only new thing in this chapter is that, instead of being given a certain number of moles or grams of a particular reactant, you will be given, for example, a certain number of

110

milliliters of a solution of a certain molarity. You will first determine how many *moles* of reactant there are in the solution; having determined the number of *moles* the rest of the calculation follows the exact pattern that was followed in Chapter 8.

Problems

13.1 How many grams of NaOH will be required to prepare 1.0 liter of 1.0 M NaOH?

SOLUTION: 1.0 M NaOH will contain 1.0 mole of NaOH dissolved in enough water to make 1 liter of solution. One mole of NaOH is 40 g of NaOH. Therefore 40 g will be required.

13.2 How many grams of K_2SO_4 will be required to prepare 1.00 liter of 0.500 M K_2SO_4?

SOLUTION: One liter of 0.500 M K_2SO_4 will contain half a mole of K_2SO_4 dissolved in enough water to make a liter of solution. Half a mole of K_2SO_4 is 87.1 g. Therefore, 87.1 g of K_2SO_4 will be required.

13.3 How many grams of $Al_2(SO_4)_3$ will be required to prepare 300 ml of 0.200 M $Al_2(SO_4)_3$?

SOLUTION: One liter of 0.200 M $Al_2(SO_4)_3$ will contain 0.200 mole of $Al_2(SO_4)_3$. 300 ml is 0.300 liter; 0.300 liter of 0.200 M $Al_2(SO_4)_3$ will contain 0.3×0.2 or 0.0600 mole of $Al_2(SO_4)_3$. One mole of $Al_2(SO_4)_3$ weighs 342 g. Therefore, 0.0600×342 g $= 20.6$ g. What has been stated above can be summarized, briefly, as follows:

$$0.300 \text{ liter} \times \frac{0.200 \text{ mole}}{\text{liter}} \times \frac{342 \text{ g}}{\text{mole}} = 20.6 \text{ g}$$

Note that liters and moles cancel, leaving the answer in grams.

13.4 If 12 g of NaOH are dissolved in enough water to give 500 ml of solution, calculate the molarity of the solution.

SOLUTION: To find the molarity means to find the number of moles of solute that are present in 1000 ml (1 liter) of solution.

$$1 \text{ mole of NaOH} = 40 \text{ g of NaOH}$$

Therefore,

$$12 \text{ g of NaOH} = \tfrac{12}{40} \text{ mole of NaOH} = 0.30 \text{ mole of NaOH}$$

The 0.30 mole of NaOH is present in 500 ml of solution. Since the molarity is the number of moles per 1000 ml, then,

$$1000 \text{ ml} \times \frac{0.30 \text{ mole}}{500 \text{ ml}} = 0.60 \text{ mole}$$

Therefore, the solution is 0.60 M.

13.5 A solution of $Cu(NO_3)_2$ contains 100 mg of the salt per milliliter. Calculate the molarity of the solution.

SOLUTION: 100 mg $= 0.1$ g. 0.1 g in 1 ml would be the same concentration as 100 g in 1000 ml. Therefore, this is a solution containing 100 g of $Cu(NO_3)_2$ per liter. To find the molarity we must find the number of moles per liter. There are 187.5 g of $Cu(NO_3)_2$ in a mole. Therefore,

$$\frac{100 \text{ g of } Cu(NO_3)_2}{187.5 \text{ g/mole}} = 0.53 \text{ mole of } Cu(NO_3)_2$$

Therefore, the molarity is 0.53.

13.6 How many grams of KOH will be required to prepare 400 ml of 0.12 M KOH?

13.7 How many liters of 0.20 M Na_2CO_3 can be prepared from 140 g of Na_2CO_3?*

13.8 A solution of NaCl contained 12 g of NaCl in 750 ml of solution. What was the molarity of the solution?

13.9 If 200 ml of 0.30 M Na_2SO_4 are evaporated to dryness, how many grams of dry Na_2SO_4 will be obtained?*

13.10 10.0 cc of a 70.0% solution of sulfuric acid of density 1.61 were dissolved in enough water to give 25.0 cc of solution. What was the molarity of the final solution?

13.11 In 3.58 M H_2SO_4 there is 29.0% H_2SO_4. Calculate the density of 3.58 M H_2SO_4.*

13.12 If 18.0 liters of dry HCl gas measured at 20°C and 750 mm are dissolved in enough water to give 400 ml of solution, calculate the molarity of the solution.

13.13 To what volume in ml must 44.20 ml of a 70.00% solution of sulfuric acid whose density is 1.610 be diluted to give 0.4000 M H_2SO_4?*

13.14 How many moles of hydrogen will be liberated from 320 ml of 0.50 M H_2SO_4 by an excess of magnesium?

SOLUTION:

$$Mg + H_2SO_4 = MgSO_4 + H_2$$

0.50 M H_2SO_4 contains 0.50 mole of H_2SO_4 per liter

$$0.320 \text{ liter of } H_2SO_4 \times \frac{0.50 \text{ mole of } H_2SO_4}{1 \text{ liter of } H_2SO_4} = 0.16 \text{ mole of } H_2SO_4$$

1 mole of H_2SO_4 liberates 1 mole of H_2
Therefore, 0.16 mole of H_2 will be liberated.

13.15 How many moles of hydrogen will be liberated from 400 ml of 0.40 M HCl by an excess of zinc?

SOLUTION:

$$Zn + 2 \text{ HCl} = ZnCl_2 + H_2$$

2 moles of HCl yield 1 mole of H_2

1 mole of HCl yields 0.5 mole of H_2

0.40 M HCl contains 0.40 moles of HCl per liter

$$0.400 \text{ liter} \times \frac{0.40 \text{ mole}}{1 \text{ liter}} = 0.16 \text{ mole of HCl}$$

Therefore, 0.080 mole ($\frac{1}{2}$ of 0.16 mole) of H_2 will be liberated.

13.16 How many liters of dry CO_2 gas, measured at standard conditions, will be evolved when 400 ml of 0.20 M H_2SO_4 are treated with an excess of K_2CO_3?

SOLUTION:

$$H_2SO_4 + K_2CO_3 = K_2SO_4 + H_2O + CO_2$$

1 mole of H_2SO_4 liberates 1 mole of CO_2

0.20 M H_2SO_4 contains 0.20 mole of H_2SO_4 per liter

0.400 liter $\times$ 0.20 mole/liter = 0.080 mole of H_2SO_4
$$= 0.080 \text{ mole of } CO_2$$

0.080 mole $\times$ 22.4 liters/mole = 1.8 liters of CO_2 evolved

The above calculations can be carried out in one operation.

$$0.400 \text{ liter} \times 0.20 \text{ mole of } H_2SO_4/\text{liter} \times \frac{1 \text{ mole of } CO_2}{1 \text{ mole of } H_2SO_4}$$

$$\times \frac{22.4 \text{ liters of } CO_2}{1 \text{ mole of } CO_2} = 1.8 \text{ liters of } CO_2$$

13.17 How many moles of hydrogen gas will be liberated when an excess of magnesium reacts with:

(a) 600 ml of 0.80 M H_2SO_4?

*(b) 600 ml of 0.80 M HCl?

13.18 How many moles of hydrogen gas will be evolved when 0.80 mole of Mg reacts with:

(a) 500 ml of 2.0 M HCl?

(b) 500 ml of 2.0 M H_2SO_4?

13.19 A solution of 447 ml of Na_2CO_3 was warmed with an excess of sulfuric acid until all action ceased. Five liters of dry CO_2 gas, measured at standard conditions, were given off. Calculate the molarity of the sodium carbonate solution.

SOLUTION: The analysis of this problem could run something like this: To find the molarity we must find the number of moles of Na_2CO_3 per liter of solution. If we knew how many moles of Na_2CO_3 there were in 447 ml, we could calculate the number in 1000 ml (1 liter).

From the equation,

$$Na_2CO_3 + H_2SO_4 = Na_2SO_4 + H_2O + CO_2$$

or, more simply, from the formulas, Na_2CO_3 and CO_2, we can see that 1 mole of Na_2CO_3 yields 1 mole of CO_2. Therefore, if we knew how many moles of CO_2 were formed we would know how many moles of Na_2CO_3 were present in the 447 ml of solution.

We know that 5 liters of CO_2 were evolved. Since 1 mole of CO_2 occupies a volume of 22.4 liters at STP, 5 liters of CO_2 is 5/22.4 mole. Therefore, 5/22.4 mole of Na_2CO_3 is present in the 447 ml (0.447 liter) of solution.

$$\frac{5}{22.4} \text{ mole} \div 0.447 \text{ liter} = 0.5 \text{ mole/liter}$$

Therefore, the solution is 0.5 M.

13.20 An excess of Mg was treated with 1340 ml of 0.400 M HCl. The evolved H_2 was dried and was then placed in an 18-liter tank which already was filled with CH_4 gas at 0°C and a pressure of 760 mm. Calculate the partial pressure of the H_2 in the resulting mixture.

13.21 A beaker contained 130 ml of hydrochloric acid. The contents were treated with excess zinc. The result was that 7.13 liters of dry hydrogen gas, measured at 22°C and 738 mm, were obtained. Calculate the molarity of the acid.*

13.22 If 12.0 g of NaOH were required to neutralize 82.0 ml of sulfuric acid, calculate the molarity of the acid.

13.23 How many milliliters of 0.250 M HCl will be required to neutralize 120 ml of 0.800 M KOH?

SOLUTION: One mole of HCl will neutralize 1 mole of KOH. Therefore, moles of HCl required = moles of KOH present in the solution. 0.800 M KOH contains 0.800 mole of KOH per liter; 0.250 M HCl contains 0.250 mole of HCl per liter.

$$0.120 \text{ liter} \times \frac{0.800 \text{ mole of KOH}}{1 \text{ liter}} = \text{moles of KOH present}$$

$$X \text{ liters} \times \frac{0.250 \text{ mole of HCl}}{1 \text{ liter}} = \text{moles of HCl required}$$

Therefore, since moles of HCl required = moles of KOH present

$$X \text{ liters of HCl} \times \frac{0.250 \text{ mole}}{1 \text{ liter}} = 0.120 \text{ liter} \times \frac{0.800 \text{ mole}}{1 \text{ liter}}$$

$$X = 0.384 \text{ liter} = 384 \text{ ml}$$

13.24 How many milliliters of 0.250 M $AgNO_3$ will be required to precipitate the chloride from 80.0 ml of 0.400 M NaCl? How many grams of AgCl will be precipitated?

13.25 An excess of $FeCl_3$ solution was added to 400 ml of 0.300 M KOH. How many grams of $Fe(OH)_3$ were precipitated?*

13.26 25.0 ml of NaOH solution exactly neutralized 40 ml of 0.10 M H_2SO_4. Calculate the molarity of the NaOH.

13.27 600 ml of 0.40 M HCl was treated with excess Mg. The evolved H_2 gas was all used to reduce CuO to Cu. How many grams of free copper were formed?*

13.28 How many liters of dry CO_2 gas, collected and measured at 0°C and 760 mm, will be liberated when 500 ml of 0.400 M HCl are treated with an excess of Na_2CO_3?

13.29 To precipitate all of the chromate, as Ag_2CrO_4, from 200 ml of a solution of K_2CrO_4 required 120 ml of 0.200 M $AgNO_3$. How many grams of Ag_2CrO_4 were precipitated? What was the molarity of the K_2CrO_4 solution?*

13.30 A 17.4-ml sample of a 70.0% solution of sulfuric acid whose density is 1.61 was diluted to a volume of 100 ml and was then treated with a large excess of zinc. The evolved hydrogen gas was combined with chlorine gas to form HCl. This HCl gas was then dissolved in enough water to form 200 ml of hydrochloric acid. There was no loss of material in the reactions. Calculate the molarity of the hydrochloric acid.

13.31 A 10.0-g sample of crude P_4S_3 containing inert impurities was first roasted in O_2 in the presence of a catalyst until all of the P_4S_3 was oxidized to P_4O_{10} and SO_3. The mixture of oxides was then dissolved in water. To neutralize the resulting solution required 900 ml of 0.600 M NaOH. Calculate the per cent of P_4S_3 in the sample.*

13.32 400 ml of a 0.500 M solution of H_2SO_4 were treated with excess Mn metal until all reaction had ceased. The evolved hydrogen gas was dried, cooled to 0°C, and was then forced into a 2.24-liter cylinder containing 0.100 mole of oxygen gas at 0°C. What was the total pressure of the mixture of gases in the cylinder?

13.33 The barium in a certain sample of pure $Ba_3(PO_4)_2$ was converted, quantitatively, to 7.005 g of $BaSO_4$. A second identical sample of pure $Ba_3(PO_4)_2$ was first converted, quantitatively, to $(NH_4)_3PO_4 \cdot 12\ MoO_3$, which was then treated with 0.920 M NaOH, with which it reacted according to the equation,

$(NH_4)_3PO_4 \cdot 12\ MoO_3 + 23\ NaOH$
$$= NaNH_4HPO_4 + (NH_4)_2MoO_4 + 11\ Na_2MoO_4 + 11\ H_2O$$

How many ml of the solution of NaOH were consumed?*

13.34 If the solution that is formed when 2.00 g of Mg is added to 400 ml of 0.25 M HCl is evaporated to dryness, how many grams of solid $MgCl_2$ will be recovered?

13.35 How many grams of KCl will be recovered when a solution obtained by dissolving 55.7 liters of HCl gas, measured at STP, in 4 liters of 1.37 M KOH is evaporated to dryness?*

13.36 What volume in liters of CO_2 gas, measured at STP, will be liberated when 55.3 g of K_2CO_3 is treated with 58.8 ml of 9.00 M H_3PO_4?

13.37 s An 85-g sample of an antimony sulfide ore containing 40% by weight of Sb_2S_3 and 60% inert material is oxidized until all of the S in the Sb_2S_3 is converted to SO_3. This SO_3 is dissolved in enough water to give 200 ml of solution. How many ml of 0.400 M NaOH will be required to completely neutralize the contents of the 200 ml solution?

13.38 s A 20-g sample of an As_2S_3 ore was roasted in air until all of its S was converted to SO_2. This SO_2 was all oxidized to SO_3, and the SO_3 was dissolved in water. A volume of 85 ml of 0.200 M NaOH was required to neutralize the solution of SO_3 in water? Calculate the per cent of As_2S_3 in the ore.

13.39 s A 16-g mixture of sodium and potassium, when allowed to react with water, gave a solution which neutralized 602.5 ml of 0.40 M H_2SO_4. How many grams of sodium were there in the mixture?

13.40 s A 14.8-g mixture of Na_2CO_3 and $NaHCO_3$ was dissolved in enough water to make 400 ml of solution. When these 400 ml of solution were treated with excess 2.00 M H_2SO_4 and boiled to remove all dissolved gas, 3.73 liters of dry CO_2 gas measured at 740 mm and 22.0°C were obtained. Calculate the molarity of the Na_2CO_3 and of the $NaHCO_3$ in the 400 ml of solution.

13.41 s A mixture of Na_2S and CaS was oxidized to SO_2 gas and a mixture of the solid oxides of Na and Ca. Exactly 400 ml of an acid solution of 0.200 M $KMnO_4$ were required to oxidize the SO_2 to SO_4^{--}. How many ml of 0.200 M HNO_3 were required to neutralize the solution formed when the mixture of oxides of Na and Ca was dissolved in water?

13.42 s A 26.95-g mixture of $BaSO_3$ and $NaHSO_3$ was analyzed by oxidation to SO_4^{--} with 0.10 M $KMnO_4$, the MnO_4^- being reduced to Mn^{++}; 600 ml of 0.10 M $KMnO_4$ were required. Calculate the per cent of $BaSO_3$ in the mixture.

13.43 s A 20.0-g mixture of H_2S and CH_4, when burned in oxygen, yielded a mixture of dry CO_2 and SO_2 in which the partial pressures of the CO_2 and SO_2 were, respectively, 200 mm and 300 mm. The SO_2

was oxidized to SO_4^{--} by treating the mixture of gases with 0.100 M $KMnO_4$; in the oxidation process MnO_4^- was reduced to Mn^{++}. How many milliliters of 0.100 M $KMnO_4$ were required to accomplish the oxidation?

13.44 s A mixture of CS_2 and CH_4, when burned in oxygen, yielded a mixture of CO_2 and SO_2 in which the partial pressures of the SO_2 and CO_2 were 400 mm and 500 mm, respectively. The mixture of SO_2 and CO_2 reduced 1200 ml of 0.200 M $KMnO_4$ to Mn^{++}. Calculate the weight in grams of the mixture of CS_2 and CH_4.

13.45 s A mixture of $FeSO_4$ and $SnSO_4$ is dissolved in water to form a liter of solution A. To replace all of the iron and tin in 200 ml of solution A required 0.020 mole of aluminum metal. To completely oxidize all of the Fe^{++} and Sn^{++} in 200 ml of solution A required 200 ml of 0.0500 M $KMnO_4$; in the reaction the MnO_4^- was reduced to Mn^{++}. Calculate the molarity of the $FeSO_4$ and the molarity of the $SnSO_4$ in solution A.

13.46 s A mixture of FeI_2 and $SnSO_4$ is dissolved in water to form a liter of solution A. To replace all of the iron and tin in 200 ml of solution A required 0.020 mole of aluminum metal. To completely oxidize all of the oxidizable ions in 200 ml of solution A required 280 ml of 0.0500 M $KMnO_4$; in the reaction the MnO_4^- was reduced to Mn^{++}. What is the molarity of the FeI_2 and the molarity of the $SnSO_4$ in solution A?

13.47 s To a beaker containing 164 ml of a solution of $CuSO_4$ was added 10.00 g of magnesium metal. When reaction was complete a mixture of Mg and Cu weighing 14.45 g remained in the beaker. Calculate the molarity of the original $CuSO_4$ solution.

Influence of a Solute on the Freezing Point and Boiling Point of a Solvent. Raoult's Law. Molality.

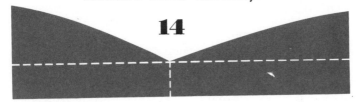

14

One gram-molecular weight (1 mole) *of a nonionizing solute* (nonelectrolyte) *when dissolved in* 1000 *g of water will raise the boiling point* 0.52°C *and will lower the freezing point* 1.86°C. (To raise the boiling point the solute must, of course, be non-volatile.) This statement represents a specific application of a relationship known as *Raoult's law*. The value, 0.52°C, is the *boiling-point constant* for water. The value, 1.86°C, is the *freezing-point constant* for water. It is believed that the reason why all nonionizing solutes, regardless of their molecular weights, have the same effect on the boiling point and freezing point of water is that a mole of such a solute contains 6.023×10^{23} molecules; 32 g (1 mole) of methyl alcohol (CH_3OH) will depress the freezing point of 1000 g of water exactly as much as will 342 g (1 mole) of sugar ($C_{12}H_{22}O_{11}$); 32 g of CH_3OH and 342 g of $C_{12}H_{22}O_{11}$ each contain 6.023×10^{23} molecules; 6.023×10^{23} molecules of CH_3OH will have the same effect on the freezing point as will 6.023×10^{23} molecules of $C_{12}H_{22}O_{11}$. *The depression of the freezing point and the increase in the boiling point is determined by the number of individual solute particles* (molecules in this case) and is independent of their weight and their chemical composition.

It should be emphasized that every pure solvent has its own characteristic boiling-point constant and freezing-point constant. In every case the boiling-point constant or freezing-point constant is the number of degrees centigrade that the boiling point or freezing point of 1000 g of solvent is raised or lowered, as the case may be, by 1 mole of solute. Thus, the boiling-point constant for CCl_4 is 5 deg per mole and the freezing-point constant for camphor is 32 deg per mole.

Since the freezing-point effect or boiling-point effect of nonelectrolytes is proportional to the number of moles of solute, it follows that, if 1 mole of solute in 1000 g of water will raise the boiling point 0.52°C and lower the freezing point 1.86°C, then 2 moles of solute in 1000 g of water will raise, or lower, it twice as much, and one half a mole will affect it only one half as much. That is, the boiling-point and freezing-point effects depend on the *concentration* of the solution expressed in moles of solute per 1000 g of solvent. The concentration of a solution expressed in moles of solute per 1000 g of solvent or millimoles of solute per gram of solvent is called *molality*.

The extent to which the boiling point or freezing point of a measured weight of water is altered by a measured weight of solute can be used as a means of determining the molecular weight of a solute. Because Raoult's law is not exact, the molecular weights obtained by this method are not exact.

Problems

14.1 A quantity of 60.0 g of a nonelectrolyte dissolved in 1000 g of H_2O lowered the freezing point 1.02°C. Calculate the approximate molecular weight of the nonelectrolyte.

SOLUTION: One mole of nonelectrolyte in 1000 g of water would have depressed the freezing point 1.86°C. Since a depression of 1.02° was observed, 1.02/1.86 mole of electrolyte must have been dissolved.

$$\frac{1.02}{1.86} \text{ mole} = 60 \text{ g}$$

$$1 \text{ mole} = \frac{1.86}{1.02} \times 60 \text{ g} = 109 \text{ g}$$

The molecular weight is approximately 109.

14.2 When 4.20 g of a nonelectrolyte were dissolved in 40.0 g of water, a solution which froze at −1.52°C was obtained. Calculate the approximate molecular weight of the nonelectrolyte.

SOLUTION: The molecular weight is the weight of solute that will depress the freezing point 1.86°C when dissolved in 1000 g of solvent. Therefore, we will first find the concentration in grams of solute per 1000 g of water.

$$1000 \text{ g of water} \times \frac{4.20 \text{ g of solute}}{40.0 \text{ g of water}} = 105 \text{ g of solute}$$

A solution containing 105 g of solute in 1000 g of water is the same *concentration* as one containing 4.20 g of solute in 40.0 g of water. Therefore, 105 g of solute will depress the freezing point of 1000 g of solvent exactly the same number of degrees that 4.20 g of solute will depress the freezing point of 40.0 g of solvent, namely, 1.52°C. Continue as in Problem 14.1.

14.3 If 20 g of $C_6H_{10}O_5$, a nonelectrolyte, were dissolved in 250 g of H_2O, calculate the boiling point of the solution at 760 mm.

SOLUTION: The molecular weight of $C_6H_{10}O_5$ is 162. That means that 162 g of $C_6H_{10}O_5$ dissolved in 1000 g of water will increase the boiling point 0.52°.
A solution containing 20 g of $C_6H_{10}O_5$ in 250 g of H_2O is the same concentration as one containing 80 g in 1000 g of H_2O (see Problem 14.2). Therefore, 80 g of $C_6H_{10}O_5$ will increase the boiling point of 1000 g of H_2O the same number of degrees that 20 g will increase the boiling point of 250 g of H_2O. 80 g of $C_6H_{10}O_5$ is 80/162 of a mole. Since 1 mole increases the boiling point 0.52°, 80/162 mole will increase it 80/162 × 0.52° or 0.26°. At 760 mm pure water boils at 100°C. Therefore, the solution will boil at 100.26°C.

14.4 When 6.00 g of a nonelectrolyte were dissolved in 54.0 g of H_2O, a solution was obtained which boiled at 100.41°C at 760 mm. Calculate the approximate molecular weight of the nonelectrolyte.

14.5 6.00 g of C_2H_5OH, a nonelectrolyte, were dissolved in 300 g of H_2O. Calculate the freezing point of the solution.*

14.6 How many grams of $C_3H_5(OH)_3$, a nonelectrolyte, must be dissolved in 600 g of H_2O to give a solution which will freeze at −4.00°C?

14.7 When 12 g of a nonelectrolyte were dissolved in 300 g of water, a solution which froze at −1.62°C was obtained. What was the approximate molecular weight of the nonelectrolyte?*

14.8 When 5.12 g of the nonionizing solute, naphthalene ($C_{10}H_8$), are dissolved in 100 g of CCl_4 (carbon tetrachloride), the boiling point of the CCl_4 is raised 2°. What is the boiling-point constant for CCl_4?

14.9 A 10% solution of a nonelectrolyte in water freezes at $-0.93°C$. Calculate the approximate molecular weight of the nonelectrolyte.*

14.10 s Calculate the density of an aqueous solution of K_2CO_3 which is 3.10 molal and 2.82 molar.

14.11 s Calculate the molality of a 28.0% $HClO_4$ solution.

14.12 s A 4.1 molar solution of NaCl in water has a density of 1.2 g per ml. Calculate the molality of 4.1 M NaCl.

14.13 s A solution prepared by dissolving 14.4 g of acetophenone (C_8H_8O) in 1000 g of acetic acid $(HC_2H_3O_2)$ freezes at a temperature 0.430°C lower than the normal freezing point of acetic acid. Acetophenone exists in solution as the monomer, C_6H_5O.

When 0.430 g of lithium iodide is dissolved in 50 g of acetic acid the freezing point of the acetic acid is lowered 0.160°C.

Calculate the average molecular weight of the lithium iodide in solution.

Assuming that lithium iodide exists only as LiI and Li_2I_2, calculate the mole per cent that is present as LiI in the above solution.

14.14 s Pure benzene freezes at 5.60°C. The freezing point constant for benzene is 4.90.

A certain alkyne has the same number of carbon atoms as a certain alkane. When a 27.8-g mixture of this alkyne and alkane is dissolved in 1000 g of benzene the resulting solution freezes at 3.15°C. The alkyne and alkane are both non-associated non-electrolytes in benzene solution. When another 27.8-g sample of this same mixture of alkyne and alkane is treated with hydrogen in the presence of a catalyst until reaction is complete 0.60 mole of H_2 is absorbed. Calculate the chemical formula of the alkyne and of the alkane.

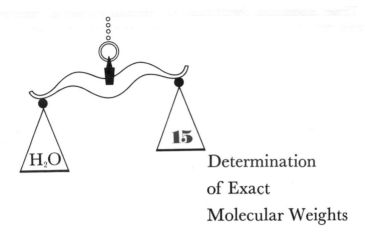

Determination
of Exact
Molecular Weights

The exact molecular weight of a compound can be determined in the following way:

1. Determine the approximate molecular weight by one of the following methods:

   (a) The vapor-density method. (One mole of a gas occupies 22.4 liters at 0°C and 760.) (See Problem 7.27.)

   (b) The boiling-point or freezing-point method. (One mole of a nonelectrolyte dissolved in 1000 g of water lowers the freezing point 1.86°C and raises the boiling point 0.52°C.) (See Problem 14.1.)

   (c) The diffusion method. (The rate of diffusion of a gas is inversely proportional to the square root of its molecular weight.) (See Problem 7.87.)

2. Determine the per cent composition by exact analysis.

3. From the per cent composition, calculate the empirical formula.

4. Knowing the empirical formula and the approximate molecular weight, calculate the true chemical formula.

5. From the true chemical formula and the known exact atomic weights calculate the exact molecular weight.

True chemical formulas of certain gaseous compounds can be determined by the type of analytical procedure illustrated in Problems 8.61, 8.62, 8.63, and 8.70. This is, in effect, a vapor-density method.

Problems

15.1   When dissolved in 1000 g of water, 20.0 g of a nonelectrolyte gave a solution which froze at 0.80°C. The compound contains 52.17% C, 34.78% O, and 13.05% H. Calculate its exact molecular weight.

SOLUTION: Carry out the steps outlined above.

1. Calculate the approximate molecular weight. (See Problem 14.1.)

$$20 \text{ g} = \frac{0.80}{1.86} \text{ mole} \qquad \text{one mole} = \frac{1.86}{0.80} \times 20 \text{ g} = 46 \text{ g}$$

2. The per cent composition is given.

3. Calculate the empirical formula.

$$C = \frac{52.17}{12} = 4.347 \qquad H = \frac{13.05}{1} = 13.05 \qquad O = \frac{34.78}{16} = 2.173$$

$$C = \frac{4.347}{2.173} = 2 \qquad H = \frac{13.05}{2.173} = 6 \qquad O = \frac{2.173}{2.173} = 1$$

The empirical formula is C_2H_6O.

4. Calculate the true chemical formula.
   The true chemical formula is either the empirical formula or some integer multiple of it. The molecular weight, calculated from the empirical formula, is 46. Since this is the calculated approximate molecular weight it can be considered that the empirical formula, C_2H_6O, is in fact the true chemical formula.

5. Using exact atomic weights, calculate the exact molecular weight of the compound whose true chemical formula is C_2H_6O.

$$
\begin{aligned}
2 \text{ C} &= 2 \times 12.011 = 24.022 \\
6 \text{ H} &= 6 \times 1.008 = 6.048 \\
1 \text{ O} &= 1 \times 15.999 = 15.999 \\
\hline
\text{exact molecular weight} &= 46.069
\end{aligned}
$$

15.2   Measured at standard conditions, 100 cc of a gas weighed 0.1232 g. The compound contained 85.71% C and 14.29% H. Calculate its exact molecular weight.

SOLUTION: Carry out the steps outlined in the preceding problem.

1. Calculate the approximate molecular weight. (The gram-molecular weight is the weight in grams of 22.4 liters at STP.)

$$22{,}400 \text{ cc} \times \frac{0.1232 \text{ g}}{100 \text{ cc}} = 27.6 \text{ g} = \text{approx. gram-mol weight}$$

2. The per cent composition is given.

3. Calculate the empirical formula.

$$C = \frac{85.71}{12} = 7.14 \qquad H = \frac{14.29}{1.008} = 14.28$$

$$C = \frac{7.14}{7.14} = 1 \qquad H = \frac{14.28}{7.14} = 2$$

The empirical formula is CH_2.

4. Calculate the true chemical formula.
   The empirical formula (CH_2) would give a molecular weight of 14. Since this is only about one half the approximate molecular weight, the true chemical formula is C_2H_4.

5. Calculate the exact molecular weight.

$$2 \text{ C} = 2 \times 12.011 = 24.022$$
$$4 \text{ H} = 4 \times \ \ 1.008 = \ \ 4.032$$
$$\text{exact molecular weight} = \overline{28.054}$$

15.3 An unknown gas was found to diffuse 2.2 ft in the same time that methane gas (CH_4) diffused 3.0 ft. The unknown gas was found to contain 80% C and 20% H. Calculate the exact molecular weight of the gas.

SOLUTION: First calculate the approximate molecular weight as follows:

$$\frac{\text{rate of diffusion of } X}{\text{rate of diffusion of } CH_4} = \frac{\sqrt{\text{mol weight of } CH_4}}{\sqrt{\text{mol weight of } X}}$$

$$\frac{2.2 \text{ ft}}{3.0 \text{ ft}} = \frac{\sqrt{16}}{\sqrt{\text{mol weight } X}}$$

$$\sqrt{\text{mol weight } X} = \frac{4 \times 3.0}{2.2} = \frac{12}{2.2} = 5.5$$

$$\text{mol weight } X = 30 = \text{approximate mol weight}$$

Then proceed as in Problem 15.2*

15.4 A compound was found, on analysis, to consist of 50.00% oxygen, 37.50% carbon, and 12.50% hydrogen. When dissolved in 100.0 cc of water, 1.666 g of the compound gave a nonconducting solution which froze at $-1.00°C$. Calculate the exact molecular weight of the compound.

15.5 When converted to a vapor, 0.347 g of a liquid compound occupied a volume of 100 cc at 0°C and 760 mm. The compound was found to consist of 92.30% carbon and 7.70% hydrogen. Calculate the exact molecular weight of the compound.*

15.6 In a given diffusion apparatus 15.0 cc of HBr gas diffused in 1 min. In the same apparatus and under the same conditions 33.7 cc of an unknown gas diffused in 1 min. The unknown gas contained 75% carbon and 25% hydrogen. Calculate its exact molecular weight.

15.7 s To completely burn 1 liter of a gaseous hydrocarbon to CO_2 and steam required 7.5 liters of O_2 gas. Five liters of CO_2 gas were formed. All volumes were measured at the same temperature and pressure. Calculate the exact molecular weight of the hydrocarbon.

15.8 s A certain hydrocarbon gas was mixed, in a steel reaction bomb, with the exact amount of O_2 gas required to burn it completely to CO_2 and H_2O (steam). The mixture was ignited by a spark, which caused all of the hydrocarbon to react with all of the O_2 to form CO_2 and H_2O. The pressures, before and after ignition, measured at the same temperature, were the same. The partial pressure of the CO_2 and steam were the same. Calculate the exact molecular weight of the hydrocarbon.

16

Chemical Equilibrium.
Equilibrium Constants.

In a great many reactions the products are capable of reacting with each other and begin to do so as soon as they are formed. A familiar example is the gas phase reaction between carbon monoxide and steam where the products, CO_2 and H_2, react with each other as indicated by the lower arrow:

$$CO + H_2O \rightleftarrows CO_2 + H_2$$

This type of reaction is called an *incomplete reaction* or *reversible reaction*. Incomplete reactions eventually reach a *state of equilibrium*. At equilibrium the rate of the reaction to the right is exactly equal to the rate of the reaction to the left.

At the start of the above reaction the CO and H_2O are present in high concentration and, therefore, react with each other at maximum speed, but they are gradually used up as the reaction progresses so the speed to the right gradually decreases.

At the beginning of the reaction, CO_2 and H_2 are present in very low concentration and, therefore, react with each other at a very low rate, but they increase in concentration as the reaction progresses and the speed to the left gradually increases. Finally the speed to the left exactly equals the speed to the right. That means that the CO, H_2O, CO_2, and H_2 are being used up as fast as they are being formed. There is no further change in the concentration of any reactant. The reaction just keeps on going "round

127

and round" without any apparent change. A state of equilibrium has been reached.

If we were to start with a mixture of CO_2 and H_2, rather than CO and H_2O, a state of equilibrium would again be reached. In this case, at the start of the reaction CO_2 and H_2 are present in high concentration, while CO and H_2O are present in very low concentration. As the reaction proceeds, the speed to the left gradually decreases as CO_2 and H_2 are used up while the speed to the right increases as more CO and H_2O are formed. Eventually, the two rates will be the same; the reaction will then be in a state of equilibrium. *It is a characteristic of any true equilibrium reaction that the same state of equilibrium will be reached by starting with either the reactants or the products.*

It is very important to note that it is not a requirement of equilibrium that the substances be present in the reaction vessel in the exact ratio in which they react with each other. Thus, if we were to place 2 moles of CO and 5 moles of steam in a 1-liter reaction vessel, 6 moles of CO and 4 moles of steam in a second liter vessel, 8 moles of CO_2 and 3 moles of H_2 in a third vessel, and 3 moles of CO, 2 moles of steam, 4 moles of CO_2 and 7 moles of H_2 in a fourth vessel, a state of equilibrium, represented by the reaction, $CO + H_2O \rightleftarrows CO_2 + H_2$, will be attained in each vessel. However, it will be observed that in each of the 4 vessels, when CO and H_2O react to form CO_2 and H_2, they always do so in the mole ratio represented by the equation, namely, 1 mole of CO with 1 mole of H_2O to form 1 mole of CO_2 and 1 mole of H_2. In any equilibrium reaction the substances will always *react* with each other in the mole ratio represented by the equation, but they can be present in all sorts of ratios.

Suppose we have, in a liter reaction vessel at a given high temperature, an equilibrium mixture consisting of 0.10 mole of CO, 0.80 mole of H_2O (steam), 0.80 mole of CO_2, and 0.50 mole of H_2 represented by the equation

$$\underset{0.10}{CO} + \underset{0.80}{H_2O} \rightleftarrows \underset{0.80}{CO_2} + \underset{0.50}{H_2}$$

Now suppose we were to force into the vessel a quantity of hydrogen gas. This, obviously, will increase the concentration of hydrogen. This increase in concentration of the hydrogen will increase the rate at which it will react with CO_2. As a result, the rate of the reaction to the left will be speeded up. This will increase the concentration of the CO and H_2O since they are, at the moment, being formed faster than they are reacting with each other. As time passes and the reaction proceeds the speed to the left gradually decreases as the concentrations of CO_2 and H_2 fall; at the same time the speed to the right gradually increases as the concentrations of CO and H_2O rise. In time the forward and reverse rates will again be equal and equilibrium will be re-established. However, at this new equilibrium the rates in the two directions will be greater than in the previous equilibrium. Also, at this new equilibrium we will find that the concentrations of the CO, H_2O, and H_2 are greater while the concentration of the CO_2 is less than before the H_2 was added. The increase in concentration of the H_2 has *shifted the equilibrium* to the left as evidenced by the fact that the concentrations of the CO and H_2O on the left have gone up, while the concentration of the CO_2 on the right has gone down. We can state that, in effect, the addition of H_2 (on the right) has pushed the equilibrium toward the left. Had we added more CO or H_2O to the reaction vessel the equilibrium would have been shifted to the right. In an equilibrium, if the concentration of a given reactant is increased, the equilibrium will be pushed toward the opposite side of the reaction. If the concentration of a reactant is reduced, by removing some of that reactant, the equilibrium will be *pulled* toward the same side of the reaction.

If we were to examine carefully, at the new equilibrium point, the increase in the *number of moles* of CO and H_2O on the left and the decrease in the *number of moles* of CO_2 on the right resulting from forcing more H_2 into the reaction vessel, we would find that the increase in the number of moles of CO is the same as the increase in the number of moles of H_2O and that the decrease in the number of moles of CO_2 is the same as the increase in the number of moles of CO. This is exactly what we would expect from the equation, $CO + H_2O \rightleftarrows CO_2 + H_2$, since it tells us that CO_2 and H_2 react in the ratio of 1 mole of CO_2 with 1 mole of H_2 to yield 1 mole of CO and 1 mole of H_2O.

Suppose we have, in a reaction vessel of fixed volume at a given high temperature, an equilibrium mixture represented by the following equation:

$$4 NH_3 + 5 O_2 \rightleftarrows 6 H_2O + 4 NO$$

If we now force into this reaction vessel, at the given temperature, some more NO gas the equilibrium will be shifted to the left. At the new equilibrium the concentrations of the NH_3 and O_2 will be higher than before addition of the extra NO and the concentration of the H_2O will be lower. In this case, however, the increase in the *number of moles* of NH_3 and O_2 and the decrease in the *number of moles* of H_2O will not be the same; we will find, as the equation testifies, that in the shift in equilibrium due to addition of more NO, for every 4 additional moles of NH_3 that are produced there will be 5 additional moles of O_2, and 6 moles of H_2O will be used up. These two examples, emphasize the very important fact that *in every equilibrium shift, the change in the number of moles of the reactants involved is strictly in accord with the mole relationships specified by the equation for the reaction.*

We have noted earlier in this discussion that, for any equilibrium reaction, the reactants can be present in all sorts of ratios. This is illustrated in Table 16.1 which gives the equilibrium concentrations of CO, H_2O, CO_2, and H_2 for the reaction $CO + H_2O \rightleftarrows H_2 + CO_2$ for five experiments, all carried out at the same temperature.

Table 16.1   RELATIVE CONCENTRATION OF REACTANTS IN AN EQUILIBRIUM SYSTEM AT CONSTANT TEMPERATURE

Reaction vessel	[CO]	[H$_2$O]	[CO$_2$]	[H$_2$]	$\dfrac{[CO_2] \times [H_2]}{[CO] \times [H_2O]}$
1	0.20	0.20	0.50	0.40	5.0
2	0.10	0.18	0.30	0.31	5.2
3	0.10	0.80	0.80	0.50	5.0
4	0.30	0.50	0.90	0.83	5.0
5	0.75	0.20	0.80	0.94	5.0

Note: the notations $[CO_2]$, $[H_2O]$, $[CO]$, and $[H_2]$ mean concentration in moles per liter of the substance within the bracket.

An examination of the data in Table 16.1 reveals one very striking fact. The answer obtained when the product of the concentrations of the products, H_2 and CO_2, is divided by the product of the concentrations of the reactants, CO and H_2O, is, within the limits of experimental error, the same for each experiment. That is,

$$\frac{[CO_2] \times [H_2]}{[CO] \times [H_2O]} = \text{a constant}$$

Similar data for the thousands of equilibria that have been studied confirm the fact that *in every reacting system in equilibrium at a given temperature the product of the concentrations of the products divided by the product of the concentrations of the reactants is a constant.* This constant, referred to by the letter, K, is called the *Equilibrium Constant* for the particular reaction at the particular temperature. For the reaction

$$A + B \rightleftarrows C + D$$

the formula for the equilibrium constant, K, is,

$$K = \frac{[C] \times [D]}{[A] \times [B]}$$

It is commonly referred to as the *Equilibrium Formula*.
It is obvious that, if

$$\frac{[C] \times [D]}{[A] \times [B]}$$

is constant, then

$$\frac{[A] \times [B]}{[C] \times [D]}$$

will also be constant; the latter constant will be the reciprocal of the former. By common agreement among scientists, the product of the concentrations of the products is placed in the numerator.

For the reaction $SO_2 + NO_2 \rightleftarrows SO_3 + NO$,

$$K = \frac{[SO_3] \times [NO]}{[SO_2] \times [NO_2]}$$

When a reaction involves more than 1 mole of a specific reactant, the concentration of that reactant is raised to a power equal to the number of moles of the reactant in the balanced equation. Thus for the reaction $2\,SO_2 + O_2 \rightleftarrows 2\,SO_3$,

$$K = \frac{[SO_3]^2}{[SO_2]^2 \times [O_2]}$$

For the reaction $N_2 + 3\,H_2 \rightleftarrows 2\,NH_3$,

$$K = \frac{[NH_3]^2}{[N_2] \times [H_2]^3}$$

For the reaction $H_2 + I_2 \rightleftarrows 2\,HI$,

$$K = \frac{[HI]^2}{[H_2] \times [I_2]}$$

For the reaction $4\,NH_3 + 5\,O_2 \rightleftarrows 4\,NO + 6\,H_2O$,

$$K = \frac{[NO]^4 \times [H_2O]^6}{[NH_3]^4 \times [O_2]^5}$$

And for the general reaction, $aA + bB \rightleftarrows cC + dD$,

$$K = \frac{[C]^c \times [D]^d}{[A]^a \times [B]^b}$$

The reason for raising the concentration of a reactant to a power equal to the number of moles may be more evident if we show each mole as a separate reactant by writing the equation for the reaction in the form

$$N_2 + H_2 + H_2 + H_2 \rightleftarrows NH_3 + NH_3$$

The equilibrium constant, K, can then be expressed in the form

$$K = \frac{[NH_3] \times [NH_3]}{[N_2] \times [H_2] \times [H_2] \times [H_2]} = \frac{[NH_3]^2}{[N_2] \times [H_2]^3}$$

The numerical value of the equilibrium constant for a given reaction is obtained by inserting the experimentally determined values of the concentrations in the Equilibrium Formula for the reaction. Thus, for the reaction,

$$\underset{0.60}{SO_2} + \underset{0.80}{NO_2} \rightleftarrows \underset{0.90}{SO_3} + \underset{1.1}{NO}$$

the calculation, using the equilibrium concentrations given in moles per liter, becomes

$$K = \frac{[SO_3] \times [NO]}{[SO_2] \times [NO_2]} = \frac{0.90 \times 1.1}{0.60 \times 0.80} = 2.1$$

(In this instance all *units* cancel, so the constant is simply a number, 2.1.)

For the reaction,

$$\underset{0.20}{2\ SO_2} + \underset{0.30}{O_2} \rightleftarrows \underset{0.60}{2\ SO_3}$$

$$K = \frac{[SO_3]^2}{[SO_2]^2 \times [O_2]} = \frac{(0.60)^2}{(0.20)^2 \times (0.30)} = 30 \text{ liters/moles}$$

(In this instance the unit, moles/liters, remains uncancelled in the denominator. Therefore, the constant has the dimension 30/moles/liters or 30 liters/moles.)

It should be noted that a *solid* reactant or product is not included in the equilibrium formula. Thus, for the equilibrium reaction,

$$SiF_4 \text{ (gas)} + 2\ H_2O \text{ (gas)} \rightleftarrows SiO_2 \text{ (solid)} + 4\ HF \text{ (gas)}$$

$$K = \frac{[HF]^4}{[SiF_4] + [H_2O]^2}$$

and for the reaction,

$$LaCl_3 \text{ (solid)} + H_2O \text{ (gas)} \rightleftarrows LaClO \text{ (solid)} + 2\ HCl \text{ (gas)}$$

$$K = \frac{[HCl]^2}{[H_2O]}$$

The reason why the solid is not included is that the *amount* of excess solid present has no effect whatever on the *equilibrium* point. The same state of equilibrium is attained whether we have a small excess or a large excess. The *rate* at which equilibrium is attained will be affected by the total surface of the solid. However, once equilibrium has been attained, the removal of some of the excess solid (in fact, all of the solid) will have no effect on the equilibrium.

Problems

16.1 At equilibrium at a given temperature and in a liter reaction vessel HI is 20 mole per cent dissociated into H_2 and I_2 according to the equation, $2 \text{ HI} \rightleftarrows H_2 + I_2$. If 1 mole of pure HI is introduced into a liter reaction vessel at the given temperature, how many moles of each component will be present when equilibrium is established?

SOLUTION: 20% of 1 mole $= 0.2$ mole $=$ the number of moles of HI that dissociate. $1 - 0.2 = 0.8$ mole of HI that is not dissociated. The equation, $2 \text{ HI} = H_2 + I_2$, tells us that 2 moles of HI yield 1 mole of H_2 and 1 mole of I_2. Therefore 0.2 mole of HI yields 0.1 mole of H_2 and 0.1 mole of I_2.

16.2 PCl_5 is 20 mole per cent dissociated into PCl_3 and Cl_2 at equilibrium at a given temperature and in a liter vessel in accordance with the equation, $PCl_5 \rightleftarrows PCl_3 + Cl_2$. One mole of pure PCl_5 was introduced into a liter reaction vessel at the given temperature. How many moles of each component were present at equilibrium?

16.3 A reaction vessel in which the following reaction had reached a state of equilibrium, $CO + Cl_2 \rightleftarrows COCl_2$, was found, on analysis, to contain 0.30 mole of CO, 0.20 mole of Cl_2, and 0.80 mole of $COCl_2$, in a liter of mixture. Calculate the equilibrium constant for the reaction.

SOLUTION: Let $K =$ the equilibrium constant

$$K = \frac{[COCl_2]}{[CO] \times [Cl_2]}$$

The notation $[COCl_2]$, by definition, means concentration of $COCl_2$ in moles of $COCl_2$ per liter. Likewise, $[CO]$ and $[Cl_2]$ mean, respectively, moles of CO per liter and moles of Cl_2 per liter. In all problems involving chemical equilibrium the concentrations will be expressed in moles per liter. Substituting in the above equation,

$$K = \frac{0.80}{0.30 \times 0.20} = 13 \text{ liters/mole}$$

16.4 A reaction vessel with a capacity of 1 liter in which the following reaction had reached a state of equilibrium, $2 SO_2 + O_2 \rightleftarrows 2 SO_3$, was found to contain 0.6 mole of SO_3, 0.2 mole of SO_2, and 0.3 mole of O_2. Calculate the equilibrium constant.

SOLUTION: Substitute in the equation

$$K = \frac{[SO_3]^2}{[SO_2]^2 \times [O_2]}$$

The total concentrations of SO_3 and SO_2 are substituted in this equation to give

$$\frac{(0.6)^2}{(0.2)^2 \times (0.3)} = \frac{0.36}{0.012} = 3 \times 10^1 \text{ liters/mole}$$

The reason why the total concentrations of SO_2 and SO_3 and not half of the total concentrations of each are used is that the 2 molecules of SO_2 that react with O_2 can each be picked from the total supply of SO_2 molecules available. The same is true of the 2 SO_3 molecules.

16.5 A quantity of PCl_5 was heated in a liter vessel at 250°C. At equilibrium the concentrations of the gases in the vessel were as follows:

$$PCl_5 = 7.05 \text{ moles/liter}; \quad PCl_3 = 0.54 \text{ mole/liter};$$
$$Cl_2 = 0.54 \text{ mole/liter}$$

Calculate the equilibrium constant, K, for the dissociation of PCl_5 at 250°C.*

16.6 An equilibrium mixture of N_2, H_2, and NH_3, which reacts according to the equation, $N_2 + 3 H_2 \rightleftarrows 2 NH_3$, was found to consist of 0.800 mole of NH_3, 0.300 mole of N_2 and 0.200 mole of H_2 in a liter. Calculate the equilibrium constant.

16.7 An equilibrium mixture, $CO + Cl_2 \rightleftarrows COCl_2$, contained 1.50 moles of CO, 1.00 mole of Cl_2 and 4.00 moles of $COCl_2$ in a 5-liter reaction vessel at a specific temperature. Calculate the equilibrium constant for the reaction at this temperature.*

SOLUTION: In calculating the equilibrium constant, concentration must be expressed in moles *per liter*.

16.8 In an equilibrium mixture of N_2, H_2, and NH_3, contained in a 5.00-liter reaction vessel at 450°C and a total pressure of 332 atm the partial pressures of the gases were: $N_2 = 47.55$ atm, $H_2 = 142.25$ atm, $NH_3 = 142.25$ atm. Calculate the equilibrium constant for the reaction.

SOLUTION: To calculate the equilibrium constant we must know the concentration of each reactant in *moles* per *liter*. To this end we will first calculate the moles of each substance per liter by use of the formula, $PV = nRT$.

16.9 An equilibrium mixture, $2 SO_2 + O_2 \rightleftarrows 2 SO_3$, contained in a 2.0-liter reaction vessel at a specific temperature was found to contain 96 g of SO_3, 25.6 g of SO_2 and 19.2 g of O_2. Calculate the equilibrium constant for the reaction at this temperature.*

SOLUTION: Concentrations must be expressed in *moles* per *liter*.

16.10 The equilibrium constant for the reaction, $CO + H_2O \rightleftarrows CO_2 + H_2$, is 4.0 at a given temperature. An equilibrium mixture of the above substances at the given temperature was found to contain 0.60 mole of CO, 0.20 mole of steam, and 0.50 mole of CO_2 in a liter. How many moles of H_2 were there in the mixture?

16.11 Exactly 1 mole of NH_3 was introduced into a liter reaction vessel at a certain high temperature. When the reaction, $2 NH_3 \rightleftarrows N_2 + 3 H_2$, had reached a state of equilibrium 0.6 mole of H_2 was found to be present. Calculate the equilibrium constant for the reaction.*

SOLUTION: Note that, when NH_3 dissociates to give N_2 and H_2, the products are formed in the ratio of 1 mole of N_2 and 3 moles of H_2 for every 2 moles of NH_3 which dissociate. To yield 0.6 mole of H_2, 0.4 mole of NH_3 must have dissociated. This leaves 0.6 mole of undissociated NH_3. The 0.4 mole of NH_3 which dissociates will yield 0.2 mole of N_2 and 0.6 mole of H_2. The equilibrium mixture will contain 0.6 mole of NH_3, 0.2 mole of N_2, and 0.6 mole of H_2.

16.12 One mole of SO_3 was placed in a liter reaction vessel at a certain temperature. When equilibrium was established in the reaction, $2 SO_3 \rightleftarrows 2 SO_2 + O_2$, the vessel was found to contain 0.60 mole of SO_2. Calculate the equilibrium constant for the reaction.

16.13 One mole of NH_3 gas is introduced into an empty liter vessel which is then heated to a certain temperature. When equilibrium is established it is found that 0.10 mole of N_2 has been formed according to the equation, $2 NH_3 \rightleftarrows N_2 + 3 H_2$. What is the numerical value of the equilibrium constant for this reaction at the certain temperature?*

16.14 The equilibrium constant for the reaction, $2 SO_2 + O_2 \rightleftarrows 2 SO_3$, is 4.5 liters/mole at 600°C. A quantity of SO_3 gas was placed in a liter reaction vessel at 600°C. When the system reached a state of equilibrium the vessel was found to contain 2.0 moles of O_2 gas. How many moles of SO_3 gas were originally placed in the reaction vessel?

SOLUTION: Note that, when SO_3 decomposes to yield SO_2 and O_2, the products are formed in the ratio of 2 moles of SO_2 and 1 mole of O_2 for every 2 moles of SO_3 decomposed. Since, in this problem, there are 2 moles of O_2 in the vessel there must also be 4 moles of SO_2 present and 4 moles of SO_3 must have decomposed to yield 4 moles of SO_2 and 2 moles of O_2. That means that, at equilibrium, the reaction vessel must contain 4 less moles of SO_3 than were originally introduced. With these facts, and knowing that the equilibrium constant is 4.5 liters/mole the number of moles of SO_3 originally added can be calculated.

16.15 The equilibrium constant for the reaction, $N_2 + 3 H_2 \rightleftarrows 2 NH_3$, is 2.00 liter^2 mole^{-2} at 300°C. A quantity of NH_3 gas was introduced into a liter reaction vessel at 300°C. When equilibrium was established the vessel was found to contain 2.00 moles of N_2. How many moles of NH_3 were originally introduced into the vessel?*

16.16 A liter reaction vessel in which the reaction,

$$C \text{ (solid)} + H_2O \text{ (gas)} \rightleftarrows CO \text{ (gas)} + H_2 \text{ (gas)},$$

has reached a state of equilibrium contains 0.16 mole of C, 0.58 mole of H_2O, 0.15 mole of CO, and 0.15 mole of H_2. Calculate the equilibrium constant for the reaction.

SOLUTION: Since C is a solid it is not included in the equilibrium formula

$$K = \frac{[CO] \times [H_2]}{[H_2O]} = \frac{[0.15] \times [0.15]}{[0.58]} = 3.9 \times 10^{-3} \text{ mole} \times \text{liter}^{-1}$$

16.17 A mixture of equal volumes of SO_2 gas and O_2 gas, measured at the same temperature and pressure, was placed in a 4-liter reaction vessel. When the temperature was raised to 727°C the reaction, $2 SO_2 + O_2 \rightleftarrows 2 SO_3$, occurred. When equilibrium was established the concentrations of the SO_2 and the SO_3 were exactly equal and the total pressure in the 4-liter vessel at 727°C was 114.8 atm. Calculate the equilibrium constant for the reaction at 727°C.*

16.18 The equilibrium mixture, $SO_2 + NO_2 \rightleftarrows SO_3 + NO$, in a liter vessel, was found to contain 0.600 mole of SO_3, 0.400 mole of NO,

0.100 mole of NO_2, and 0.800 mole of SO_2. How many moles of NO would have to be forced into the reaction vessel, volume and temperature being kept constant, in order to increase the amount of NO_2 to 0.300 mole?

SOLUTION: First calculate the equilibrium constant.

$$K = \frac{[SO_3] \times [NO]}{[SO_2] \times [NO_2]} = \frac{0.6 \times 0.4}{0.8 \times 0.1} = 3.00$$

Let X = moles of NO that must be added. We can see from the equation, $SO_2 + NO_2 \rightleftarrows SO_3 + NO$, that in order to produce 0.2 more mole of NO_2 we must also produce 0.2 more mole of SO_2 and we must use up 0.2 mole of SO_3 and 0.2 mole of NO. Therefore, when we have 0.3 mole of NO_2 we will have 1 mole $(0.8 + 0.2)$ of SO_2, 0.4 mole $(0.6 - 0.2)$ of SO_3 and $X + 0.2$ mole $(0.4 + X - 0.2)$ of NO. Substituting the values in the equilibrium formula, we have

$$\frac{0.4 \times (X + 0.2)}{1 \times 0.3} = 3.00 \qquad (X = 2.05 \text{ moles})$$

16.19 An equilibrium mixture, $CO + H_2O \rightleftarrows CO_2 + H_2$, contains 0.20 mole of H_2, 0.80 mole of CO_2, 0.10 mole of CO, and 0.40 mole of H_2O in a liter. How many moles of CO_2 would have to be added at constant temperature and volume to increase the amount of CO to 0.20 mole?*

16.20 An equilibrium mixture, $CO_2 + H_2 \rightleftarrows CO + H_2O$, was found to contain 0.6 mole of CO_2, 0.2 mole of H_2, 0.8 mole of CO, and 0.3 mole of H_2O in a liter. How many moles of CO_2 would have to be removed from the system at constant volume and temperature in order to reduce the amount of CO to 0.6 mole?

16.21 A reaction system in equilibrium according to the reaction, $2 SO_2 + O_2 \rightleftarrows 2 SO_3$, in a liter reaction vessel at a given temperature was found to contain 0.11 mole of SO_2, 0.12 mole of SO_3, and 0.050 mole of O_2. Another liter reaction vessel contains 64 g of SO_2 at the above temperature. How many grams of O_2 must be added to this vessel in order that, at equilibrium, half of the SO_2 is oxidized to SO_3?*

16.22 The equilibrium constant for the reaction, $PCl_5 \rightleftarrows PCl_3 + Cl_2$, at 250°C is 0.041 mole $\times$ liter^{-1}. Set up, but do not solve, an algebraic equation in one unknown, X, which, if solved for X, will give the number of *grams* of Cl_2 that will be present at equilibrium when 0.3 mole of PCl_5 is heated in a liter vessel at 250°C.

16.23 An equilibrium mixture, $H_2 + I_2 \rightleftarrows 2 HI$, contains 3 moles of H_2, 2 moles of I_2, and 2 moles of HI in a liter. How many moles of I_2 must be added at constant temperature to have half the added I_2 react to form HI? Let $X =$ moles of I_2 added. Set up the equilibrium expression but do not solve.

16.24 The equilibrium constant for the reaction,

$$4 NH_3 + 5 O_2 \rightleftarrows 4 NO + 6 H_2O,$$

at 600°C is 360 moles/liter. A 1-liter reaction vessel at 600° contains, in equilibrium, a moles of NH_3, b moles of O_2, c moles of NO, and d moles of steam. Z additional moles of O_2 are introduced. Set up, but *do not solve*, an algebraic expression involving an unknown X, and the known quantities, a, b, c, d, Z, and 360, which, when solved, will enable you to determine the concentration of each of the four reactants at the new equilibrium. Be sure to specify what X represents.

16.25 The equilibrium mixture, $SO_2 + NO_2 \rightleftarrows SO_3 + NO$, was found to contain 0.60 mole of SO_3, 0.40 mole of NO, 0.80 mole of SO_2 and 0.10 mole of NO_2 per liter. One mole of NO was then forced into the reaction vessel, temperature and volume being kept constant. Calculate the number of moles of each gas in the new equilibrium mixture.

SOLUTION: First calculate the equilibrium constant. Its value is 3.0 We can see from the equation, $SO_2 + NO_2 \rightleftarrows SO_3 + NO$, that if the concentration of NO is increased the equilibrium will be shifted to the left. Let X be the number of additional moles of SO_2 formed as a result of this shift. There will then be $0.8 + X$ moles of SO_2. But when X new moles of SO_2 are formed, X new moles of NO_2 will also be formed; X moles of SO_3 and X moles of NO will be used up. There will, therefore, be present in the new mixture $0.8 + X$ moles of SO_2, $0.1 + X$ moles of NO_2, $0.6 - X$ moles of SO_3, and $1 + 0.4 - X$ or $1.4 - X$ moles of NO. If we insert these values in the equilibrium formula, for which the constant 3 has been calculated, we have

$$\frac{[SO_3] \times [NO]}{[SO_2] \times [NO_2]} = \frac{(0.6 - X) \times (1.4 - X)}{(0.8 + X) \times (0.1 + X)} = 3.0$$

Solving, $X = 0.12$ moles. Substituting this value of X we find the concentrations of the 4 reactants to be $SO_3 = 0.48$ mole, $NO = 1.3$ moles, $SO_2 = 0.92$ mole, and $NO_2 = 0.22$ mole.

16.26 At a given temperature a liter reaction vessel contained 0.60 mole of $COCl_2$, 0.30 mole of CO, and 0.10 mole of Cl_2. $CO + Cl_2 \rightleftharpoons COCl_2$. An amount of 0.40 mole of Cl_2 was added to the vessel at constant temperature and volume. Calculate the number of moles of CO, Cl_2, and $COCl_2$, in the new equilibrium system.

16.27 The equilibrium constant for the reaction,

$$CO + H_2O \rightleftharpoons CO_2 + H_2$$

is 4.00 at a given temperature. A combination of 0.400 mole of CO and 0.600 mole of steam was brought together in a liter vessel at this temperature. How many moles of CO_2 were present when the system reached a state of equilibrium?*

16.28 Calculate the number of moles of Cl_2 produced when 1.0 mole of PCl_5 is heated at 250°C in a vessel having a capacity of 1.0 liter. PCl_5 dissociates according to the equation, $PCl_5 \rightleftharpoons PCl_3 + Cl_2$. The equilibrium constant for this reaction at 250°C is 0.041 mole × liter^{-1}.

16.29 A mixture of equal volumes of CO and H_2O, measured at the same temperature and pressure, was placed in a 4.0-liter reaction vessel which was then heated to 1220°C. When equilibrium was established in the reaction, $CO + H_2O \rightleftharpoons CO_2 + H_2$, the vessel was found to contain 3.0 moles of H_2 and the total pressure of the equilibrium mixture was 490 atm.

(a) How many moles of CO were originally placed in the reaction vessels?*

(b) How many additional moles of CO must be added to the vessel in order to increase the concentration of H_2 to 1.0 mole per liter, temperature being kept at 1220°C?*

16.30 Equal volumes of CO and H_2O (steam) were introduced into a 0.500-liter reaction vessel at 1207°C. When the reaction,

$$CO + H_2O \rightleftharpoons CO_2 + H_2$$

had reached a state of equilibrium the vessel contained a total of 2.00 moles of gases. The partial pressure of the H_2 in this equilibrium mixture was 97.2 atm.

(a) How many grams of CO gas must be forced into the vessel to increase the concentration of the H_2 to 1.00 mole per liter, temperature being kept constant?

(b) What will be the partial pressure of the H_2 in this new equilibrium system?

16.31 s A mixture of 2 moles of CH_4 gas and 1 mole of H_2S gas was placed in an evacuated container which was then heated to and maintained at a temperature of 727°C. When equilibrium was established in the gaseous reaction, $CH_4 + 2\ H_2S \rightleftarrows CS_2 + 4\ H_2$, the total pressure in the container was 0.92 atm and the partial pressure of the hydrogen gas was 0.20 atm. What was the volume of the container?

16.32 s A mixture of $COCl_2$, CO, and Cl_2, formed from $COCl_2$ gas in equilibrium according to the reaction, $COCl_2 \rightleftarrows CO + Cl_2$, has a density of 1.207 g/liter at 327°C and a pressure of 1.0 atm. Calculate the equilibrium constant for the reaction at 327°C.

16.33 s To the system $LaCl_3$ (solid) + H_2O (gas) + heat $\rightleftarrows$ LaClO (solid) + 2 HCl (gas) already at equilibrium we add more water vapor without changing either the temperature or the volume of the system. When equilibrium is re-established the pressure of water vapor is found to have been doubled. Hence, the pressure of HCl present in the system has been multiplied by what factor?

16.34 s The empirical formula for sulfur monochloride is known to be SCl. To determine the true chemical formula (whether it is S_1Cl_1, S_2Cl_2, S_3Cl_3, S_4Cl_4, etc.) the following equilibrium reaction is studied in a 1-liter vessel at 327°C:

$$3\ Cl_2\ (gas) + \frac{2}{X}S_xCl_x\ (gas) + 8\ NaF\ (solid)$$

$$\rightleftarrows 2\ SF_4\ (gas) + 8\ NaCl\ (solid)$$

The solid NaF and NaCl have zero vapor pressures.

In the above reaction, at equilibrium at 327°C, the 1-liter vessel was found to contain 0.0040 mole of SF_4, 0.020 mole of Cl_2, 2.16 g of S_xCl_x, 0.36 g of NaF and 0.94 g of NaCl. The total pressure was 1497.6 mm.

Calculate the true chemical formula of the sulfur monochloride at 327°C and the value of the equilibrium constant.

16.35 s A mixture of equal volumes of SO_2 and O_2, measured at the same temperature and pressure, was placed in a 4.00-liter reaction vessel which was then heated to 527°C. When equilibrium was established in the reaction, $2 SO_2 + O_2 \rightleftarrows 2 SO_3$, the vessel was found to contain 4.00 moles of SO_3 and the total pressure in the vessel was 164 atm.

(a) How many moles of SO_2 were originally placed in the vessel?

(b) How many additional moles of SO_2 would have to be forced into the 4.00-liter vessel, in order that, at equilibrium at 527°C, the number of moles of SO_3 would be twice the number of moles of O_2?

16.36 s A 5.0-liter reaction vessel in which the reaction, $2 NH_3 \rightleftarrows N_2 + 3 H_2$, had reached equilibrium at a certain temperature, was found to contain 3.0 moles NH_3, 2.0 moles of N_2, and 5.0 moles of H_2. By pushing down on a piston the volume of the reaction vessel was reduced to 4.0 liters; at the same time X moles of N_2 were forced into the vessel; during the entire experiment the temperature was kept constant. When equilibrium had been re-established the 4.0-liter vessel was found to contain 5.0 moles of NH_3. How many moles of N_2 were forced into the vessel? When equilibrium had been re-established what were the concentrations, in moles per liter, of the N_2 and the H_2?

16.37 s An equilibrium, $2 NH_3 \rightleftarrows N_2 + 3 H_2$, taking place in a 3.0 liter volume in a cylinder was found to contain 4.0 moles NH_3, 3.0 moles N_2, and 2.0 moles H_2. A piston fitted to this cylinder was then withdrawn until the final volume was 5.0 liters. Then Z moles of NH_3 were forced into the container. When equilibrium had been re-established, 5.0 moles N_2 were found in the container. Find Z and find final concentrations of all the gases in moles per liter. Temperature is constant.

16.38 s At 450°C and in a 5.0-liter reaction vessel the partial pressures of the reactants in the equilibrium, $N_2 + 3 H_2 \rightleftarrows 2 NH_3$, are: $N_2 = 11.85$ atm, $H_2 = 23.70$ atm, $NH_3 = 35.55$ atm.
A liter reaction vessel at 450°C contains 1.0 mole of H_2 gas. How many grams of N_2 must be added to the vessel in order that, at equilibrium, 60 mole per cent of the H_2 will be converted to NH_3?

16.39 s A mixture of SO_3, SO_2, and O_2 gases in equilibrium in a 4.0-liter reaction vessel at 527°C according to the equation, $2 SO_2 + O_2 \rightleftarrows 2 SO_3$, was found to contain 2.0 moles of SO_2, 4.0 moles of O_2, and 4.0 moles of SO_3. The volume of the reaction system was then reduced by means of a piston until the number of moles of SO_3 at equilibrium at 527°C was increased to 5.0. What was the final volume of the reaction system?

16.40 s An equilibrium mixture of hydrogen, ammonia, and nitrogen contains 4.0 moles of hydrogen, 5.0 moles of ammonia, and 3.0 moles of nitrogen, in a 4.0-liter cylinder. The volume of the cylinder is changed at constant temperature by moving a piston such that at equilibrium this new volume now contains 7.0 moles of hydrogen. Calculate the final volume of the cylinder.

16.41 s To determine the equilibrium constant at a given temperature for the gas-phase reaction, $N_2 + 3 H_2 \rightleftarrows 2 NH_3$, 0.326 mole of H_2 and 0.439 mole of N_2 were mixed in a 1.00-liter vessel. At equilibrium the system was found to contain a total of 0.657 mole.

(a) Calculate the equilibrium constant for the reaction as written above and state the units in which this value is expressed.

(b) Call the constant calculated in part (a) K_1. Call the constant for the following reaction K_2; $NH_3 \rightleftarrows \frac{1}{2} N_2 + \frac{3}{2} H_2$. State the units in which K_2 would be expressed. State the algebraic relation between K_1 and K_2.

16.42 s When N_2O_5 gas is heated it dissociates into N_2O_3 gas and O_2 gas according to the reaction, $N_2O_5 \rightleftarrows N_2O_3 + O_2$. K_1 for this reaction at a specific temperature, t°C, is 7.75 moles/liter. The N_2O_3 dissociates to give N_2O gas and O_2 gas according to the reaction, $N_2O_3 \rightleftarrows N_2O + O_2$. K_2 for this reaction at the same specific temperature, t°C, is 4.00 moles/liter.
When 4.00 moles of N_2O_5 are heated in a 1.00-liter reaction vessel at t°C the concentration of O_2 at equilibrium is 4.50 moles/liter. Calculate the concentrations in moles per liter of all other species in the equilibrium system.

SOLUTION: Let X equal the moles per liter of O_2 derived from the N_2O_5 and Y equal the moles per liter of O_2 derived from the N_2O_3. Then:

$$[O_2] = X + Y \qquad [N_2O_5] = 4.00 - X$$
$$[N_2O_3] = X - Y \qquad [N_2O] = Y$$

Since three equations involving X and Y are available the value of X and of Y, and hence the concentrations of all species, can be calculated.

Equilibrium Constants in Units of Pressure

When the gas law equation, $PV = nRT$, is written in the form, $n/V = P/RT$, the term, n/V, represents the concentration of the gas in moles per liter. The equation, $n/V = P/RT$, tells us that, at constant temperature, the concentration of a gas in moles per liter is directly proportional to its partial pressure. It follows, therefore, that for a gaseous equilibrium reaction an equilibrium constant, K_p, can be written in terms of the partial pressures of the reacting gases. The forms of the K_p expressions for some typical equilibria are given below:

REACTION	EQUILIBRIUM EXPRESSION
(1) $CO + H_2O \rightleftarrows CO_2 + H_2$	$K_p = \dfrac{P_{CO_2} \times P_{H_2}}{P_{CO} \times P_{H_2O}}$
(2) $COCl_2 \rightleftarrows CO + Cl_2$	$K_p = \dfrac{P_{CO} \times P_{Cl_2}}{P_{COCl_2}}$
(3) $2\,NH_3 \rightleftarrows N_2 + 3\,H_2$	$K_p = \dfrac{P_{N_2} \times (P_{H_2})^3}{(P_{NH_3})^2}$
(4) $4\,H_2 + CS_2 \rightleftarrows CH_4 + 2\,H_2S$	$K_p = \dfrac{P_{CH_4} \times (P_{H_2S})^2}{(P_{H_2})^4 \times P_{CS_2}}$

Note that the form of the K_p expression is the same as that for the K_c expression (concentration expressed in concentration units) except that P_a is substituted for $[a]$. K_p is expressed in pressure units of atmospheres or millimeters.

Relation Between K_p and K_c for a Specific Equilibrium

Since, as has been noted above, $n/V = P/RT$, and since n/V represents concentration in moles per liter, it follows that, at constant temperature, P/RT can be substituted for the concentration term, $[\ \ ]$, in the K_c expression. Thus for the reaction, $CO + H_2O \rightleftarrows CO_2 + H_2$,

$$K_c = \frac{[CO_2] \times [H_2]}{[CO] \times [H_2O]} = \frac{\dfrac{P_{CO_2}}{RT} \times \dfrac{P_{H_2}}{RT}}{\dfrac{P_{CO}}{RT} \times \dfrac{P_{H_2O}}{RT}}$$

Since the temperature is constant all of the RT terms will cancel, leaving

$$K_c = \frac{P_{CO_2} \times P_{H_2}}{P_{CO} \times P_{H_2O}}$$

But we have learned that

$$\frac{P_{CO_2} \times P_{H_2}}{P_{CO} \times P_{H_2O}} = K_p$$

Therefore, for this particular reaction, K_c is numerically equal to K_p. K_c will be equal to K_p for all equilibria in which the number of moles of gaseous reactants equals the number of moles of gaseous products.

For the equilibrium, $COCl_2 \rightleftarrows CO + Cl_2$,

$$K_c = \frac{[CO] \times [Cl_2]}{[COCl_2]} = \frac{\dfrac{P_{CO}}{RT} \times \dfrac{P_{Cl_2}}{RT}}{\dfrac{P_{COCl_2}}{RT}} = \frac{P_{CO} \times P_{Cl_2}}{P_{COCl_2}} \times \frac{1}{RT} = K_p \times \frac{1}{RT}$$

For the equilibrium, $2\,NH_3 \rightleftarrows N_2 + 3\,H_2$,

$$K_c = \frac{[N_2] \times [H_2]^3}{[NH_3]^2} = \frac{\dfrac{P_{N_2}}{RT} \times \left(\dfrac{P_{H_2}}{RT}\right)^3}{\left(\dfrac{P_{NH_3}}{RT}\right)^2}$$

$$= \frac{P_{N_2} \times (P_{H_2})^3}{(P_{NH_3})^2} \times \left(\frac{1}{RT}\right)^2 = K_p \times \left(\frac{1}{RT}\right)^2$$

For the equilibrium, $4\,H_2 + CS_2 \rightleftarrows CH_4 + 2\,H_2S$,

$$K_c = \frac{[CH_4] \times [H_2S]^2}{[H_2]^4 \times [CS_2]} = \frac{\dfrac{P_{CH_4}}{RT} \times \left(\dfrac{P_{H_2S}}{RT}\right)^2}{\left(\dfrac{P_{H_2}}{RT}\right)^4 \times \dfrac{P_{CS_2}}{RT}}$$

$$= \frac{P_{CH_4} \times (P_{H_2S})^2}{(P_{H_2})^4 \times P_{CS_2}} \times \left(\frac{1}{RT}\right)^{-2} = K_p \times \left(\frac{1}{RT}\right)^{-2}$$

Examining the four examples given above we conclude that for any gas-phase equilibrium

$$K_c = K_p \times \left(\frac{1}{RT}\right)^{\Delta n}$$

where Δn is the change in the number of moles of gas when the reaction goes from left to right.

Problems

16.43 s In an equilibrium mixture, $CO_2 + H_2 \rightleftarrows CO + H_2O$, contained in a 6.0-liter reaction vessel at $1007°C$ the partial pressures of the reactants are: $CO_2 = 63.1$ atm, $H_2 = 21.1$ atm, $CO = 84.2$ atm,

$H_2O = 31.6$ atm. Enough CO_2 was then removed from the vessel to reduce the partial pressure of the CO to 63.0 atm, temperature being kept constant.

(a) Calculate the partial pressure of the CO_2 in the new equilibrium system.

(b) For the above reaction how does the numerical value of K_c, in which concentration is expressed in moles per liter, compare with the numerical value of K_p, in which concentrations are expressed in atmospheres?

(c) Suppose the volume of the new equilibrium system was reduced to 3 liters by depressing a piston, what would the partial pressure of the CO_2 be?

SOLUTION:

(a)
$$\overset{\text{63.1 atm}}{CO_2} + \overset{\text{21.1 atm}}{H_2} \;\rightleftarrows\; \overset{\text{84.2 atm}}{CO} + \overset{\text{31.6 atm}}{H_2O}$$

$$K_p = \frac{P_{CO} \times P_{H_2O}}{P_{CO_2} \times P_{H_2}} = \frac{84.2 \text{ atm} \times 31.6 \text{ atm}}{63.1 \text{ atm} \times 21.1 \text{ atm}} = 2.0$$

Let $x =$ the partial pressure of the CO_2 in the system after removal of CO_2. Since the partial pressure of the CO is reduced to 63.0 atm, a quantity of CO with a partial pressure of 21.2 atm must have reacted with H_2O to form CO_2 and H_2. Therefore, 21.2 atm worth of H_2O must have reacted and 21.2 atm worth of both CO_2 and H_2 must have been produced. The partial pressures of each reactant in the new equilibrium system will then be

$$\overset{\text{X atm}}{CO_2} + \overset{\text{42.3 atm}}{H_2} \;\rightleftarrows\; \overset{\text{63.0 atm}}{CO} + \overset{\text{10.4 atm}}{H_2O}$$

$$K_p = \frac{63.0 \text{ atm} \times 10.4 \text{ atm}}{X \text{ atm} \times 42.3 \text{ atm}} = 2.0$$

Solving, $X = 7.8$ atm

(b) Since there is no change in the number of moles, $K_c = K_p$.

(c) Since, in the gaseous equilibrium represented by the reaction, $CO_2 + H_2 \rightleftarrows CO + H_2O$, there is no change in the number of moles, increase in pressure by reducing the volume to one half its original value will not shift the equilibrium. All that will happen will be that the partial pressure of each reactant will be doubled. Therefore, the partial pressure of the CO_2 will be 2×7.8 atm or 15.6 atm.

16.44 s Derive an expression to show how K_c is related to K_p for the gas-phase equilibrium, $aA + bB \rightleftarrows cC + dD$.
How is K_c related to K_p:

(a) When $a + b = c + d$?

(b) When $a + b > c + d$?

(c) When $a + b < c + d$?

16.45 s Pure water vapor is present at a pressure of 1.5 atm in a clean reaction vessel. To the vessel we add, without change of volume or temperature, excess solid $LaCl_3$. When equilibrium is established the total pressure in the vessel is found to be 2.0 atm. What is the equilibrium constant, in terms of atmospheres, for the reaction? (s = solid, g = gas.)

$$LaCl_3 \text{ (s)} + H_2O \text{ (g)} \rightleftarrows LaClO \text{ (s)} + 2 \text{ HCl (g)}$$

16.46 s When a mixture of 2.0 moles of CH_4 and 1.0 mole of H_2S is heated at 973°K over a suitable accelerator (MoS_2), the chemical reaction, $CH_4 \text{ (g)} + 2 H_2S \text{ (g)} \rightleftarrows CS_2 \text{ (g)} + 4 H_2 \text{ (g)}$, takes place. When the final total pressure is 1.0 atm, the partial pressure of H_2 (g) is 0.16 atm. Calculate K_p and K_c.

16.47 s A sample of gas that was initially pure NO_2 was heated to a temperature of 337°C. The NO_2 partially dissociates according to the equation $2 NO_2 \rightleftarrows 2 NO + O_2$. At equilibrium, the observed density of the gas mixture at 0.750 atm pressure is 0.520 g per liter. Calculate K_c and K_p for this reaction.

16.48 s A 1-liter reaction vessel in which the reaction, $A \text{ (g)} + B \text{ (g)} \rightleftarrows AB \text{ (g)}$, has reached a state of equilibrium at 727°C contains 0.0200 mole of solid B. The partial pressures of the gaseous reactants in the equilibrium system are: $A = 8.20$ atm; $B = 4.92$ atm; $AB = 11.48$ atm. Calculate the minimum number of moles of A that must be added to the above equilibrium system at 727°C in order that no solid B shall be present at equilibrium.

16.49 s A reaction vessel at 850°C contains $SrCO_3$ (s), SrO (s), and C (s) in equilibrium with CO_2 (g) and CO (g). The total pressure of the CO_2 and CO is 169 mm. K_p for the reaction, $SrCO_3 \text{ (s)} \rightleftarrows SrO \text{ (s)} + CO_2 \text{ (g)}$, is 2.45 mm at 850°C. Calculate K_p for the reaction, $C \text{ (s)} + CO_2 \text{ (g)} \rightleftarrows 2 CO \text{ (g)}$, at 850°C.

17

Ionic Equilibria.

Ionization Constants.

Formality.

Buffer Action.

Complex Ions.

When certain types of covalent compounds such as HCl, NH$_3$, and HC$_2$H$_3$O$_2$ are dissolved in an ionizing solvent such as water, ionization takes place. For all of these substances the ionization reaction is incomplete, and a state of equilibrium is reached, as is represented by the reaction,

$$HC_2H_3O_2 \rightleftarrows H^+ + C_2H_3O_2^-$$

The equilibrium constant for this reaction is

$$\frac{[H^+] \times [C_2H_3O_2^-]}{[HC_2H_3O_2]} = K$$

K is called the *ionization constant*. Its value varies with temperature.

Covalent compounds which are sparingly ionized and, hence, have small ionization constants, are referred to as *weak electrolytes*; covalent compounds such as HCl, HNO$_3$ and H$_2$SO$_4$, which are practically 100% ionized, are called *strong electrolytes*. With a very few exceptions (AlCl$_3$ is one) salts are ionic compounds and are 100% ionized.

147

Weak electrolytes, such as H_2S, H_2CO_3, H_2SO_3, and H_3PO_4, which can yield more than one ion of a particular species, ionize in steps.

$$H_2S \rightleftarrows H^+ + HS^-$$

$$HS^- \rightleftarrows H^+ + S^{--}$$

Equilibrium is established for each of these reaction steps and, therefore, each has its own ionization constant:

$$K_1 = \frac{[H^+] \times [HS^-]}{[H_2S]} = 1.0 \times 10^{-7} \, M$$

(*M*, for reactions in solution, means moles per liter.)

$$K_2 = \frac{[H^+] \times [S^{--}]}{[HS^-]} = 1.3 \times 10^{-13} \, M$$

The constant, K_i, for the over-all reaction is the product of K_1 and K_2.

$$K_i = K_1 \times K_2 = \frac{[H^+]^2 \times [S^{--}]}{[H_2S]} = 1.3 \times 10^{-20} \, M^2$$

Note that, in line with what was stated about equilibrium constants in Chapter 16, the concentration of an ion species is raised to a power equal to the number of that ion formed. Table 2, page 240, lists the ionization constants for ammonium hydroxide and a number of weak acids.

The Concept of Formality

When 0.10 mole of the soluble salt, NaCl, is dissolved in enough water to form a liter of solution, 100% dissociation into Na^+ and Cl^- occurs. The resulting solution is 0.10 M in Na^+ and 0.10 M in Cl^-.

When 0.10 mole of the soluble salt, K_2SO_4, is dissolved in enough water to form a liter of solution, 100% dissociation into K^+ and SO_4^{--} occurs. The resulting solution is 0.20 M in K^+ and 0.10 M in SO_4^{--}.

When 0.10 mole of the strong acid, HCl, is dissolved in a liter of solution, 100% ionization occurs and the resulting solution is 0.10 M in H^+ and 0.10 M in Cl^-.

When 0.0100 mole of the weak acid, $HC_2H_3O_2$, is dissolved in enough water to form a liter of solution only 4.17% of the $HC_2H_3O_2$ is ionized. The resulting solution is $4.17 \times 10^{-4} \, M$ in H^+, $4.17 \times 10^{-4} \, M$ in $C_2H_3O_2^-$ and $9.58 \times 10^{-3} \, M$ in $HC_2H_3O_2$.

When 0.10 mole of the soluble salt, $NaC_2H_3O_2$, is dissolved in water 100% dissociation into Na^+ and $C_2H_3O_2^-$ occurs. However, as we shall learn later, a certain per cent of the $C_2H_3O_2^-$ ions undergo hydrolysis to form $HC_2H_3O_2$ and OH^-. As a consequence, the resulting solution is found to be 0.10 M in Na^+, 7.5 $\times$ 10^{-6} M in OH^-, 1.3 $\times$ 10^{-9} M in H^+, 7.5 $\times$ 10^{-6} M in $HC_2H_3O_2$, and (0.10 $-$ 7.5 $\times$ 10^{-6}) M in $C_2H_3O_2^-$.

From these examples it is obvious that, when electrolytes are dissolved, the concentrations of the species in solution, expressed in moles per liter, are not necessarily the same as the moles per liter of original solute dissolved. To help avoid the ambiguity that may arise from this state of affairs the concepts of *formality* and *formal solutions* have been introduced and are now widely used. The formality of a solution with respect to a particular solute represents the number of gram-formula-weights (moles) of that solute dissolved per liter of solution. Thus a 0.10 formal (abbreviated 0.10 F) solution of Na_2SO_4 is prepared by dissolving 0.10 gram-formula-weight (0.10 mole) of solid Na_2SO_4 in enough water to form a liter of solution. Since Na_2SO_4 is 100% dissociated into Na^+ and SO_4^{--}, 0.10 F Na_2SO_4 will be 0.10 M in SO_4^{--} and 0.20 M in Na^+. *The quantity of original solute* (sodium sulfate, potassium chloride, sodium acetate, acetic acid etc.) *dissolved per liter of solution, is designated as the* **formality**. *The concentration, in moles per liter, of each species in solution is designated as* **molarity**. Thus, 0.010 F KCl is 0.010 M in K^+ and 0.010 M in Cl^-. Likewise, 0.0100 F acetic acid is 4.17 $\times$ 10^{-4} M in H^+, 4.17 $\times$ 10^{-4} M in $C_2H_3O_2^-$, and 9.58 $\times$ 10^{-3} M in $HC_2H_3O_2$. Similarly, 0.10 F $NaC_2H_3O_2$ is 0.10 M in Na^+, 7.5 $\times$ 10^{-6} M in OH^-, 7.5 $\times$ 10^{-6} M in $HC_2H_3O_2$, and 0.10 M in $C_2H_3O_2^-$.

It is important to note that formality, as now defined, is synonymous with molarity as that term is used in Chapter 13.

From this point on the term *formality will be used to designate the number of moles of an original solute dissolved per liter of solution*; there should, therefore, never be any ambiguity about the use of the term. *The concentration of a species in solution, whether it is an ion or a neutral molecule, will be designated by molarity*, never by formality. Thus 0.010 F $HC_2H_3O_2$ is 9.6 $\times$ 10^{-3} M in $HC_2H_3O_2$; 0.10 F Na_2SO_4 is 0.20 M in Na^+ and 0.10 M in SO_4^{--}; 0.10 F $C_{12}H_{22}O_{11}$ (a non-associated non-electrolyte) is 0.10 M in $C_{12}H_{22}O_{11}$.

Many textbooks do not use the concept of formality; concentration of the original solute as well as that of each of the species in solution is designated in terms of molarity (0.20 M $KMnO_4$, 0.50 M KOH, 0.25 M H_2SO_4). There need be no confusion in the reading of such a textbook; *molarity* alone covers what we will cover by *formality* and *molarity*. Confusion will be avoided if the chemical formula of the species being considered is always given. Thus, 0.20 M $KMnO_4$ means, clearly, a solution prepared by dissolving 0.20 mole of $KMnO_4$ in a liter of solution. Likewise, 0.50 M

$K_2Cr_2O_7$ means, clearly, a solution prepared by dissolving 0.50 mole of $K_2Cr_2O_7$ in a liter of solution

Problems

17.1 A 0.010 F solution of $HC_2H_3O_2$ is 4.17% ionized. Calculate its ionization constant.

SOLUTION:

$$HC_2H_3O_2 \rightleftarrows H^+ + C_2H_3O_2^-$$

$$K = \frac{[H^+] \times [C_2H_3O_2^-]}{[HC_2H_3O_2]}$$

4.17% expressed in decimal form, is 0.0417.

0.0417×0.10 moles $= 0.00042$ moles of $HC_2H_3O_2$ ionized.

Since 1 mole of $HC_2H_3O_2$ yields 1 mole of H^+ and 1 mole of $C_2H_3O_2^-$, the 4.2×10^{-4} mole of $HC_2H_3O_2^-$ will yield 4.2×10^{-4} mole each of H^+ and $C_2H_3O_2^-$; $[H^+]$ and $[C_2H_3O_2^-]$ will each be 4.2×10^{-4} mole/liter. The concentration of un-ionized $HC_2H_3O_2$ molecules will then be $0.010 - 0.00042$ or 0.0096 mole/liter. Substituting these values in the equilibrium formula,

$$K = \frac{(4.2 \times 10^{-4}) \times (4.2 \times 10^{-4})}{(9.6 \times 10^{-3})}$$

$$= 1.8 \times 10^{-5} \text{ mole/liter} = 1.8 \times 10^{-5} M$$

When calculating the ionization constants of acids and bases in water solution, the small concentrations of H^+ or OH^- ions due to the ionization of water are generally ignored.

17.2 Calculate the ionization constant of:

(a) A 0.10 F solution of NH_4OH which is 1.3% ionized

(b) A 0.0010 F solution of $HC_2H_3O_2$ which is 12.6% ionized

(c) A 0.01 F solution of HCN which is 0.02% ionized

17.3 If a 0.500 F solution of the weak base, MOH, contains 0.00500 mole of OH^- ion in 400 ml, calculate the per cent ionization and the ionization constant.

17.4 For the weak acid, HA, derive an expression for K_i in terms of the formality, F, of HA and the fraction, X, of HA ionized.

17.5 The ionization constant for HCN is $4 \times 10^{-10} \, M$ at 25°C. Calculate the formality of and the H^+ ion concentration of a solution of HCN which is 0.010% ionized.

SOLUTION:

$$HCN \rightleftarrows H^+ + CN^-$$

(1) $$K = \frac{[H^+] \times [CN^-]}{[HCN]} = 4 \times 10^{-10} \, M$$

Let $X =$ formality. Since the solution is 0.010% ionized, and since 0.010%, expressed as decimal, is 0.00010, the concentration of H^+ will be 0.00010 X. The concentration of CN^- will also be 0.00010 X. The concentration of un-ionized HCN will be $X - 0.00010 \, X$. Substituting these values in the above equilibrium formula.

(2) $$\frac{0.00010 \, X \times 0.00010 \, X}{X - 0.00010 \, X} = 4 \times 10^{-10} \, M$$

Solving, $X = 4 \times 10^{-2} =$ the formality

$$[H^+] = 0.00010 \, X = 1 \times 10^{-4} \times 4 \times 10^{-2}$$

$$= 4 \times 10^{-6} \, M$$

17.6 The ionization constant for NH_4OH is $1.80 \times 10^{-5} \, M$. Calculate the formality and OH^- concentration of a solution in which the NH_4OH is 1.3% ionized.

17.7 The ionization constant for $HC_2H_3O_2$ is $1.8 \times 10^{-5} \, M$. Calculate the hydrogen-ion concentration of 0.01 F $HC_2H_3O_2$.

SOLUTION:

$$HC_2H_3O_2 \rightleftarrows H^+ + C_2H_3O_2^-$$

Let $X = [H^+] = [C_2H_3O_2^-]$

$$0.01 - X = [HC_2H_3O_2]$$

$$K = \frac{[H^+] \times [C_2H_3O_2^-]}{[HC_2H_3O_2]} = 1.8 \times 10^{-5} \, M$$

Substituting the values of $[H^+]$, $[C_2H_3O_2^-]$, and $[HC_2H_3O_2]$ in the equilibrium formula:

(1) $$\frac{X^2}{0.01 - X} = 1.8 \times 10^{-5} \, M$$

The term, X, can be dropped from the expression, $0.01 - X$, in the denominator of Equation (1) if the value of X is so small that

$0.01 - X = 0.01$. We can estimate the value of X as follows: Drop X from the expression, $0.01 - X$. As a result, $X^2 = 1.8 \times 10^{-7}$ and X is about 4×10^{-4} or 0.0004. $0.01 - 0.0004 = 0.0096$. When rounded off to one significant figure 0.0096 becomes 0.01. Therefore, X can be dropped.

$$(2) \qquad \frac{X^2}{0.01} = 1.8 \times 10^{-5} \, M$$

$$X = 4 \times 10^{-4} \, M = [H^+]$$

This example illustrates the rule that a term, n, *which is added to or subtracted from* a term, m, in an expression, $m + n$ or $m - n$, can be dropped if it is so small that $m - n$ (or $m + n$), when rounded off to the permissible significant figures, is equal to m.

It should be emphasized that a small term can be dropped only in expressions involving its *addition to* or *subtraction from* a large term, never in an expression involving its multiplication or division by a large term.

17.8 The ionization constant for NH_4OH is $1.8 \times 10^{-5} \, M$. Calculate the hydroxide-ion concentration of $0.10 \, F \, NH_4OH$.

17.9 Referring to Table 2, page 240, for the ionization constants, calculate:

(a) The formality of a solution of HCN which is 0.2% ionized.*

(b) The concentration of HCO_3^- and CO_3^{--} ions in a $0.034 \, F$ solution of CO_2 in water.

SOLUTION: The reactions that occur when CO_2 is dissolved in water are:

(1) $CO_2 + H_2O = H_2CO_3$

(2) $H_2CO_3 \rightleftarrows H^+ + HCO_3^-$

(3) $HCO_3^- \rightleftarrows H^+ + CO_3^{--}$

The ionization constant for (2) is

$$\frac{[H^+][HCO_3^-]}{[H_2CO_3]} = 4.2 \times 10^{-7} \, M = K_1$$

and for (3) is

$$\frac{[H^+][CO_3^{--}]}{[HCO_3^-]} = 4.8 \times 10^{-11} \, M = K_2$$

Referring to Reaction (2) and its ionization constant, K_1, let

$$X = \text{conc of } HCO_3^- \qquad X = \text{conc of } H^+$$

$$0.034 - X = \text{conc of } H_2CO_3$$

Substituting these values in the equation for K_1

$$\frac{X^2}{0.034 - X} = 4.2 \times 10^{-7} M$$

X is so small by comparison with 0.034 that it can be dropped from the expression, $0.034 - X$.

$$X^2 = 1.43 \times 10^{-8} M^2$$

$$X = 1.2 \times 10^{-4} M = [HCO_3^-] = [H^+]$$

Since the equilibria represented by K_1 and K_2 both occur in the same solution $[H^+]$ is the same for both. Since K_2 is so much smaller than K_1, the value of $[H^+]$ calculated from K_1 will be the $[H^+]$ of the solution and can be inserted in the formula for K_2.
Letting $\Upsilon = [CO_3^{--}]$ and $1.2 \times 10^{-4} = [H^+]$

$$\frac{1.2 \times 10^{-4} \Upsilon}{1.2 \times 10^{-4} - \Upsilon} = 4.8 \times 10^{-11} M$$

Since K_2 is very small, Υ will be so small by comparison with 1.2×10^{-4} that it can be dropped from the term, $1.2 \times 10^{-4} - \Upsilon$. Therefore,

$$\frac{1.2 \times 10^{-4} \Upsilon}{1.2 \times 10^{-4}} = 4.8 \times 10^{-11} M$$

$$\Upsilon = 4.8 \times 10^{-11} M = [CO_3^{--}]$$

NOTE: The equation for the over-all ionization is

$$H_2CO_3 \rightleftarrows 2\,H^+ + CO_3^{--}$$

The over-all ionization constant, K_i, is

$$K_i = \frac{[H^+]^2 \times [CO_3^{--}]}{[H_2CO_3]} = K_1 \times K_2 = 2.0 \times 10^{-17} M^2$$

It should be emphasized that this over-all ionization equation and constant can not be used to solve for $[CO_3^{--}]$, $[HCO_3^-]$ and $[H^+]$ in a solution of CO_2 in pure water. Using the over-all equation assumes that $[H^+] = 2 \times [CO_3^{--}]$. This is not a valid assumption. Suppose we solve for $[H^+]$ and $[CO_3^{--}]$ by using K_i.
Let $X = [CO_3^{--}]$; $2X = [H^+]$; $0.034 - X = [H_2CO_3]$.

$$\frac{(2\,X)^2\,X}{0.034 - X} = 2.0 \times 10^{-17}\,M^2$$

$$4\,X^3 = 6.8 \times 10^{-19}\,M^3$$

$$X = 5.5 \times 10^{-7}\,M = [CO_3{}^{--}]$$

$$2\,X = 1.1 \times 10^{-6}\,M = [H^+]$$

These answers are quite different from those obtained by the correct method, in which K_1 and K_2 were used separately. That these new answers are not correct can be seen by using them to calculate $[HCO_3{}^-]$.

$$[HCO_3{}^-] = K_1 \frac{[H_2CO_3]}{[H^+]} \quad \text{and} \quad [HCO_3{}^-] = \frac{[H^+][CO_3{}^{--}]}{K_2}$$

The value of $[HCO_3{}^-]$ thus obtained, $1.3 \times 10^{-2}\,M$, is obviously incorrect, for this high a concentration of $HCO_3{}^-$ could not be present without an equally high $[H^+]$.

It is worth noting, however, that although the over-all ionization constant *cannot* be used to calculate correctly $[H^+]$ and $[CO_3{}^{--}]$, the value of this over-all ionization constant *must be satisfied*. Substituting the correct values, $[H^+] = 1.2 \times 10^{-4}\,M$, $[CO_3{}^{--}] = 4.8 \times 10^{-11}\,M$, and $[H_2CO_3] = 3.4 \times 10^{-2}\,M$, into the equation for the over-all ionization, it is seen that this is indeed the case.

If the H^+ *concentration is fixed* by the addition of a strong acid to a solution of CO_2 in water K_i can then be used in solving for $[CO_3{}^{--}]$. This case is presented in Problem 17.17.

17.10 Calculate the concentrations of $H_2PO_4{}^-$, $HPO_4{}^{--}$, and $PO_4{}^{---}$ ions in $0.10\,F\,H_3PO_4$.

SOLUTION: The three equilibria and their constants are

(1) $H_3PO_4 \rightleftarrows H^+ + H_2PO_4{}^-$ $K_1 = \dfrac{[H^+] \times [H_2PO_4{}^-]}{[H_3PO_4]}$

$$= 7.5 \times 10^{-3}\,M$$

(2) $H_2PO_4{}^- \rightleftarrows H^+ + HPO_4{}^{--}$ $K_2 = \dfrac{[H^+] \times [HPO_4{}^{--}]}{[H_2PO_4{}^-]}$

$$= 6.2 \times 10^{-8}\,M$$

(3) $HPO_4{}^{--} \rightleftarrows H^+ + PO_4{}^{---}$ $K_3 = \dfrac{[H^+] \times [PO_4{}^{---}]}{[HPO_4{}^{--}]}$

$$= 1.0 \times 10^{-12}\,M$$

Since all three equilibria occur in the same solution, the value of $[H^+]$ must be the same in each. Since K_1 is so much larger than K_2 and K_3, it will determine the value of $[H^+]$. Likewise, K_1 will determine the value of $[H_2PO_4^-]$. Accordingly, we will first calculate $[H^+]$ and $[H_2PO_4^-]$ from K_1.

Let $X = [H^+]$. Then $X = [H_2PO_4^-]$ and $0.10 - X = [H_3PO_4]$

$$\frac{X^2}{0.10 - X} = 7.5 \times 10^{-3}\ M$$

It is obvious that X will be too large in comparison with 0.10 to allow it to be dropped.

Solving this quadratic, $X = 2.4 \times 10^{-2}\ M = [H^+] = [H_2PO_4^-]$

We will next substitute these values in K_2, letting $\Upsilon = [HPO_4^{--}]$

$$K_2 = \frac{(2.4 \times 10^{-2})(\Upsilon)}{(2.4 \times 10^{-2} - \Upsilon)} = 6.2 \times 10^{-8}\ M$$

Since K_2 is very small, Υ will be so small by comparison with 2.4×10^{-2} that it can be dropped from the term, $2.4 \times 10^{-2} - \Upsilon$. This leaves

$$\frac{2.4 \times 10^{-2}\ \Upsilon}{2.4 \times 10^{-2}} = 6.2 \times 10^{-8}$$

$$\Upsilon = 6.2 \times 10^{-8}\ M = [HPO_4^{--}]$$

We will then substitute the calculated values of $[H^+]$ and $[HPO_4^{--}]$ in K_3, letting $\mathcal{Z} = [PO_4^{---}]$.

$$K_3 = \frac{(2.4 \times 10^{-2})(\mathcal{Z})}{(6.2 \times 10^{-8} - \mathcal{Z})} = 1.0 \times 10^{-12}\ M$$

Since K_3 is extremely small, $\mathcal{Z}$ will be so small by comparison with 6.2×10^{-8} that it can be dropped from the term, $6.2 \times 10^{-8} - \mathcal{Z}$. That leaves

$$\frac{2.4 \times 10^{-2}\ \mathcal{Z}}{6.2 \times 10^{-8}} = 1.0 \times 10^{-12}$$

$$\mathcal{Z} = 2.5 \times 10^{-18}\ M = [PO_4^{---}]$$

17.11 Calculate the concentration of S^{--} in $0.10\ F\ H_2S.$*

17.12 Calculate the concentration of CrO_4^{--} in $0.10\ F\ H_2CrO_4$.

The Common Ion Effect

We have noted in Chapter 16 that if after a chemical reaction of the general type, $A + B \rightleftarrows C + D$, has reached a state of equilibrium, more C is added to the reaction vessel, the equilibrium is shifted to the left. In exactly the same manner the equilibrium in an ionic equilibrium such as, $HC_2H_3O_2 \rightleftarrows H^+ + C_2H_3O_2^-$, will be shifted to the left if acetate ions are added to the system. This shift in an ionization equilibrium by increasing the concentration of one of the ions involved is called *the common ion effect*.

Problems

17.13 The ionization constant for $HC_2H_3O_2$ is $1.8 \times 10^{-5} M$. How many moles of hydrogen ions will there be in a liter of $0.10 F \ HC_2H_3O_2$ containing 0.20 mole of $NaC_2H_3O_2$?

SOLUTION:

$$HC_2H_3O_2 \rightleftarrows H^+ + C_2H_3O_2^-; \qquad NaC_2H_3O_2 = Na^+ + C_2H_3O_2^-$$

Let X = concentration of H^+

$0.20 + X$ = concentration of $C_2H_3O_2^-$

$0.10 - X$ = concentration of $HC_2H_3O_2$

$$K = \frac{[H^+] \times [C_2H_3O_2^-]}{[HC_2H_3O_2]} = 1.8 \times 10^{-5} M$$

Substituting the values of $[H^+]$, $[C_2H_3O_2^-]$, and $[HC_2H_3O_2]$ in the above equation,

$$\frac{X(0.20 + X)}{0.10 - X} = 1.8 \times 10^{-5} M$$

In solving for X in the above equation we will assume that, since acetic acid is weak, the value of X (the concentration of H^+ ions) will be very much less than 0.10. If this assumption is true X can then be dropped from the terms, $0.20 + X$ and $0.10 - X$. That leaves the expression

$$\frac{0.20 \, X}{0.10} = 1.8 \times 10^{-5} M \qquad (X = 9.0 \times 10^{-6} \text{ mole of } H^+ \text{ per liter})$$

The fact that the value of X turns out to be very much less than 0.10 means that the assumption made above is justified.

17.14 The ionization constant for NH_4OH is $1.8 \times 10^{-5} M$. How many moles of OH^- are there in a liter of $0.10 F \ NH_4OH$ which contains 0.10 mole of NH_4Cl?

17.15 The weak base, NH_4OH, has an ionization constant of 1.8×10^{-5} M. What is the OH^- concentration of a solution prepared by dissolving 0.25 mole of NH_3 and 0.75 mole of NH_4Cl in enough water to make a liter of solution?*

17.16 How many moles of NaCN must be dissolved in a liter of 0.2 F HCN to yield a solution with a hydrogen-ion concentration of 1×10^{-6} mole per liter?

17.17 The hydrogen ion concentration of a 0.034 F solution of CO_2 in dilute HCl is 0.10 M. Calculate the molar concentration of CO_3^{--}.

SOLUTION: This problem differs from 17.9 in that H^+ has been added (in the form of HCl) to give a total $[H^+]$ of 0.10 M. Using the first ionization constant for H_2CO_3 we will first solve for $[HCO_3^-]$.

$H_2CO_3 \rightleftarrows H^+ + HCO_3^-$

Let $X = [HCO_3^-]$

$0.10 = [H^+]$

$0.034 - X = [H_2CO_3]$

$$K_1 = \frac{[H^+][HCO_3^-]}{[H_2CO_3]} = 4.2 \times 10^{-7} M = \frac{0.10\ X}{0.034 - X}$$

Since K_1 is very small and $[H^+]$ is high (0.10 M), $[HCO_3^-]$ will be very small in comparison with $[H^+]$ and $[H_2CO_3]$. Therefore we can drop the X in the term, $0.034 - X$. That leaves

$$\frac{0.10\ X}{0.034} = 4.2 \times 10^{-7} M$$

$0.10\ X = 1.4 \times 10^{-8} M$

$X = 1.4 \times 10^{-7} M = [HCO_3^-]$

We can now substitute this value of $[HCO_3^-]$ and the value of 0.10 M for $[H^+]$ in the second ionization constant to give

$$K_2 = \frac{[H^+][CO_3^{--}]}{[HCO_3^-]} = 4.8 \times 10^{-11} M = \frac{0.10 \times Y}{1.4 \times 10^{-7} - Y}$$

In this formula $Y = [CO_3^{--}]$.

Since Y will be very small by comparison with 1.4×10^{-7}, it can be dropped from the term, $1.4 \times 10^{-7} - Y$. This leaves

$$\frac{0.10\ Y}{1.4 \times 10^{-7}} = 4.8 \times 10^{-11} M$$

$0.10\ Y = 6.7 \times 10^{-18} M \qquad Y = 6.7 \times 10^{-17} M = [CO_3^{--}]$

NOTE: It should be pointed out that, when the hydrogen ion concentration of a solution of a weak polybasic acid such as H_2CO_3 (H_2S, H_3PO_4, etc.) is fixed by the addition of a strong acid, the overall ionization constant, K_i, can be used in solving for $[CO_3^{--}]$. Thus

$$K_i = K_1 \times K_2 = \frac{[H^+]^2 \times [CO_3^{--}]}{[H_2CO_3]} = 2.0 \times 10^{-17}$$

If we substitute the values of $[H^+]$ and $[H_2CO_3]$ in this equation:

$$\frac{(0.10)^2[CO_3^{--}]}{0.034} = 2.0 \times 10^{-17}$$

$$[CO_3^{--}] = 6.8 \times 10^{-17}$$

This, it will be noted, is the same value for $[CO_3^{--}]$ that was obtained when the calculation was made via K_1 and K_2.

17.18 (a) Calculate the concentrations of $H_2AsO_4^-$, $HAsO_4^{--}$, and AsO_4^{---} in 0.20 F H_3AsO_4 which is 0.10 F in HCl.

(b) Calculate the sulfide ion concentration of a 0.10 F solution of H_2S in 0.10 F HCl.*

Buffer Action

If 0.10 mole of solid NaCN is added to a liter 0.010 F HCl the following reaction occurs:

(1) $CN^- + H^+ \rightleftarrows HCN$

Because HCN is a very weak acid ($K_i = 4.0 \times 10^{-10}$) and because *excess* CN^- was added, practically all of the H^+ from the HCl is tied up as HCN. As a result the $[H^+]$ of the solution drops from 0.010 M down to an extremely low value.

If an additional 0.010 mole of HCl (as a gas so that there will be no appreciable change in volume) is added to the solution there then is no appreciable change in $[H^+]$; the excess CN^- combines with the additional hydrogen ions from the added HCl to form more HCN.

If we now add 0.010 mole of NaOH to the solution there still is no appreciable change in $[H^+]$. As fast as the added OH^- ions react with H^+ ions to form water, more HCN ionizes, thereby keeping the $[H^+]$ practically constant; the equilibrium, $CN^- + H^+ \rightleftarrows HCN$, is shifted to the left. If we continue to add NaOH we will find that a total of 0.020 mole of

NaOH will be required to neutralize the H^+ ions in the solution. This means that, although the CN^- ions have reduced, enormously, the $[H^+]$ of the solution by tieing them up as HCN, they have not altered the total available H^+ in the solution.

The salt of any weak acid, when added to a solution of a strong acid, will behave as did NaCN. Likewise, the salt of any weak base (NH_4Cl for example) when added to a solution of a strong base (KOH, NaOH) will depress the $[OH^-]$ by tieing the OH^- ions up in the form of the weak base (NH_4OH).

The behavior described above is called *buffer action*. The salt of a weak acid will *buffer* a strong acid; it reduces the concentration of H^+ and, when present in reasonable excess, will keep it practically constant at this low value. Likewise, the salt of a weak base will *buffer* a strong base.

Problems

17.19 (a) Calculate the hydrogen ion concentration of a liter of solution which is 0.1 F in $NaC_2H_3O_2$ and 0.001 F in HCl. K for $HC_2H_3O_2 = 1.8 \times 10^{-5} M$.

SOLUTION: 0.1 F $NaC_2H_3O_2$ will yield 0.1 M Na^+ and 0.1 M $C_2H_3O_2^-$. 0.001 F HCl will yield 0.001 M H^+ and 0.001 M Cl^-. The 0.001 mole of H^+ will combine with 0.001 mole of $C_2H_3O_2^-$ to form 0.001 mole of $HC_2H_3O_2$.
That will leave $0.1 - 0.001$ or 0.1 mole of $C_2H_3O_2^-$.
Therefore, $[C_2H_3O_2^-] = 0.1$ M and $[HC_2H_3O_2] = 0.001$ M.

$$K = \frac{[H^+] \times [C_2H_3O_2^-]}{[HC_2H_3O_2]} = 1.8 \times 10^{-5} M$$

Substituting in the above formula:

$$\frac{[H^+] \times 0.1 \ M}{0.001 \ M} = 1.8 \times 10^{-5} M$$

$$[H^+] = 2 \times 10^{-8} M$$

(b) Calculate the hydrogen ion concentration of a solution which is 0.2 F in NaF and 0.002 F in HCl. K for HF $= 6.9 \times 10^{-4}$

(c) What concentrations of $NaC_2H_3O_2$ and $HC_2H_3O_2$ must be used in preparing a solution buffered to a hydrogen ion concentration of 1.0×10^{-6} M?*

Complex Ions

When an ion combines with one or more other ions or neutral molecules to form a new ion, this new ion is called a *complex ion*. Complex ions are weak electrolytes and, as such, dissociate incompletely to form the original species. Thus

$$Zn^{++} + 4\,NH_3 \rightleftarrows Zn(NH_3)_4{}^{++}$$

and

$$Zn(NH_3)_4{}^{++} \rightleftarrows Zn^{++} + 4\,NH_3$$

The equilibrium constants for ionization of complex ions are referred to as instability constants. (See Table 3, page 241.)

Problems

17.20 s (a) Calculate the concentration of Cu^{++} in a solution which is 0.10 F in $CuSO_4$ and 1.40 F in NH_3. The instability constant for $Cu(NH_3)_4{}^{++}$ is 4.7×10^{-15} mole⁴/liter⁴.

SOLUTION: The very low value of the instability constant means that essentially all the copper ion in solution will be in the form of the ammine complex. Therefore, $[Cu(NH_3)_4{}^{++}] = 0.10$ mole/liter. Then, $[NH_3] = 1.40 - 4\,(0.10) = 1.00$ mole/liter

$$\frac{[Cu^{++}][NH_3]^4}{[Cu(NH_3)_4{}^{++}]} = 4.7 \times 10^{-15}\ \text{mole}^4/\text{liter}^4$$

and

$$[Cu^{++}] = 4.7 \times 10^{-16}\ \text{mole/liter}$$

The low $[Cu^{++}]$ thus calculated justifies the assumption that $Cu(NH_3)_4{}^{++}$ is by far the predominant copper-containing species. It should be noted that, in effect, the NH_3 acts as a *buffer*; it ties up the Cu^{++} in the form of the weak electrolyte, $Cu(NH_3)_4{}^{++}$.

(b) The instability constant for $Ag(NH_3)_2{}^{+}$ is 6.0×10^{-8} mole²/liter².

(1) What is the molar concentration of NH_3 needed to convert exactly 50% of the silver ion to the ammine complex in $Y\,F\,AgNO_3$?

(2) What is the formal concentration of NH_3 in this solution?

17.21 s A mixture of 500 ml of $1.0 \, F \, HNO_3$ and 100 ml of $15 \, F \, NH_4OH$ was diluted with water to 1.0 liter. Calculate the $[H^+]$ of the solution.

17.22 s A $0.100 \, F$ aqueous solution of the weak acid, HY, freezes at $-0.240°C$. The freezing point constant for water is 1.86. Calculate the ionization constant for HY.

17.23 s To what volume must a liter of a solution of the weak acid, HZ, be diluted with water in order to give a hydrogen ion concentration one-half that of the original solution?

SOLUTION:

$$HZ \rightleftarrows H^+ + Z^-$$

Let $X = [H^+]$ at equilibrium

Then $X = [Z^-]$ at equilibrium

Let $Y = [HZ]$ at equilibrium

$$K = \frac{X^2}{Y}$$

Since diluting the solution does not affect the value of K,

$$\frac{X^2}{Y} = \frac{\left(\dfrac{X}{2}\right)^2}{\dfrac{Y}{V}} \qquad (V = \text{volume in liters of diluted solution})$$

Solving, $V = 4$ liters.

17.24 s HA is a weak acid with an ionization constant of $1.0 \times 10^{-8} \, M$. HA forms the complex ion, HA_2^-. The instability constant for the reaction, $HA_2^- \rightleftarrows HA + A^-$, is $0.25 \, M$. Calculate $[H^+]$, $[A^-]$, and $[HA_2^-]$ in $1.0 \, F \, HA$.

SOLUTION:

$$HA \rightleftarrows H^+ + A^-$$

$$A^- + HA \rightleftarrows HA_2^-$$

$$K_i = \frac{[H^+] \times [A^-]}{[HA]} = 1.0 \times 10^{-8} \, M$$

$$K_{inst} = \frac{[HA] \times [A^-]}{[HA_2^-]} = 0.25 \, M$$

Since K_i is very small the number of moles of HA that ionize will be so small that HA will be $1.0 \, M$. (This does not mean, of course, that no H^+, A^-, or HA_2^- will be formed. It simply means that, when calculations are made, the value of $[HA]$, when rounded off to two significant figures, will be the same as the original formality of HA.) Therefore,

$$[H^+] \times [A^-] = 1 \times 10^{-8}$$

Since $K_{inst} = 0.25$ M, and $[HA] = 1.0$, $[HA_2^-] = 4 \times [A^-]$. Also, we see that $[H^+] = [A^-] + [HA_2^-]$.
Therefore, if we let $X = [A^-]$, then $[HA_2^-] = 4\,X$, and $[H^+] = 5X$. Substituting in K_i:

$$5\,X^2 = 1 \times 10^{-8}\,M^2$$
$$X = 4.5 \times 10^{-5} = [A^-]$$
$$5\,X = 2.2 \times 10^{-4} = [H^+]$$
$$4\,X = 1.8 \times 10^{-4} = [HA_2^-]$$

17.25 s Write the equilibrium expression for the following equation, and give the units in which it will be expressed.

$$CaCO_3\ (s) + CO_2\ (g) + H_2O = Ca^{++} + 2\ HCO_3^-$$

17.26 s A saturated CO_2 solution in pure water is 3.4×10^{-2} molar in CO_2. How many moles of CO_2 will dissolve in 1.00 liter of 0.100 F NaOH?

SOLUTION: Write the net equation for the reaction that takes place when excess CO_2 is added to a solution of a strong base. How many moles of OH^- are present in a liter of 0.100 F NaOH? With how many moles of CO_2 will this OH^- react? What, then, is the total solubility of CO_2 in 0.100 F NaOH?

17.27 s How much water and how much 6.0 F HCl must be added to 2.0 ml of 0.30 F NaAsO$_2$ to yield a solution which is 0.10 M in the very weak acid, HAsO$_2$, and 1.0 M in H^+?

SOLUTION: How many moles of AsO_2^- are present in 2.0 ml of 0.30 F NaAsO$_2$? Keeping in mind that HAsO$_2$ is a *very weak* acid, how many moles of HAsO$_2$ will these AsO_2^- ions yield when treated with HCl? In what volume, V, of solution must this number of moles of HAsO$_2$ be dissolved to yield a solution which is 0.10 M in HAsO$_2$? How many moles of HCl will be used up in producing this number of moles of HAsO$_2$? How many ml of 6.0 F HCl will be needed to provide this amount of HCl? How many moles of H^+ are present in the above volume, V, of a solution which is 1.0 M in

H+? How many ml of 6.0 F HCl will provide this many moles of H+? How many ml of water must then be added in order to satisfy the requirements of the problem?

17.28 s A volume of 4.0 ml of 0.10 F NaCN was mixed with 2.0 ml of hydrochloric acid and 4.0 ml of water to give 10.0 ml of solution with a hydrogen ion concentration of 0.10 M. What was the formality of the hydrochloric acid?

17.29 s The element Q has stable oxidation states of 2, 3, and 4. A mixture weighing 207 g contains "a" moles of QCl_2, "b" moles of $Q_2(SO_4)_3$, and "c" moles of $Q(CrO_4)_2$.

(1) 1.35 moles of Ba^{++} are needed to precipitate all the sulfate and chromate in a 207 g sample.

(2) A second identical 207 g sample requires 0.180 mole of MnO_4^- to oxidize all the Q to the +4 state (MnO_4^- is reduced to Mn^{++}).

(3) A third identical 207 g sample requires 2.60 moles of ammonia to completely convert Q^{++} and Q^{++++} to their very stable ammine complexes, $Q(NH_3)_4^{++}$, and $Q(NH_3)_6^{++++}$ (Q^{+++} forms neither a stable ammine complex nor an insoluble hydroxide).

(a) How many moles of each compound were in a 207 g sample of this mixture?

(b) Calculate the atomic weight of Q.

17.30 s An amount of 0.22 mole of the weak acid, HX, was dissolved in 100 ml of 0.20 F KOH. The hydrogen ion concentration of the resulting solution was determined to be 1.0×10^{-5} M. Calculate the ionization constant for HX.

18 pH and the Ionization Equilibrium of Water. Hydrolysis.

Pure water is very slightly ionized as follows:

(1) $$H_2O \rightleftarrows H^+ + OH^-$$

The concentration of H^+ ions has been shown experimentally to be 1×10^{-7} mole/liter at 25°C. The concentration of OH^- ions is the same as the concentration of H^+ ions, namely 1×10^{-7} mole/liter; for this reason water is neutral.

The ionization constant for water is expressed by the familiar equation,

(2) $$K = \frac{[H^+] \times [OH^-]}{[H_2O]}$$

A liter of water (1000 g) will contain 55.6 moles of H_2O; since, as noted above, it contains 1×10^{-7} mole of H^+ and 1×10^{-7} mole of OH^- the equilibrium constant will be calculated as follows:

(3) $$\underset{55.6 - 1 \times 10^{-7}}{H_2O} \quad \rightleftarrows \quad \underset{1 \times 10^{-7}}{H^+} + \underset{1 \times 10^{-7}}{OH^-}$$

(4) $$K = \frac{(1 \times 10^{-7})(1 \times 10^{-7})}{(55.6 - 1 \times 10^{-7})}$$

It is obvious from Equation (3) that, not only is $[H_2O]$ enormous by comparison with $[H^+]$ and $[OH^-]$, but that, regardless of how much the equilibrium in (3) is shifted to the left (by adding H^+ or OH^-), the actual change in the number of moles of H_2O is negligible. Even if the concentration of H^+ is so high that the equilibrium is shifted completely to the left the number of moles of H_2O will increase only by 10^{-7} mole; for all practical purposes that is no change at all. That means that the concentration of H_2O molecules in equilibrium with H^+ and OH^- is constant. Therefore, Equation (4) becomes

(5)
$$K = \frac{(1 \times 10^{-7})(1 \times 10^{-7})}{\text{A constant whose value is 55.6}}$$

The constant whose value is 55.6 can then be multiplied by the ionization constant, K, to give a new constant called the *ion product constant* for water; it is designated by the symbol, K_w. That is

(6)
$$K_w = (1 \times 10^{-7}) \times (1 \times 10^{-7}) = 1 \times 10^{-14} \, M^2$$

Equation (6) states that, at 25°C, *the product of $[H^+]$ and $[OH^-]$ in water, or any water solution, is always* 1×10^{-14}.

If the H^+ concentration is greater than 10^{-7} mole/liter (10^{-6} or 10^{-1}) the solution will be acidic, while if the hydrogen-ion concentration is less than 10^{-7} mole/liter the solution will be alkaline. One can, therefore, designate whether a solution is acid or alkaline by stating, for example, that the value of the hydrogen-ion concentration is $1 \times 10^{-6.2}$ mole/liter, meaning thereby, that it is slightly acid.

Because the use of numbers such as $1 \times 10^{-6.2}$ and $1 \times 10^{-9.37}$ is cumbersome, the acidity or alkalinity of a system is commonly designated by a term referred to as *p*H. The *p*H *is the logarithm of the reciprocal of the hydrogen-ion concentration*, when this concentration is expressed as moles per liter. This is equivalent to saying that *the p*H *is the negative of the logarithm of the hydrogen ion concentration.* To illustrate, suppose the concentration of H^+ is 1×10^{-6} mole/liter. The reciprocal of this is $1/(1 \times 10^{-6})$, which is equal to 10^6. The logarithm of 10^6 is 6; the *p*H of the solution is 6. Likewise, the logarithm of 10^{-6} is -6. The negative of -6 is 6. Therefore, a *p*H of 6 means a hydrogen-ion concentration of 1×10^{-6} mole/liter. Likewise, a *p*H of 8.2 represents a hydrogen-ion concentration of $1 \times 10^{-8.2}$ mole/liter.

A solution whose *p*H is 7 is neutral. A solution whose *p*H is greater than 7 is alkaline while one whose *p*H is less than 7 is acidic.

It is important to remember that an increase in *p*H represents a decrease in hydrogen-ion concentration, that is, a decrease in acidity.

Problems

18.1 Calculate the OH⁻ concentration in moles of OH⁻ per liter, of a solution which contains 1×10^{-2} mole of H⁺ per liter. Will the solution be neutral, acidic, or alkaline?

SOLUTION: In any water solution the product of the concentration of H⁺ and the concentration of OH⁻, when these concentrations are expressed in moles per liter, is always equal to 1×10^{-14}. That is

$$[H^+] \times [OH^-] = 1 \times 10^{-14} \, M^2$$

$$[OH^-] = \frac{1 \times 10^{-14}}{[H^+]} = \frac{1 \times 10^{-14}}{1 \times 10^{-2} \text{ mole H}^+ \text{ per liter}}$$

$$= 1 \times 10^{-12} \text{ mole OH}^- \text{ per liter}$$

If the concentration of H⁺ is 1×10^{-7} mole of H⁺ per liter, the concentration of OH⁻ will also be 1×10^{-7} mole of OH⁻ per liter, and the solution will be neutral. If the concentration of H⁺ is greater than 1×10^{-7} mole/liter, the solution will be acidic; if less, it will be alkaline. Since 1×10^{-2} mole of H⁺ per liter is a higher concentration than 1×10^{-7} mole of H⁺ per liter, the solution will be acidic.

18.2 Calculate the OH⁻ concentration, in g of OH⁻ per liter, of a solution containing 1×10^{-10} mole of H⁺ per liter.

SOLUTION:

$$[H^+] \times [OH^-] = 1 \times 10^{-14} \, M^2$$

$$[OH^-] = \frac{1 \times 10^{-14}}{[H^+]} = \frac{1 \times 10^{-14}}{1 \times 10^{-10} \text{ mole H}^+ \text{ per liter}}$$

$$= 1 \times 10^{-4} \text{ mole of OH}^- \text{ per liter}$$

$$1 \times 10^{-4} \text{ mole of OH}^-/\text{liter} \times \frac{17 \text{ g of OH}^-}{1 \text{ mole of OH}^-}$$

$$= 1.7 \times 10^{-3} \text{ g of OH}^-/\text{liter}$$

18.3 Calculate the OH⁻ concentration, in grams of OH⁻ per liter, of a solution whose H⁺ concentration is:

(a) 1.0×10^{-6} mole of H⁺ per liter

*(b) 3.0×10^{-4} g of H⁺ per liter

18.4 Calculate the H^+ concentration, in grams of H^+ per liter, of a solution whose OH^- concentration is:

   (a) 2.0×10^{-5} mole of OH^- per liter

  *(b) 3.4×10^{-2} g of OH^- per liter

18.5 Calculate the pH of a solution which contains 1×10^{-5} mole of H^+ per liter.

   SOLUTION: By definition, pH is the negative logarithm of the hydrogen-ion concentration when this concentration is expressed in moles of H^+ per liter.

$$pH = -\log [H^+] = -\log 10^{-5} = 5$$

18.6 Calculate the pH of a solution which contains 3×10^{-4} mole of H^+ per liter.

   SOLUTION:

$$pH = \log \frac{1}{[H^+]} = \log \frac{1}{3 \times 10^{-4}} = \log \frac{10^4}{3}$$

$$pH = \log \frac{10^4}{3} = \log 10^4 - \log 3$$

$$\log 10^4 = 4 \qquad \log 3 = 0.477$$

$$pH = 4 - 0.477 = 3.523$$

18.7 Calculate the pH of a solution which contains:

   (a) 1×10^{-8} mole of H^+ per liter

  *(b) 0.0020 g of H^+ per liter

   (c) 0.0030 mole of H^+ per liter

  *(d) 0.00017 g of OH^- per 100 cc

   (e) 2.0×10^{-3} mole of OH^- per liter

18.8 Calculate the pH of:

  *(a) $0.010\ F\ HC_2H_3O_2$ which is 4.17% ionized

   (b) $0.10\ F\ NH_4OH$ which is 4.10% ionized

  *(c) $0.010\ F\ KOH$

  *(d) $1.00 \times 10^{-8}\ F\ HCl$

18.9 Calculate the H^+ concentration in moles of H^+ per liter, of a solution whose pH is 5.

SOLUTION: pH is, by definition, the negative of the logarithm of the H^+ concentration. Since the pH is 5, $[H^+]$ must be 10^{-5} mole/liter.

18.10 Calculate the H^+ concentration in moles per liter of a solution whose pH is 4.8.

SOLUTION: Since pH is 4.8, $[H^+]$ must be $10^{-4.8}$ mole/liter. But $10^{-4.8} = 10^{-5} \times 10^{0.2}$

$$10^{0.2} = 1.59 \qquad (\log 10^{0.2} = 0.2 \text{ and antilog of } 0.2 = 1.59)$$

Therefore, $10^{-4.8} = 1.59 \times 10^{-5}$

$$[H^+] = 1.59 \times 10^{-5} \text{ mole/liter}$$

18.11 Calculate the H^+ concentration in moles of H^+ per liter of a solution whose:

(a) pH is 1.5

*(b) pH is 13.6

18.12 Calculate the OH^- concentration in moles of OH^- per liter of a solution whose:

(a) pH is 3.6

*(b) pH is 6.2

18.13 Which is more strongly acid:

(a) a solution with a pH of 2?

(b) a solution containing 0.020 g of H^+ per liter?

18.14 A 0.0010 F solution of HF has a pH of 4. Calculate the per cent ionization of the HF.*

Hydrolysis

The hydrolysis equilibrium that is established when a salt, such as $NaC_2H_3O_2$, which is derived from the weak acid, $HC_2H_3O_2$, is dissolved in water may be represented by the net equation,

(1) $\qquad C_2H_3O_2^- + H_2O \rightleftarrows HC_2H_3O_2 + OH^-$

The equilibrium constant for this reaction is represented by the equation,

(2) $\qquad K = \dfrac{[HC_2H_3O_2] \times [OH^-]}{[C_2H_3O_2^-] \times [H_2O]}$

In comparison with the concentrations of the other ions involved in this equilibrium, $[H_2O]$ is extremely large; this is particularly true in dilute solution. Since $[H_2O]$ is large, and since the degree of hydrolysis is in most instances small, the change in the value of $[H_2O]$ when the equilibrium Equation (1) is shifted is negligible. For that reason $[H_2O]$ can be considered to be constant. In dilute solutions the constant value of $[H_2O]$ is approximately 55.6 moles/liter. This constant value of $[H_2O]$ can then be multiplied by the equilibrium constant, K, in Equation (2) to give a new constant K_h, called the *hydrolysis constant*. The formula for the hydrolysis constant will then be

(3) $$K_h = \frac{[HC_2H_3O_2] \times [OH^-]}{[C_2H_3O_2^-]}$$

The constant for the hydrolysis of the ammonium ion is represented by the formula,

(4) $$K_h = \frac{[NH_4OH] \times [H^+]}{[NH_4^+]}$$

The argument that has been used above in determining the formula for the hydrolysis constant, when applied to other systems, leads to the general rule that *the concentration of the liquid solvent never appears in the formula for an equilibrium constant* even if it is a reactant.

The numerical value of the hydrolysis constant for a particular ion can be calculated from the ion product constant for water and the ionization constant for the weak acid or weak base formed during hydrolysis in the following way:

In Equation (3) we will multiply both numerator and denominator by $[H^+]$, giving thereby,

(5) $$K_h = \frac{[HC_2H_3O_2]}{[H^+] \times [C_2H_3O_2^-]} \times [OH^-] \times [H^+]$$

The first term to the right of the $=$ sign is the reciprocal of the ionization constant, K_i, for $HC_2H_3O_2$ and the rest of the expression is the ion product constant, K_w, for water.

If we substitute the numerical values of K_w and K_i we obtain the numerical value of K_h.

(6) $$K_h = \frac{K_w}{K_i} = \frac{1 \times 10^{-14} \, M^2}{1.8 \times 10^{-5} \, M} = 5.6 \times 10^{-10} \, M$$

It is obvious from these calculations that *the weaker the acid* (or base) *the greater the per cent hydrolysis of its anion* (or cation).

If the salt is derived from a weak acid and a weak base both the cation and the anion undergo hydrolysis. Thus, for the salt, NH_4F, the reactions are:

$$(7) \qquad NH_4^+ + H_2O \rightleftarrows NH_4OH + H^+$$

$$(8) \qquad F^- + H_2O \rightleftarrows HF + OH^-$$

The H^+ and OH^- formed in Equations (7) and (8) will react

$$(9) \qquad H^+ + OH^- = H_2O$$

Equations (7), (8) and (9), when totalled, give the net equation for the hydrolysis,

$$(10) \qquad NH_4^+ + F^- + H_2O \rightleftarrows NH_4OH + HF$$

The equilibrium constant for this reaction is

$$(11) \qquad K = \frac{[NH_4OH] \times [HF]}{[NH_4^+] \times [F^-] \times [H_2O]}$$

As in the previous hydrolysis, $[H_2O]$ is constant, and can be combined with K to give a new constant, the hydrolysis constant K_h.

$$(12) \qquad K_h = \frac{[NH_4OH] \times [HF]}{[NH_4^+] \times [F^-]}$$

By multiplying both numerator and denominator by $[H^+] \times [OH^-]$, Equation (12) is resolved into three separate equilibria.

$$(13) \quad K_h = \frac{[NH_4OH]}{[NH_4^+] \times [OH^-]} \times \frac{[HF]}{[H^+] \times [F^-]} \times [H^+] \times [OH^-]$$

$$(14) \quad K_h = \frac{1}{K_{NH_4OH}} \times \frac{1}{K_{HF}} \times K_w = \frac{K_w}{K_{NH_4OH} \times K_{HF}}$$

By substituting, in Equation (14), the numerical values of the three constants, the numerical value of K_h can be calculated.

$$(15) \qquad K_h = \frac{1.0 \times 10^{-14}}{1.8 \times 10^{-5} \times 6.9 \times 10^{-4}} = 8.0 \times 10^{-7}$$

Other Equilibria Involving Weak Electrolytes

The technique of resolving a given equilibrium constant into its component constants, which was used in calculating hydrolysis constants, can be applied to other systems. To illustrate, when sodium formate

(NaHCO$_2$) is added to a solution of acetic acid the following equilibrium is set up.

$$CHO_2^- + HC_2H_3O_2 \rightleftharpoons HCHO_2 + C_2H_3O_2^-$$

The equilibrium constant for this reaction is

$$K = \frac{[HCHO_2] \times [C_2H_3O_2^-]}{[CHO_2^-] \times [HC_2H_3O_2]}$$

By multiplying both numerator and denominator by $[H^+]$ we obtain

$$K = \frac{[HCHO_2^-]}{[H^+] \times [CHO_2^-]} \times \frac{[H^+] \times [C_2H_3O_2^-]}{[HC_2H_3O_2]}$$

$$K = \frac{1}{K_{HCHO_2}} \times K_{HC_2H_3O_2} = \frac{1.8 \times 10^{-5}}{2 \times 10^{-4}} = 9 \times 10^{-2}$$

Problems

18.15 Calculate the OH^- ion concentration of 0.2 F KCN.

SOLUTION: The net equation for the hydrolysis is

$$CN^- + H_2O \rightleftharpoons HCN + OH^-$$

$$K_h = \frac{[HCN] \times [OH^-]}{[CN^-]} = \frac{[HCN]}{[H^+] \times [CN^-]} \times [H^+] \times [OH^-]$$

$$= \frac{K_w}{K_{HCN}} = \frac{1.0 \times 10^{-14}}{4.0 \times 10^{-10}} = 2.5 \times 10^{-5} M$$

Let $X = [OH^-] = [HCN]$

$$0.2 - X = [CN^-]$$

$$\frac{X^2}{0.2 - X} = 2.5 \times 10^{-5} M$$

$$X^2 = 5 \times 10^{-6} M^2$$

$$X = 2 \times 10^{-3} M = [OH^-]$$

18.16 Calculate the pH of 0.10 F KHCO$_2$ (potassium formate).

18.17 Calculate the H^+ ion concentration of 0.10 F NH$_4$Cl.*

18.18 Calculate the concentration of HCN and of OH^- in 0.20 F NH$_4$CN.

18.19 Calculate the pH of 0.1 F NH$_4$Ac.*

18.20 s Calculate the concentration of K^+, SO_3^{--}, H^+, OH^-, and H_2SO_3 in 0.10 F K_2SO_3.

SOLUTION: The net equations for the hydrolysis reactions are:

(1) $$SO_3^{--} + H_2O \rightleftarrows HSO_3^- + OH^-$$

(2) $$HSO_3^- + H_2O \rightleftarrows H_2SO_3 + OH^-$$

The hydrolysis constants, calculated in the manner illustrated in Problem 18.15, are:

(3) K_h for $SO_3^{--} = \dfrac{[HSO_3^-] \times [OH^-]}{[SO_3^{--}]} = 1.8 \times 10^{-7} M$

(4) K_h for $HSO_3^- = \dfrac{[H_2SO_3] \times [OH^-]}{[HSO_3^-]} = 7.7 \times 10^{-13} M$

It is obvious that the hydrolysis of the HSO_3^- formed in (1) is negligible, and that $[OH^-]$ and $[HSO_3^-]$ will be determined by the hydrolysis of SO_3^{--}.

Let $X = [OH^-] = [HSO_3^-]$

$$0.10 - X = [SO_3^{--}]$$

$$\frac{X^2}{0.10 - X} = 1.8 \times 10^{-7} M$$

$$X^2 = 1.8 \times 10^{-8} M^2$$

$$X = 1.3 \times 10^{-4} M = [OH^-] = [HSO_3^-]$$

$$[H^+] = \frac{1.0 \times 10^{-14}}{1.3 \times 10^{-4}} = 7.5 \times 10^{-11}$$

$$[SO_3^{--}] = 0.10 - 1.3 \times 10^{-4} = 0.10$$

$$[H_2SO_3] = \frac{7.7 \times 10^{-13} \times [HSO_3^-]}{[OH^-]} = 7.7 \times 10^{-13}$$

$$[K^+] = 0.20$$

NOTE: This problem is an example of a situation which will be encountered in many problems, in which many equilibria exist. Thus, in addition to the two hydrolysis reactions given in Equations (1) and (2), the following equilibria are set up:

(5) $$SO_3^{--} + H^+ \rightleftarrows HSO_3^-$$

(6) $$HSO_3^- + H^+ \rightleftarrows H_2SO_3$$

(7) $$H^+ + OH^- \rightleftarrows H_2O$$

Since all of these equilibria occur in the same solution the concentration of a given species must be the same in each; a concentration that satisfies one equilibrium must satisfy all other equilibria in which that species is involved. Thus, in this particular problem, the concentrations of SO_3^{--}, HSO_3^- and H^+ that are calculated for Equations (1) and (7) must satisfy the K for Equation (5) and the concentration of H_2SO_3 calculated for Equation (6) must be the same as that derived for Equation (2).

In solving such a problem the *main equilibrium* should be selected and used as the basis for the calculations. The choice of the main equation is, generally, quite obvious, since it involves the predominant reactants (in this instance, SO_3^{--} and H_2O).

18.21 s Calculate the formate-ion concentration in moles per liter of a 0.2 F solution of NaF in 0.1 F HCOOH (formic acid).

18.22 s Calculate the CN^- ion concentration, in moles per liter, of a 0.1 F solution of $NaC_2H_3O_2$ in 0.1 F HCN.

18.23 s A liter of solution prepared by dissolving H_2SO_4 in pure water has a pH of 3.00.

(a) Calculate the molarity of each species in solution.

(b) How many moles of H_2SO_4 were dissolved? The first ionization of H_2SO_4 is complete. The ionization constant for HSO_4^- is 1.26×10^{-2} M.

SOLUTION: Let X equal the moles of H_2SO_4 dissolved. Let Y equal the moles of SO_4^{--}. Then, since the first ionization of H_2SO_4 is complete,

$$\begin{array}{ccc} X & X & X - Y \end{array}$$
(a) $H_2SO_4 = H^+ + HSO_4^-$

$$\begin{array}{ccc} X - Y & Y & Y \end{array}$$
(b) $HSO_4^- \rightleftarrows H^+ + SO_4^{--}$

(c) $X + Y = 1.00 \times 10^{-3} = [H^+]$

(d) $Y/(X - Y) = [SO_4^{--}]/[HSO_4^-] = K_2/[H^+] = 12.6$

From (c) and (d) we find that

$X = 5.18 \times 10^{-4}$ moles = moles of H_2SO_4 dissolved

$Y = 4.82 \times 10^{-4}$ moles per liter = $[SO_4^{--}]$

$$X - Y = 3.6 \times 10^{-5} \text{ moles per liter} = [HSO_4^-]$$

$$1.00 \times 10^{-14} \div 1.00 \times 10^{-3} = 1.00 \times 10^{-11} = [OH^-]$$

18.24 s In a solution prepared by dissolving $NaC_2H_3O_2$ and $HC_2H_3O_2$ in pure water the sum of the formalities of the 2 solutes is 1.0. The pH of the solution is 5.0.

(a) Calculate the formality of each of the 2 solutes.

(b) Calculate the molarity of each of the species in solution. K_i for $HC_2H_3O_2$ is $1.8 \times 10^{-5} M$.

SOLUTION: Since $[H^+]$ is 1.0×10^{-5} and $K = 1.8 \times 10^{-5} M$, the ratio, $[C_2H_3O_2^-]/[HC_2H_3O_2]$ will be 1.8. Since we know that $[C_2H_3O_2^-] + [HC_2H_3O_2] = 1.0$, the values of $[C_2H_3O_2^-]$ and $[HC_2H_3O_2]$ can be calculated to be 0.64 M and 0.36 M, respectively. The fact that $[H^+]$ is 1×10^{-5} means that a negligible amount of $HC_2H_3O_2$ ionizes and a negligible amount of $C_2H_3O_2^-$ is produced by this ionization. Therefore, the molarity of the $C_2H_3O_2^-$ equals the formality of the $NaC_2H_3O_2$ and the molarity of the $HC_2H_3O_2$ equals its formality.

18.25 s A solution which is 0.020 F in oxalate has a pH of 4.0. Calculate the molarity of each species in the solution. For $H_2C_2O_4$, $K_1 = 6.5 \times 10^{-2} M$ and $K_2 = 6.1 \times 10^{-5} M$.

SOLUTION: Since $[H^+]$ is 1.0×10^{-4}, and since the ionization constants are known, the ratios, $[HC_2O_4^-]/[H_2C_2O_4]$, $[C_2O_4^{--}]/[HC_2O_4^-]$, and $[C_2O_4^{--}]/[H_2C_2O_4]$ can be calculated. From these ratios, and the fact that $[H_2C_2O_4] + [HC_2O_4^-] + [C_2O_4^{--}] = 0.020$, the molarity of each species in solution can be calculated.

18.26 s Calculate the pH of 0.20 F $NaHCO_3$. The principal equilibrium is $2 HCO_3^- \rightleftarrows H_2CO_3 + CO_3^{--}$.

18.27 s How many grams of solid anhydrous $NaC_2H_3O_2$ must be added to 100 ml of 0.110 F HCl to give a solution with a pH of 4.60? Assume that the volume of the solution is unchanged. K_i for $HC_2H_3O_2$ is $1.75 \times 10^{-5} M$.

18.28 s Calculate the pH of a solution

(a) 0.014 F in Na_2SO_4 and 0.010 F in HNO_3. K_2 for H_2SO_4 is 1.2×10^{-2}.

(b) 0.10 F in HCl and 0.35 F in $NaC_2H_3O_2$.

18.29 s (a) Calculate the concentration of NH_4OH in a solution containing both $0.1\ F\ HC_2H_3O_2$ and $0.1\ F\ NH_4Cl$.

SOLUTION: The principal reactions with their equilibrium constants are:

(1) $HC_2H_3O_2 \rightleftarrows H^+ + C_2H_3O_2^-$ $K_i = 1.8 \times 10^{-5}$

(2) $NH_4^+ + H_2O \rightleftarrows H^+ + NH_4OH$ $K_{hyd} = 5.6 \times 10^{-10}$

Since K_{hyd} is so much smaller than K_i the amount of H^+ derived from the hydrolysis of NH_4^+ is negligible by comparison with the amount derived from the ionization of $HC_2H_3O_2$. Therefore, calculate the $[H^+]$ derived from the ionization of $HC_2H_3O_2$ as in Problem 17.7. The value of $[H^+]$ thus calculated is $1.3 \times 10^{-3}\ M$.

To calculate $[NH_4OH]$, substitute the above value of $[H^+]$, $1.3 \times 10^{-3}\ M$, for $[H^+]$ and $0.1\ M$ for $[NH_4^+]$ in K_{hyd}.

(b) Calculate the molar concentration of each species in a solution which is $0.20\ F$ in NH_3 and $0.20\ F$ in $NaC_2H_3O_2$.

(c) Calculate the molar concentration of each species in a solution which is $0.20\ F$ in NH_3 and $0.20\ F$ in $NaCN$.

SOLUTION: The principal reactions with their equilibrium constants are:

(1) $NH_3 + H_2O \rightleftarrows NH_4^+ + OH^-$

$$K_i = \frac{[NH_4^+] \times [OH^-]}{[NH_3]} = 1.8 \times 10^{-5}$$

(2) $CN^- + H_2O \rightleftarrows HCN + OH^-$

$$K_{hyd} = \frac{[HCN] \times [OH^-]}{[CN^-]} = 2.5 \times 10^{-5}$$

Since the two equilibria occur in the same solution the value of $[OH^-]$ is the same for each. Therefore, K_i and K_{hyd} can be equated to give:

(3) $$\frac{1.8 \times 10^{-5} \times [NH_3]}{[NH_4^+]} = \frac{2.5 \times 10^{-5} \times [CN^-]}{[HCN]}$$

But $[NH_3]$ is $0.20\ M$ and $[CN^-]$ is $0.20\ M$. Substituting these values in Equation (3)

(4) $$\frac{[HCN]}{[NH_4^+]} = \frac{2.5 \times 10^{-5}}{1.8 \times 10^{-5}}$$

or

(5) $[HCN] = 1.4 \times [NH_4^+]$.

Let $X = [NH_4^+]$.

Then $1.4\,X = [HCN]$.

Since the OH^- derived in the ionization of NH_3 is, according to Equation (1), equal to $[NH_4^+]$ and since the OH^- derived from the hydrolysis of CN^- is, according to Equation (2), equal to $[HCN]$, the total $[OH^-]$ will be equal to $[NH_4^+] + [HCN]$, or $2.4\,X$. Substituting X for $[NH_4^+]$, $2.4\,X$ for $[OH^-]$, and $0.20\,M$ for $[NH_3]$ in the formula for K_i the value of X and, hence, the molar concentration of each species in solution can be calculated.

18.30 s The acid HX is a weak acid. In a $0.10\,F$ aqueous solution of the salt, NaX, 1.0% of the X^- ion is hydrolyzed. Calculate the pH of $0.10\,F$ NaX and the ionization constant of HX.

18.31 s In a $0.5\,F$ solution of KClO, the OH^- ion concentration is $3 \times 10^{-4}\,M$. What is the ionization constant for HClO?

18.32 s The solubility of a gas in a solution is directly proportional to its partial pressure. The principal equilibrium for the hydrolysis of Cl_2 in water is $Cl_2 + H_2O \rightleftarrows Cl^- + H^+ + HClO$.

In a solution prepared by bubbling gaseous chlorine into pure water, to what power of the pressure of Cl_2 over the solution is the molar chloride-ion concentration proportional?

18.33 s How would you prepare a solution with pH 9.25 from $0.30\,F$ NH_3 and $0.30\,F$ HCl?

SOLUTION: Calculate the $[NH_3]/[NH_4^+]$ ratio.

18.34 s One g of the solid weak base, MOH, whose molecular weight is 50, was neutralized by a certain volume of $1\,F$ HCl and exactly half that volume of $1\,F$ NaOH was added to the solution. The resulting solution has a pH of 8. Calculate the ionization constant of the weak base, MOH. The volume of the solid MOH can be neglected.

18.35 s A mixture of solid Na_2CO_3 and $NaHCO_3$ weighs 59.2 g. The mixture is dissolved in enough water to give 2.00 liters of solution. The pH of this solution is found to be 10.62. How many grams of Na_2CO_3 were there in the mixture? The ionization constants for H_2CO_3 are:

$$K_1 = 4.2 \times 10^{-7}\,M, \quad K_2 = 4.8 \times 10^{-11}\,M$$

18.36 s The molar concentration of H_2S in equilibrium with gaseous H_2S at a pressure of 1.00 atm is 0.10 M.

(a) Calculate the molarities of all species present in 0.020 F NaOH saturated with H_2S at 0.10 atm pressure.

(b) A solution which is 5.0 F in NH_3 is saturated with H_2S until no further reactions take place and the pressure of H_2S over the solution is 1.00 atm. Calculate the molarities of all species in this solution.

18.37 s The isotope of hydrogen, tritium, represented by the symbol, $_1^3H$ or T, forms the weak acid, tritium fluoride, TF, in which the T^+ ion, formed in the ionization reaction, TF $\rightleftarrows T^+ + F^-$, is equivalent in its properties to the H^+ ion. Tritium undergoes slow radioactive decay according to the equation

$$_1^3H = {_2^3He} + \text{one beta particle } (-_1^0e)$$

A freshly prepared aqueous solution of the weak acid, TF, has a pT (the equivalent of pH) of 1.50 and freezes at $-0.372°C$. If a 600-ml portion of this solution were allowed to stand for 24.8 yr a total of 4.50×10^{22} beta particles would be emitted.
The molecular weight of TF is 22.0. The freezing point constant for water is 1.86. The density of the above aqueous solution of TF is 1.0. The half life of tritium is 12.4 yr.
On the basis of the above data and facts calculate:

(a) The ionization constant for TF.

(b) The numerical value of the Avogadro number.

(c) What happens to the fluorine atoms when tritium decays?

18.38 s $BaSO_4$ is insoluble. The first ionization of H_2SO_4 is 100% complete; the second ionization constant is 1.2×10^{-2}. Exactly 0.0500 mole of barium metal was added to 2.00 liters of 0.0500 F H_2SO_4. When reaction was complete what was the pH of the solution?

18.39 s A mixture of HCl and SO_3 gases was contained in a 1.00-liter flask at 127°C and a pressure of 374.40 mm. The mixture was dissolved in enough water to give one liter of solution; this solution had a pH of 1.77. Calculate the number of moles of SO_3 in the original mixture. K_2 for H_2SO_4 is 1.2×10^{-2} M.

18.40 s A mixture of equal grams of Na and Ca was added to enough water to give 500 ml of solution; this solution had a pH of 12.8. How many grams of Na were in the mixture?

18.41 s The pH of a solution 0.240 F in HA (a weak acid) and 0.080 F in NaA, is 5.30.

(a) Calculate the molar concentrations of all species and also the ionization constant for HA.

(b) The solution is now made 0.010 F in HCl. Calculate the molar concentrations of all species in the solution.

18.42 s A solution of the weak acid, HCN, is diluted with water so that the final molarity of HCN is exactly 0.01 times the initial molarity.

(a) How will the hydrogen ion concentration in the diluted solution compare with that in the original?

(b) How will the pH of the diluted solution compare with that of the original?

(c) How will the per cent ionization of the HCN in the diluted solution compare with that in the original?

18.43 s (a) You are given a solution, S_1, of the weak acid, HA. A portion of this solution is then diluted with enough water to give a solution, S_2, in which the final molarity of HA is 0.0001 times the original molarity. How does [H+] in S_1 compare with [H+] in S_2?

(b) The solid soluble salt, KA, is added to S_1 so that the molarity of A− in S_1 is 10,000 times its molarity in S_2. There is no change in volume when KA is added. How does the [H+] in S_1 now compare with the [H+] in S_2?

(c) KA is now added to S_2 until the molarity of A− in S_2 is equal to its molarity in S_1. How will the pH of S_2 compare with that of S_1?

18.44 s (a) Calculate the pH of 0.10 F H_2S.

(b) To 1.00 liter of this solution is added solid KOH until the pH is 7.00. Compute the amount of KOH added.

(c) What is the pH of the solution when 0.090 formula weight of KOH has been added all told?

(d) Calculate how much KOH must be added (in total) to bring the pH to 13.00.

18.45 s The ionization constant of the weak acid, HCN, is $4.0 \times 10^{-10}\ M$. A solution is prepared by dissolving 0.20 mole of NaCN in enough water to make 1.00 liter of solution.

(a) Calculate the pH of this solution.

(b) The strong acid, HCl, is then added to this solution (as a gas, so there is no change in the volume of the solution) until the pH of the resulting solution is 9.60. How many moles of HCl were added?

18.46 s The pressure of HCN (g) over $1.00\ M$ HCN is 0.020 atm. To $0.333\ F$ NaCN is added HNO_3 until the pH is 9.69. What pressure of HCN (g) is over this solution? (Assume that a negligible volume change takes place when the acid is added; assume that the volume of the gas phase over the solution is small, so that not much HCN need vaporize to establish this pressure.)

18.47 s H_3A is a weak acid. A solution 0.100 F in Na_3A and 0.070 F in HCl has a pH of 8.0. A solution 0.100 F in Na_3A and 0.150 F in HCl has a pH of 1.30. What can be said about the three ionization constants of H_3A?

18.48 s A solution is prepared by dissolving 1.07 moles of NaH_2PO_4 and 3.32 moles of Na_3PO_4 in enough water to make a liter of solution. What is the pH of the solution? What are the molar concentrations of $H_2PO_4^-$, HPO_4^{--}, PO_4^{---}, and H_3PO_4?

SOLUTION: The main equilibrium is

$$PO_4^{---} + H_2PO_4^- \rightleftarrows 2\ HPO_4^{--}$$

18.49 s A solution is 0.10 F in formic acid and 0.025 F in hydrocyanic acid. To 40 ml of this solution is added 10 ml of 0.050 F NaOH. Calculate the pH of the resulting solution.

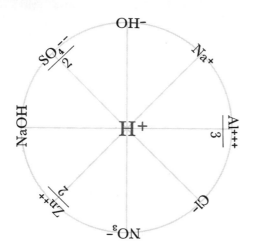

19

The Concept
of
Equivalent Weights.
Normality of Solutions.
Faraday's Law
and Electrochemical
Equivalence.

In chemical terminology two quantities of substances are *equivalent* to each other if they will react with each other or replace each other. Thus, 24.3 g of Mg (1 mole of Mg) will combine with 16.0 g of O (1 mole of O); the quantity, 24.3 g of Mg, is *equivalent to* the quantity, 16.0 g of O. Likewise, 23.0 g of sodium will combine with 1.0 g of hydrogen; 23.0 g of Na is equivalent to 1.0 g of H. One mole of H_2SO_4 will neutralize 2 moles of NaOH; 1 mole of H_2SO_4 is equivalent to 2 moles of NaOH. Two moles of $KMnO_4$ will oxidize 5 moles of H_2SO_3; that means that 1 mole of $KMnO_4$ is equivalent to 2.5 moles of H_2SO_3. Two moles of aluminum metal will replace 3 moles of copper according to the equation, $2 \text{ Al} + 3 \text{ Cu}^{++} = 3 \text{ Cu} + 2 \text{ Al}^{+++}$; that means that 1 mole of Al is equivalent to 1.5 moles of Cu. One mole of Al will replace 3 moles of H according to the reaction, $\text{Al} + 3 \text{ H}^+ = \text{Al}^{+++} + 1.5 \text{ H}_2$; 1 mole of H is equivalent to $\frac{1}{3}$ mole of Al.

To facilitate comparison of equivalent quantities of different substances, 1.008 g (1 mole) of H is selected as a standard and is defined as *one gram-equivalent weight of hydrogen. One gram-equivalent weight of any substance is then, by definition, the weight in grams of that substance which will react with or replace one gram-equivalent weight (1.008 g) of hydrogen or its equivalent.*

In the combination of H with O to form H_2O, 1.008 g of H combine with 7.999 g of O; therefore, 7.999 g is 1 gram-equivalent weight of O. To replace 1.008 g of H from HCl requires 12.15 g of Mg; therefore, 12.15 g is 1 gram-equivalent weight of Mg.

The formula, HCl, tells us that 1 mole of Cl is equivalent to 1 mole (1.008 g) of H.

Since the number of moles of H with which 1 mole of an element, X, will react is determined by the valence of X, it follows that *the equivalent weight of an element,* when it combines with or replaces another element, *is its atomic weight divided by its valence.*

Since 1 mole of Na (which is 1 gram-equivalent weight of Na) will react with one mole of HCl as represented by the equation

$$Na + HCl = NaCl + \tfrac{1}{2} H_2$$

1 mole of HCl is 1 gram-equivalent weight of HCl. This leads to the conclusion, from the reaction, $NaOH + HCl = NaCl + H_2O$, that 1 mole of NaOH is 1 gram-equivalent weight of NaOH. Likewise, from the reaction

$$2\,NaOH + H_2SO_4 = Na_2SO_4 + 2\,H_2O$$

we conclude that $\tfrac{1}{2}$ a mole is 1 gram-equivalent weight of H_2SO_4, while the equation

$$3\,NaOH + H_3PO_4 = Na_3PO_4 + 3\,H_2O$$

tells us $\tfrac{1}{3}$ of a mole is 1 gram-equivalent weight of H_3PO_4, and the equation

$$6\,NaOH + Fe_2(SO_4)_3 = 3\,Na_2SO_4 + 2\,Fe(OH)_3$$

shows that $\tfrac{1}{6}$ of a mole is 1 gram-equivalent weight of $Fe_2(SO_4)_3$.

From the above examples, and many similar examples, we conclude that, *in any simple replacement reaction or direct* (non-redox) *combination between oppositely charged ions the equivalent weight of a substance is its formula weight divided by the total valence of its + or − ion.*

In any redox reaction the equivalent weight of a substance is its formula weight divided by the change in oxidation number of its component atoms. This is illustrated by the reaction

$$KClO_3 + 6\,(H) = KCl + 3\,H_2O$$

Since 1 mole of $KClO_3$ reacts with 6 moles of H, the equivalent weight of $KClO_3$ is, obviously, $\tfrac{1}{6}$ of its formula weight. In the change from $KClO_3$ to KCl the oxidation number of Cl changes from $+5$ to -1, for a total change of 6. The equivalent weight of $KClO_3$, *in this particular reaction,* is, therefore, its formula weight divided by the change in oxidation number of its component atoms.

In the reaction

$$2\,MnO_4^- + 5\,H_2SO_3 = 2\,Mn^{++} + 5\,SO_4^{--} + 4\,H^+ + 3\,H_2O$$

the change in oxidation number of Mn per mole of MnO_4^- is 5; therefore, the equivalent weight of MnO_4^- (or of $KMnO_4$, if that is the compound used in the reaction) is $\frac{1}{5}$ of its formula weight. The change in oxidation number of S per mole of H_2SO_3 is 2; therefore, the equivalent weight of H_2SO_3 is $\frac{1}{2}$ its formula weight. That means that 1 mole of MnO_4^- is 5 equivalents of MnO_4^-, and 2 MnO_4^- represents 10 equivalents of MnO_4^-. Likewise, 1 mole of H_2SO_3 is 2 equivalents of H_2SO_3 and 5 H_2SO_3 represents 10 equivalents. Therefore, in this reaction, it is a fact that the number of equivalents of MnO_4^- is equal to the number of equivalents of H_2SO_3.

It follows from the definition of equivalence given in the first sentence of this chapter, that, *in any reaction between any two substances, A and B, one equivalent of A will always react with one equivalent of B and the number of equivalents of A that react will always equal the number of equivalents of B that react.*

The concentration of a solution, expressed in units of *equivalents of solute per liter of solution*, is referred to as the *normality* of the solution. Thus, a *normal solution*, abbreviated 1 N, of any solute contains 1 equivalent weight of solute per liter of solution. A 0.5 N solution contains 0.50 equivalent of solute per liter of solution, etc.

Since 1 equivalent weight of reactant A, H_2SO_4 for example, will react with 1 equivalent weight of B, NaOH for example, and since a 1 N solution contains 1 equivalent of solute per liter of solution, it must follow that 1 liter of 1 N H_2SO_4 will neutralize exactly 1 liter of 1 N NaOH and 50 ml of 1 N H_2SO_4 will neutralize 50 ml of 1 N NaOH.

Since the concentration of 0.25 N HCl is 0.25 equivalent per liter, it follows that 400 ml (0.400 liter) of 0.25 N HCl will contain 0.400×0.25 or 0.10 equivalent of HCl. For any solution of any solute,

$$\text{liters of solution} \times \frac{\text{equivalents of solute}}{1 \text{ liter of solution}} = \text{total equivalents of solute}$$

Since the normality of a solution represents the number of equivalent weights of solute per liter of solution and since the equivalent weight of a solute will depend on how it reacts, it follows that a solution which has a certain normality for one reaction may have a different normality for another reaction. To illustrate, suppose a solution is prepared by dissolving 1 mole of K_2CrO_4 in enough water to give 1 liter of solution. This, then, is 1.0 formal K_2CrO_4 (1.0 F K_2CrO_4). When this solution is treated with $Ba(NO_3)_2$, the simple non-redox reaction, $Ba^{++} + CrO_4^{--} = BaCrO_4$, occurs. In this reaction the equivalent weight of K_2CrO_4 is equal to $\frac{1}{2}$ the formula weight. Therefore, when used to carry out this reaction, the above solution of K_2CrO_4 can properly be labeled 2 N K_2CrO_4.

When K_2CrO_4 is treated with Na_2SO_3 under proper conditions, the following reaction occurs:

$$10 \ H^+ + 2 \ CrO_4^{--} + 3 \ SO_3^{--} = 2 \ Cr^{+++} + 3 \ SO_4^{--} + 5 \ H_2O$$

This is a redox reaction. Since the change in oxidation number of Cr is 3 its equivalent weight is $\frac{1}{3}$ of its formula weight. When used in this reaction, 1 F K_2CrO_4 should be labeled 3 N K_2CrO_4.

This means that, in all problems dealing with equivalent weights and normal solutions, the kind of reaction must always be kept in mind.

Problems

19.1 When 0.300 g of a metal was treated with excess HCl, 0.0177 g of hydrogen was liberated. Calculate the equivalent weight of the metal.

SOLUTION: To find the equivalent weight we simply find the weight of the metal that will liberate 1.008 g of H_2.

$$1.008 \text{ g of } H_2 \times \frac{0.300 \text{ g of metal}}{0.0177 \text{ g of H}} = 16.9 \text{ g of metal}$$

$$\text{equivalent weight} = 16.9$$

19.2 When 0.030 g of a metal will combine with 0.020 g of oxygen, what is the equivalent weight of the metal?

SOLUTION: 1 mole of H is equivalent to $\frac{1}{2}$ mole of O. Therefore, to find the equivalent weight we simply find the weight of the metal that will combine with 8.0 g of oxygen.

$$8.0 \text{ g of oxygen} \times \frac{0.030 \text{ g of metal}}{0.020 \text{ g of oxygen}} = 12 \text{ g of metal}$$

$$\text{equivalent weight} = 12$$

19.3 If 12 g of NaOH were required to neutralize 400 ml of a solution of HCl in water, calculate the concentration of the HCl solution in equivalents of HCl per liter.

SOLUTION: equivalents of NaOH = equivalents of HCl. The number of equivalents of NaOH in 12 g of NaOH equals the number of equivalents of HCl in 400 ml of solution. The equivalent weight of

NaOH is equal to its formula weight, 40. Therefore, 12 g of NaOH is 12/40 or 0.30 equivalent of NaOH, and 0.30 equivalent of NaOH will neutralize 0.30 equivalent of HCl. That means that there is 0.30 equivalent of HCl in 400 ml of solution. The number of equivalents per liter will then be

$$1000 \text{ ml} \times \frac{0.30 \text{ equivalent}}{400 \text{ ml}} = 0.75 \text{ equivalent}$$

19.4 A solution containing 12.0 g of NaOH was added to a solution containing 0.400 equivalent of Fe^{+++}. How many grams of $Fe(OH)_3$ were precipitated?

soLUTION: 12.0 g of NaOH is 12.0/40.0 or 0.300 equivalent. 0.300 equivalent of NaOH will react with 0.300 equivalent of Fe^{+++} to form 0.300 equivalent of $Fe(OH)_3$. (There is an excess of Fe^{+++}) 1 equivalent of $Fe(OH)_3 = \frac{1}{3} \times$ formula weight $= \frac{1}{3} \times 106.8$ g

$$0.300 \text{ equivalent} \times \frac{106.8}{3} \text{ g/equivalent} = 10.7 \text{ g}$$

19.5 How many equivalents of $KMnO_4$ will be required to react with 30 g of $FeSO_4$ in the following reaction?

$$5 \text{ Fe}^{++} + \text{MnO}_4{}^- + 8 \text{ H}^+ = 5 \text{ Fe}^{+++} + \text{Mn}^{++} + 4 \text{ H}_2\text{O}$$

soLUTION: equivalents of $KMnO_4$ = equivalents of $FeSO_4$.

$$\text{equivalent weight of FeSO}_4 = \frac{\text{formula weight of FeSO}_4}{\text{oxidation number change of Fe}}$$

$$= \frac{151.9}{1} = \frac{151.9 \text{ g of FeSO}_4}{\text{equivalent of FeSO}_4}$$

$$\text{equivalents of FeSO}_4 = \frac{30 \text{ g of FeSO}_4}{151.9 \text{ g/equivalent of FeSO}_4}$$

$$= 0.20 \text{ equivalent of FeSO}_4$$

Therefore, 0.20 equivalent of $KMnO_4$ is required.

19.6 How many grams of KOH will be required for the preparation of 500 ml of 0.400 N KOH for use in neutralization reactions?

soLUTION: 0.400 N KOH contains 0.400 equivalent of KOH per liter (1000 ml). Therefore, 500 ml will contain 0.200 equivalent of KOH. The equivalent weight of KOH is its formula weight, 56.1.

$$0.200 \text{ equivalent of KOH} \times \frac{56.1 \text{ g}}{\text{equivalent}} = 11.2 \text{ g of KOH}$$

The problem can be solved in one operation.

$$500 \text{ ml} \times \frac{0.400 \text{ equivalent}}{1000 \text{ ml}} \times \frac{56.1 \text{ g of KOH}}{1 \text{ equivalent}} = 11.2 \text{ g of KOH}$$

19.7 What is the normality of a solution of NaOH which contains 8 g of NaOH per 400 ml of solution?

SOLUTION: The solution, 8 g of NaOH in 400 ml, is the same concentration as 20 g of NaOH in 1000 ml of solution. One equivalent weight of NaOH is 40 g; 20 g of NaOH is 0.5 of an equivalent weight. Since 0.5 equivalent of NaOH is present in a liter of solution the normality is 0.5 N. The problem can be solved in one operation.

$$1000 \text{ ml} \times \frac{8 \text{ g of NaOH}}{400 \text{ ml}} \times \frac{1 \text{ equivalent of NaOH}}{40 \text{ g of NaOH}}$$
$$= 0.5 \text{ equivalent of NaOH}$$

19.8 A sample of 50 ml of hydrochloric acid was required to react with 0.40 g of NaOH. Calculate the normality of the hydrochloric acid.

SOLUTION: To find the normality we must find the number of equivalents of HCl in a liter of acid.

$$\text{equivalents of HCl} = \text{equivalents of NaOH}$$

The equivalent weight of NaOH is 40. Therefore 0.40 g of NaOH is 0.010 equivalent of NaOH. Since there is 0.010 equivalent of NaOH there must be 0.010 equivalent of HCl in the 50 ml of hydrochloric acid that were required. To find the number of equivalents per 1000 ml, which is the normality,

$$1000 \text{ ml} \times \frac{0.010 \text{ equivalent}}{50 \text{ ml}} = 0.20 \text{ equivalent}$$

Therefore, the solution is 0.20 N.
The above calculation can be carried out in one operation:

$$\frac{0.40 \text{ g of NaOH} \times \dfrac{1 \text{ equivalent}}{40 \text{ g of NaOH}}}{50 \text{ ml of HCl}}$$
$$\times 1000 \text{ ml of HCl} = 0.20 \text{ equivalent}$$

19.9 How many grams of KOH will be required to react with 100 ml of 0.80 N HCl?

SOLUTION: equivalents of KOH = equivalents of HCl.

$$\text{equivalents of KOH} = \frac{\text{g of KOH}}{56.1 \text{ g of KOH per equivalent}}$$

$$\text{equivalents of HCl} = 100 \text{ ml of HCl} \times \frac{0.80 \text{ equivalent of HCl}}{1000 \text{ ml of HCl}}$$

$$\frac{\text{g of KOH}}{56.1 \text{ g of KOH per equivalent}}$$

$$= 100 \text{ ml of HCl} \times \frac{0.80 \text{ equivalent of HCl}}{1000 \text{ ml of HCl}}$$

$$\text{g of KOH} = \frac{56.1 \times 100 \times 0.80}{1000} = 4.5 \text{ g}$$

Since normality is defined as equivalents of solute per liter of solution, since equivalents of KOH equals equivalents of HCl, and since 100 ml is 0.10 liter, the entire calculation can take the simple form,

0.10 liter × 0.80 equivalent/liter × 56.1 g/equivalent = 4.5 g

19.10 How many milliliters of 0.30 N HNO_3 will be required to react with 24 ml of 0.25 N KOH?

SOLUTION: equivalents of HNO_3 = equivalents of KOH.

$$\frac{\text{ml of } HNO_3 \times 0.30 \text{ equivalent}}{1000 \text{ ml}} = \frac{24 \text{ ml of KOH} \times 0.25 \text{ equivalent}}{1000 \text{ ml}}$$

$$\text{milliliters of } HNO_3 = \frac{24 \text{ ml} \times 0.25 \text{ equivalent}}{0.30 \text{ equivalent}} = 20 \text{ ml}$$

19.11 What would be the concentration, in grams per liter, of 0.100 N $KMnO_4$ when used in the following reaction?

$$2 \text{ MnO}_4^- + 10 \text{ Cl}^- + 16 \text{ H}^+ = 2 \text{ Mn}^{++} + 5 \text{ Cl}_2 + 8 \text{ H}_2\text{O}$$

SOLUTION: 0.100 N $KMnO_4$ contains 0.100 equivalent (equivalent weights) of $KMnO_4$ per liter.

The oxidation number of Mn changes from +7 in $KMnO_4$ to +2 in $MnCl_2$. This represents an oxidation number change of 5.

$$\text{redox equivalent weight} = \frac{\text{formula weight}}{\text{oxidation number change}}$$

$$= \frac{158}{5} = 31.6$$

0.100 equivalent = 3.16 g   concentration = 3.16 g/liter

19.12 If 18 ml of 0.2 N H_2SO_4 were required to liberate the CO_2 from 82 ml of sodium carbonate solution, calculate the normality of the sodium carbonate solution.

19.13 How many milliliters of 0.250 N HCl will be required to neutralize 500 ml of solution containing 8.00 g of NaOH?*

19.14 Calculate the normality of a H_3PO_4 solution, 40 ml of which neutralized 120 ml of 0.53 N NaOH.

19.15 How many milliliters of 0.25 N NaOH will be required to neutralize 116 ml of 0.0625 N H_2SO_4?*

19.16 It took 40 ml of 0.20 N H_2SO_4 to precipitate completely the Ba^{++} ion (as $BaSO_4$) from a $BaCl_2$ solution. Calculate the number of grams of $BaCl_2$ that were originally present in the $BaCl_2$ solution.

19.17 How many grams of commercial sodium hydroxide containing 91.0% NaOH will be required for the preparation of 600 ml of 2.00 N NaOH?*

19.18 If 0.664 g of phthalic acid, $H_6C_9O_4$, was required to neutralize 20.0 ml of 0.400 N NaOH, calculate the equivalent weight of the acid.

19.19 A sample of 79 ml of hydrochloric acid was treated with an excess of magnesium. The hydrogen gas that evolved was collected and measured over water at 30°C and 780 mm; its volume was 500 cc. Calculate the normality of the hydrochloric acid.*

19.20 A sample of 200 ml of 1.000 N H_2SO_4 was treated with an excess of Na_2CO_3. How many liters of dry CO_2 gas, measured at STP, were given off?

19.21 Each of the following solutions is used in non-redox reactions.

*(a) Calculate the normality of a 77.0% solution of H_2SO_4 whose density is 1.70.

(b) Calculate the per cent of HCl in 12.0 N HCl of density 1.20.

*(c) Calculate the density of 7.36 N HCl containing 24.0% HCl.

(d) What is the formality of 0.015 N H_3PO_4?

*(e) What is the formality of 0.12 N H_2SO_4?

(f) What is the formality of 0.25 N HCl?

*(g) What is the normality of 0.02 F H_2SO_4?

(h) What is the normality of 0.15 F $Al_2(SO_4)_3$?

19.22 A 25-ml sample of 0.50 N H_2SO_4 was diluted to 30 ml. Calculate the normality of the resulting solution.

SOLUTION: Since no H_2SO_4 was lost in the diluting process, equivalent of H_2SO_4 before dilution = equivalent of H_2SO_4 after dilution.

$$25 \text{ ml} \times \frac{0.50 \text{ equivalent}}{1000 \text{ ml}} = 30 \text{ ml} \times \frac{X \text{ equivalent}}{1000 \text{ ml}}$$

$$X = 0.42 \text{ equivalent}$$

Solution is 0.42 N.

19.23 To what volume in ml must 100 ml of 2.00 N HCl be diluted to give 0.400 N HCl?*

19.24 Given some 2.00 F K_2SO_4, how would you prepare 400 ml of 0.100 N K_2SO_4?

19.25 To what volume must 1.00 ml of a 70.0% solution of nitric acid of density 1.42 be diluted to give a solution with a pH of 2? What is the normality of this diluted solution?*

19.26 Calculate the pH of each of the following:

(a) A solution containing 2×10^{-5} equivalent of H^+ per liter.

(b) A solution containing 3×10^{-3} equivalent of OH^- per liter.*

(c) A solution containing 0.022 equivalent of $Ca(OH)_2$ per liter.

19.27 A volume of 600 ml of HCl of a certain normality was mixed with 400 ml of NaOH of the same normality. The resulting solution had a pH of 1. Calculate the normality of the HCl and NaOH.*

19.28 How many grams of $KClO_3$ will be required for the preparation of 400 ml of 0.20 N $KClO_3$ for use in the reaction,

$$ClO_3^- + 3 H_2SO_3 = Cl^- + 3 SO_4^{--} + 6 H^+?$$

19.29 How many milliliters of 0.50 N H_2SO_3 will be required to reduce 120 ml of 0.40 N $K_2Cr_2O_7$?*

$$Cr_2O_7^{--} + 3 H_2SO_3 + 2 H^+ = 2 Cr^{+++} + 3 SO_4^{--} + 4 H_2O$$

19.30 How many grams of $FeSO_4$ will be oxidized by 24 ml of 0.25 N $KMnO_4$ in the following reaction?

$$MnO_4^- + 5 Fe^{++} + 8 H^+ = Mn^{++} + 5 Fe^{+++} + 4 H_2O$$

19.31 A 2.0 g sample of crude sulfur containing inert impurities was analyzed by burning in air to SO_2. The SO_2 was absorbed in water and the resulting solution was acidified with dilute HCl and was then titrated with 0.25 N $KMnO_4$. In the reaction the MnO_4^- was reduced to Mn^{++}. Exactly 400 ml of this 0.25 N $KMnO_4$ were required. Calculate the per cent of sulfur in the sample.*

19.32 A 3.0 g sample of crude zinc sulfide ore containing sand and clay as impurities was roasted completely in air, and the evolved SO_2 was passed into 0.20 N $K_2Cr_2O_7$. The $Cr_2O_7^{--}$ was reduced to Cr^{+++}. It was found that 200 ml of this 0.20 N $K_2Cr_2O_7$ were required to react with the evolved gas. Calculate the per cent of ZnS in the crude ore.

19.33 $Cr_2O_7^{--}$ will oxidize NO_2^- to NO_3^- in acid solution, the $Cr_2O_7^{--}$ being reduced to Cr^{+++}.

In one student's experiment 20 ml of 0.100 F $K_2Cr_2O_7$ solution reacted with 1.020 g of a mixture of KNO_2 and KNO_3. For this experiment calculate:

*(a) The normality of the $K_2Cr_2O_7$.

*(b) The number of equivalents of $K_2Cr_2O_7$ used.

*(c) The number of equivalents of KNO_2 present in the mixture.

*(d) The gram-equivalent weight of KNO_2.

*(e) Grams of KNO_2 in the mixture.

*(f) Per cent of KNO_2 in the mixture.

19.34 112 cc of HCl gas at STP are passed into 30 ml of a 0.20 N $Ba(OH)_2$ solution.

(a) Will the final solution be acid, basic, or neutral?

(b) How many grams of $BaCl_2$ could be recovered from the solution?

Faraday's Law and Electrochemical Equivalence

One faraday of electricity, when passed through a solution of an electrolyte, will cause one gram-equivalent weight of substance to react, be deposited, or be liberated at each electrode. This important generalization is a part of a broader generalization known as *Faraday's Law*.

It should be noted that, since 1 gram-equivalent weight of a substance such as Ag^+ contains 6.023×10^{23} ions, 6.023×10^{23} electrons will be required to electrodeposit 1 gram-equivalent weight of silver according to the reaction, $Ag^+ + e^- = Ag$. Since 1 faraday of electricity will deposit 1 gram-equivalent weight of silver, 1 faraday must represent 6.023×10^{23} electrons. This is the basis for stating that 1 faraday is a *mole of electrons*.

One faraday of electricity is 96,500 coulombs. One coulomb is the charge that is carried when one ampere of current flows for one second. Therefore, 1 faraday = 96,500 ampere-seconds = 26.8 ampere-hours. It will be assumed in the problems that follow that the efficiency of the process (the current efficiency) is 100% unless stated otherwise.

Problems

19.35 Electricity was allowed to flow until 20 g of copper were deposited from a solution of $CuSO_4$. How many coulombs of electricity passed through the solution?

SOLUTION: The equivalent weight of Cu in $CuSO_4$ is 31.8.

$$\frac{20.0 \text{ g of Cu}}{31.8 \text{ g of Cu/equivalent}} \times \frac{96,500 \text{ coulombs}}{1 \text{ equivalent}} = 60,700 \text{ coulombs}$$

19.36 A current of 2.00 amp was allowed to flow through a solution of $AgNO_3$ for 6.00 hr. How many grams of silver were deposited?

SOLUTION: 6.00 hr = 21,600 sec. Two amp of current flowing for 21,600 sec is 43,200 coulombs of electricity. The equivalent weight of Ag in $AgNO_3$ is 107.9.

$$\frac{43,200 \text{ coulombs}}{96,500 \text{ coulombs/equivalent}} \times \frac{107.9 \text{ g of Ag}}{1 \text{ equivalent}} = 48.4 \text{ g of Ag}$$

19.37 A certain amount of electricity deposited 50.0 g of silver from a solution of $AgNO_3$. How many grams of copper will this same amount of current deposit from a solution of $CuSO_4$?

SOLUTION: Since 1 faraday of electricity will deposit 1 equivalent of any element, it follows that the weight of one element deposited by a given amount of electricity will be to the weight of another element deposited by the same amount of electricity as the equivalent weight of the first element is to the equivalent weight of the second element.

$$\frac{\text{weight of copper deposited}}{\text{weight of silver deposited}} = \frac{\text{equivalent weight of copper in } CuSO_4}{\text{equivalent weight of silver in } AgNO_3}$$

The equivalent weight of Ag in $AgNO_3$ is 107.9. The equivalent weight of Cu in $CuSO_4$ is 31.8. Therefore,

$$\frac{\text{grams of copper}}{50.0 \text{ g of Ag}} = \frac{31.8}{107.9}$$

$$\text{grams of copper} = \frac{31.8}{107.9} \times 50.0 \text{ g} = 14.7 \text{ g}$$

19.38 How many grams of cobalt will be deposited from a solution of $CoCl_2$ by 40,000 coulombs of electricity?

19.39 How many coulombs of electricity will be required to deposit 100 g of chromium from a solution of $CrCl_3$?*

19.40 How many grams of zinc would be deposited from a solution of $ZnCl_2$ by a current of 3.00 amp flowing for 20.0 hr?

19.41 A quantity of electricity which deposited 70 g of nickel from a solution of $NiCl_2$ will deposit how many grams of hydrogen from a solution of HCl?*

19.42 A solution of $CuSO_4$ contains Cu^{++}. A solution of $Na_2Cu(CN)_3$ contains Cu^+ ions in equilibrium with $Cu(CN)_3^{--}$ ions and CN^- ions. A quantity of electricity which deposits 12 g of copper from a solution of copper sulfate will deposit how many grams of copper from a solution of $Na_2Cu(CN)_3$?

19.43 How many grams of nickel will be deposited from a solution of $NiCl_2$ by 4.00 amp of current flowing for 24.0 hr if the current efficiency of the process is 96.0%*

19.44 Calculate the charge, in coulombs, on an electron.

19.45 A current of 2.0 amp was passed through a solution of H_2SO_4 for 20 min. How many milliliters of O_2 gas, measured at STP, were liberated?*

19.46 A solution of $CuSO_4$ was electrolyzed, using platinum electrodes. A volume of 6.0 liters of O_2 gas, measured at STP, was liberated at the positive electrode. How many grams of copper were deposited at the negative electrode?

19.47 s A 0.2000 g portion of pure $Na_2C_2O_4$ requires 21.00 ml of $KMnO_4$ solution for titration. How many milligrams of As_2O_3 are in a sample which requires 29.00 ml of the $KMnO_4$ for titration?

19.48 s Exactly 25.0 ml of a certain thiocyanate (SCN^-) solution are required to react with 0.015 equivalent of permanganate in the reaction:

$$5\ SCN^- + 6\ MnO_4^- + 13\ H^+$$
$$= 6\ Mn^{++} + 5\ HCN + 5\ SO_4^{--} + 4\ H_2O$$

To another solution containing 0.015 equivalent of permanganate are added 40.0 ml of the above thiocyanate solution. How many milliliters of 0.20 N silver nitrate solution will be required to precipitate all the unreacted thiocyanate as the insoluble silver salt, according to the reaction, $Ag^+ + SCN^- = AgSCN$? (Note that the equivalent weight of SCN^- differs in the two reactions.)

19.49 s The concentration of a hypochlorite solution (OCl^-) can be determined by adding an excess of a solution of As_2O_3 of known concentration and then titrating the unreacted (excess) As_2O_3 with an iodine solution of known concentration. The following reactions occur:

$$2\ OCl^- + As_2O_3 = As_2O_5 + 2\ Cl^-$$

$$2\ I_2 + As_2O_3 + 2\ H_2O = 4\ I^- + As_2O_5 + 4\ H^+$$

A student added 20.0 ml of 2.00 N As_2O_3 to a 30-ml sample of an unknown solution of OCl^-. A total of 50.0 ml of a 0.2 N solution of I_2 was needed to react with the excess As_2O_3. What was the formality of the unknown solution of OCl^-?

19.50 s In concentrated HCl solution IO_3^- reacts with $SbCl_4^-$ as follows:

$$2\ SbCl_4^- + IO_3^- + 5\ H_2O = 2\ H_3SbO_4 + ICl + 7\ Cl^- + 4\ H^+$$

Exactly 25.0 ml of a certain iodate solution is just enough to react with 0.020 equivalent of $SbCl_4^-$.
To a solution containing 0.028 equivalent of $SbCl_4^-$ is added 42.0

ml of this same IO_3^- solution. What volume of 0.20 N Ba^{++} solution is required to precipitate the excess (unreacted) IO_3^-?

$$Ba^{++} + 2\ IO_3^- = Ba(IO_3)_2\ (s)$$

19.51 s A solution of $Cr_2O_7^{--}$ ions also contains CrO_4^{--} ions as represented by the equilibrium, $Cr_2O_7^{--} + H_2O \rightleftarrows 2\ CrO_4^{--} + 2\ H^+$. This solution of $Cr_2O_7^{--}$ reacts with a solution of Fe^{++} ions according to the equation

$$6\ Fe^{++} + Cr_2O_7^{--} + 14\ H^+ = 6\ Fe^{+++} + 2\ Cr^{+++} + 7\ H_2O$$

and with Ba^{++} ions to form insoluble $BaCrO_4$ according to the equation

$$2\ Ba^{++} + Cr_2O_7^{--} + H_2O = 2\ BaCrO_4 + 2\ H^+$$

To react with the Fe^{++} in 300 ml of 0.600 N $FeSO_4$ required 250 ml of a certain solution of $Cr_2O_7^{--}$. How many milliliters of this solution of $Cr_2O_7^{--}$ will be required to precipitate all of the Ba^{++} from 400 ml of 0.200 F $BaCl_2$?

19.52 s A mixture of Na and Ba was first completely oxidized by oxygen. The mixture of oxides was then dissolved in 1000 g of water. The boiling point of the resulting solution was found to be 100.208°C at 760 mm; 500 ml of 0.500 N H_2SO_4 were required to neutralize the solution. Calculate the number of grams of Na and of Ba in the original mixture.

19.53 s A mixture of CS_2 and H_2S when oxidized, yielded a mixture of CO_2, SO_2 and H_2O (steam) which exerted a pressure of 748.8 mm when collected in a 60-liter vessel at 327°C. To oxidize the SO_2 in the mixture required 700.0 ml of a 2.00 N solution of I_2. What was the mole fraction of the CS_2 in the mixture of CS_2 and H_2S?

19.54 s A mixture of HCl and SO_3 gases was contained in a 2.00-liter flask at 127°C and a pressure of 374.40 mm. The mixture was dissolved in enough water to give 2000 ml of solution. To neutralize this solution required 400 ml of 0.100 N NaOH. Calculate the weight in grams of the mixture of HCl and SO_3 and the mole per cent of HCl in the mixture.

19.55 s To electrodeposit all of the Cu and Cd from a solution of $CuSO_4$ and $CdSO_4$ in water required 1.20 faradays of electricity. The mixture of Cu and Cd that was deposited weighed 50.36 g. How many grams of $CuSO_4$ were there in the solution?

19.56 s A sample of water was a mixture of ^1H_2O, ^2H_2O, and ^3H_2O; it contained ordinary oxygen, atomic weight 16.00, but contained some of each of the 3 hydrogen isotopes, ^1H (at. wt 1.00), ^2H (at. wt 2.00), and ^3H (at. wt 3.00). A total of exactly 1.00 faraday of electricity was required to electrolyze the sample; the mixture of ^1H, ^2H, and ^3H which was produced weighed exactly 1.75 g. On standing the ^3H all decayed according to the reaction, $^3_1H = ^3_2He$ + beta particle. By the time all of the ^3H had decayed a total of 1.5×10^{23} disintegrations had been counted. Calculate the mole per cent of ^2H_2O in the sample. (The Avogadro number is 6.0 $\times 10^{23}$.)

19.57 s A current of 2.0 amp was passed through a cell containing 800 ml of 1.0 F H_2SO_4. The following electrode reactions took place:

$$\text{Anode: } 2\,H_2O = O_2\,(g) + 4\,H^+ + 4\,e^-$$

$$\text{Cathode: } 2\,H^+ + 2\,e = H_2\,(g)$$

(a) What time (in sec) was required to liberate 0.050 mole of O_2?

(b) What volume of H_2 gas, measured over water at 25°C and a barometric pressure of 740 mm, was produced at the same time?

(c) How many electrons were involved in the anode reaction in this experiment?

(d) What volume of 2 F NaOH would be required to neutralize all the acid remaining in the cell at the end of the electrolysis?

19.58 s When a hot, alkaline solution of NaCl is electrolyzed oxidation to chlorate ion (ClO_3^-) takes place at the positive electrode in accordance with the reaction, $Cl^- + 6\,OH^- = ClO_3^- + 3\,H_2O + 6\,e^-$. Assuming that the current efficiency is 100 per cent and that all chlorate is recovered, how long must a current of 10 amp be passed through the above solution to produce 21.3 g of $NaClO_3$?

19.59 s A certain solution of K_2SO_4 was electrolyzed using platinum electrodes. The combined volume of the dry gases that were evolved was 67.2 cc at STP. Assuming 100 per cent current efficiency and no loss of gases during measurement, how many coulombs of electricity were consumed?

19.60 s The atomic weight of metal M is 52.01. When the melted chloride of M is electrolyzed, for every gram of metal deposited on the cathode 725 cc of dry chlorine gas, measured at 25°C and 740 mm, are liberated at the anode. Calculate the formula of the chloride of M.

19.61 s The following electrode reactions occur in a "dry" cell:

$$Zn = Zn^{++} + 2 e$$

$$2 NH_4^+ + 2 MnO_2 + 2 e = Mn_2O_3 + 2 NH_3 + H_2O$$

A certain dry cell contains 11.74 g of MnO_2 and 17.60 g of NH_4Cl plus enough water to enable it to function properly. The zinc can weighs 150 g. Calculate the maximum theoretical lifetime of this battery in ampere-hours.

19.62 s A potassium salt of a ternary acid of molybdenum (Mo, at. wt 95.95) has the formula K_2MoO_x. When an acidified solution of K_2MoO_x is electrolyzed between platinum electrodes only oxygen gas is liberated at the positive electrode and only molybdenum metal is deposited at the negative electrode. When electrolysis is continued until 0.3454 g of molybdenum are deposited 121.0 cc of O_2 gas, measured at STP, are liberated. Calculate the formula of the salt.

19.63 s When 0.20 faraday of electricity is passed through a solution of $Pb(NO_3)_2$, a compound containing 20.7 g of Pb is deposited at the positive electrode. What is the oxidation number of lead in the compound that is deposited?

19.64 s Calculate a value for Avogadro's number using only the following information:

(a) the atomic weight of chlorine is 35.5

(b) 1.00 coulomb of electricity will cause 3.61×10^{-4} g of chlorine to be liberated from melted NaCl

(c) a quantity of radioactive material emits 9.40×10^{10} alpha particles per sec; the current which accompanies this radio-activity is 2.80×10^{-8} coulombs/sec.

19.65 s When 1 g of yttrium metal (at. wt 88.92) is treated with excess H_2SO_4 378 cc of H_2 gas, measured at STP, are liberated. When the resulting solution of yttrium sulfate is electrolyzed with platinum electrodes, using a steady current of 2 amp, 1 g of pure yttrium is deposited on the negative electrode and O_2 gas is liberated at the positive electrode. Calculate:

(a) the formula for yttrium sulfate

(b) the number of minutes the electrolysis had to proceed to deposit the 1 g of Y, and

(c) the volume, measured at STP, of the oxygen gas liberated.

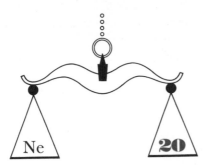

Determination
of Exact
Atomic Weights

The experimental determination of the exact atomic weight of an element can be carried out as follows:

1. Determine the approximate atomic weight.

   (a) By the use of the mass spectrometer. By the use of this instrument one can determine the exact mass of each isotope present in the naturally occurring element and the approximate mole per cent of each. From this information the approximate chemical atomic weight can be calculated. It should be pointed out, however, that with many of the newer mass spectrometers, mole per cent can be determined with such great accuracy that the calculated atomic weight is as exact as can be determined by any other method.

   (b) By applying the law of Dulong and Petit. This law states that the product of the atomic weight of an element and the specific heat of that element is equal to 6.4. That is,

$$\text{atomic weight} \times \text{specific heat} = 6.4$$

or

$$\text{atomic weight} = \frac{6.4}{\text{specific heat}}$$

197

Therefore, if we know the specific heat of an element we can calculate its approximate atomic weight. Since the law of Dulong and Petit is not exact, the atomic weights calculated by this law are not exact.

(c) By determining the smallest weight of the element contained in 1 mole of a large number of its compounds. This smallest weight is then taken to be the weight of 1 gram atom, the assumption being that 1 molecule of the particular compound contains 1 atom of the element in question.

2. Determine the exact equivalent weight. (See Problems 19.1 and 19.2.)

3. Calculate the valence by dividing the approximate atomic weight by the exact equivalent weight.

4. Calculate the exact atomic weight by multiplying the exact equivalent weight by the valence.

Exact atomic weights can also be determined by an analytical method which is illustrated in Problems 20.6, 20.7, and 20.8.

Problems

20.1 The specific heat of an element is 0.0310 cal/g × deg. It was determined that 25.90 g of the element combined with 4.000 g of oxygen. Calculate the exact atomic weight of the element.

SOLUTION: Proceed as directed above.

1. Calculate the approximate atomic weight.

$$\text{atomic weight} = \frac{6.4}{\text{specific heat}} = \frac{6.4}{0.0310} = 206.4$$

2. Calculate the exact equivalent weight.

$$\text{equivalent weight} = 7.999 \text{ g of oxygen} \times \frac{25.90 \text{ g of element}}{4.000 \text{ g of oxygen}}$$
$$= 51.80$$

3. Calculate the valence.

$$\text{valence} = \frac{\text{atomic weight}}{\text{equivalent weight}} = \frac{206.4}{51.80} = 4$$

(The valence is always a small *whole* number.)

4. Calculate the exact atomic weight.

valence $\times$ exact equivalent weight = exact atomic weight

$4 \times 51.80 = 207.2$, the exact atomic weight

20.2 Three compounds of an element X were found, by the vapor-density method, to have molecular weights of 32.4, 47.1, and 59.3, respectively. These compounds contained 37.5%, 52.2%, and 60.0%, respectively, of the element X. The oxide of X contained 27.27% X. Calculate the exact atomic weight of X.

SOLUTION:

1. Calculate the approximate atomic weight.

$$37.5\% \text{ of } 32.4 = 12.2$$
$$52.2\% \text{ of } 47.1 = 24.6$$
$$60.0\% \text{ of } 59.3 = 35.6$$

Since the smallest weight of X per mole is 12.2 g, 12.2 is taken as the approximate atomic weight. Then proceed as in Problem 20.1.

20.3 An element X has a specific heat of 0.0330 cal/g $\times$ deg. 2.212 g of the oxide of X were found to contain 1.972 g of X. Calculate the exact atomic weight of X.*

20.4 The vapor densities of three substances referred to hydrogen as 1 are 16.0, 23.0, and 30.0, respectively, and the per cent of element X in each substance is 37.5, 52.18, and 60.0, respectively. If 0.440 g of the oxide of X contains 0.120 g of X, calculate the exact atomic weight of X.

20.5 An element X forms a chloride which contains 29.34% chlorine. The approximate atomic weight of X as determined by the use of the mass spectrometer is 85.42. Calculate the exact atomic weight of X.*

20.6 The atomic weights of Ag and Cl are 107.87 and 35.453, respectively. In a very exact analysis 1.0000 g of LiCl, when treated with $AgNO_3$, gave 3.3806 g of AgCl. Calculate the exact atomic weight of lithium.

SOLUTION: Let X represent the exact atomic weight of Li. The formula weight of LiCl is then $X + 35.453$.

$$LiCl + AgNO_3 = AgCl + LiNO_3$$

This molecular equation tells us that

$$\frac{\text{weight of LiCl}}{\text{weight of AgCl}} = \frac{\text{formula weight of LiCl}}{\text{formula weight of AgCl}} = \frac{X + 35.453}{143.32}$$

$\dfrac{\text{weight of LiCl}}{\text{weight of AgCl}}$ was found, by exact analysis, to be $\dfrac{1.0000}{3.3806}$

Therefore,

$$X + 35.453 = 143.32 \times \frac{1.0000}{3.3806}$$

$$X = 6.942 = \text{the exact atomic weight of Li}$$

20.7 The atomic weights of Ag and Br are 107.88 and 79.916, respectively. In a very exact analysis 1.0000 g of KBr, when treated with $AgNO_3$, gave 1.5779 g of AgBr. Calculate the exact atomic weight of K.*

20.8 The atomic weights of Cl and Ag are 35.453 and 107.88, respectively. In a very exact analysis 2.5682 g of NaCl yielded 6.2971 g of AgCl. Calculate the exact atomic weight of Na.

20.9 s A metal M is known to form the fluoride MF_2. When 3300 coulombs of electricity are passed through the molten fluoride 1.950 g of M are plated out. What is the exact atomic weight of M?

20.10 s When a solution of KI is electrolyzed using porous silver electrodes, H_2 gas is liberated at the negative electrode (cathode) and insoluble AgI is deposited in the pores of the positive electrode (anode). All of the AgI that is formed remains in the pores of the anode. At the conclusion of the experiment the anode had increased in weight 5.076 g and 530 cc of dry H_2 gas, measured at 27°C and 720 mm, had been liberated. Calculate the atomic weight of iodine.

20.11 s An aqueous solution of the soluble salt MSO_4 is electrolyzed between inert (platinum) electrodes until 0.0327 g of metal, M, are deposited on the negative electrode (cathode). To neutralize the solution that was formed in the electrolytic cell required 50 ml of 0.020 F KOH. Calculate the atomic weight of metal M.

20.12 s The specific heat of cerium metal is 0.0440. When a solution of the sulfate of cerium in pure water is electrolyzed using platinum electrodes, 0.4671 g of pure cerium metal is deposited on the negative electrode. To neutralize the acidity which was acquired by the solution during the electrolysis required 25.0 ml of 0.400 F NaOH. Calculate:

(a) the exact atomic weight of cerium

(b) the formula of cerium sulfate

(c) the number of faradays of electricity required for the electrolysis.

20.13 s The specific heat of element M is 0.0270 cal/g × deg. Element M forms a compound with the element fluorine (at. wt 19.00); a solution of 2.5 g of this fluoride in 250 g CCl_4 forms a non-conducting solution which freezes at $-23.8°C$. The normal freezing point of CCl_4 is $-22.9°C$; the molal freezing point constant for CCl_4 is 32. Calculate the formula of the fluoride. What additional experimental data is needed to determine the exact atomic weight of M?

20.14 s On careful heating, 7.478 g of $BaCl_2 \cdot 2 H_2O$ yields 6.378 g of $BaCl_2$. When this $BaCl_2$ is treated with excess Ag^+, 8.761 g of AgCl are formed. Given the following atomic weights: $H = 1.00$, $O = 16.0$, $Ag = 107.9$, calculate the exact atomic weights of Ba and Cl.

20.15 s A sample of pure I_2O_5 weighing 4.509 g was dissolved in water and quantitatively reduced to I^-. This I^- was then quantitatively precipitated as AgI by treatment with Ag^+. A total of 6.345 g of AgI was formed and 2.916 g of Ag^+ were consumed. The atomic weight of $O = 16.0$. Calculate the atomic weights of I and Ag.

20.16 s An element X forms a compound whose weight composition is 21.83% X, 27.85% P, and 50.32% O. The specific heat of X is 0.257 cal × g^{-1} × deg^{-1}. The atomic weights of P and O are known to be 31.0 and 16.0, respectively. What is the atomic weight of X?

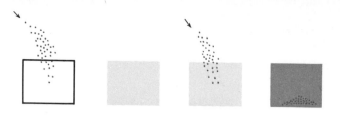

21
Solubility Products

When a saturated solution of sugar is prepared by shaking an excess of sugar with water the following equilibrium is set up:

solid sugar $\rightleftarrows$ sugar molecules in solution

When a saturated solution of a very slightly soluble salt, such as AgCl, is prepared by shaking excess AgCl with water, a somewhat different type of equilibrium is set up. AgCl is a salt; hence, it is 100% ionized. Therefore, the saturated solution which is in equilibrium with solid AgCl contains silver ions and chloride ions but no un-ionized AgCl molecules. These silver ions and chloride ions are in equilibrium with the excess solid AgCl. We may, therefore, represent the equilibrium which exists in such a saturated solution of AgCl as follows:

$$AgCl \text{ (solid)} \rightleftarrows Ag^+ + Cl^-$$

Since this is a true equilibrium it will have an equilibrium constant. As has already been noted in Chapter 16, solid reactants are not involved in the equilibrium equation. Therefore

$$K = [Ag^+] \times [Cl^-]$$

This equation tells us, simply, that the product of the concentrations of the solute ions in a saturated solution of a very slightly soluble electrolyte is constant at a given temperature. This constant, K, is called the *solubility product constant,* or simply the *solubility product,* and is usually designated by the notation K_{sp} or S.P.

If the concentration of silver ions and the concentration of chloride ions, expressed in moles per liter, is such that their product is less than K_{sp} for AgCl, or is just barely equal to K_{sp}, no precipitate of AgCl will form. If, on the other hand, the product of the concentrations of Ag^+ and Cl^- is greater than K_{sp}, silver chloride will precipitate; furthermore, AgCl will keep on precipitating until enough Ag^+ ions and Cl^- ions have been removed to lower the product of their concentrations to the value of K_{sp}.

The solubility product represents a typical ionic equilibrium. As such it behaves exactly like the other ionic equilibria discussed in Chapter 17.

The following problems will point out how solubility products are determined and how they can be used in certain types of calculations. The solubility product constants used are normally those determined at 20°C. In certain of the problems the calculations are based on data obtained at temperatures other than 20°C. Because the recorded solubility product is a function of the temperature as well as the accuracy of the determination, the value of K_{sp} for a certain substance may not be the same in all problems. Since such lack of agreement will in no way affect the calculation, it need not be the source of any concern.

It should be emphasized that the solubility product concept applies only to *very slightly soluble strong electrolytes.* It does not apply to *highly soluble* strong electrolytes such as NaCl, $MgSO_4$, and KOH, or to *weak* electrolytes, regardless of their solubility.

Problems

21.1 A solution in equilibrium with a precipitate of AgCl was found, on analysis, to contain 1.0×10^{-4} mole of Ag^+ per liter and 1.7×10^{-6} mole of Cl^- per liter. Calculate the solubility product for AgCl.

SOLUTION: The solubility product is, by definition, the product of the concentrations of the ions in equilibrium with a precipitate of a very sparingly soluble (insoluble) substance.

For AgCl,

$$K_{sp} = [Ag^+] \times [Cl^-]$$
$$= 1.0 \times 10^{-4} \text{ mole } Ag^+ \text{ per liter} \times 1.7 \times 10^{-6} \text{ mole } Cl^- \text{ per liter}$$
$$= 1.7 \times 10^{-10} M^2 \quad (M \text{ means moles per liter.})$$

Note that, in the equilibrium with which this problem is concerned, the concentration of Ag^+ ions is not the same as the concentration of Cl^- ions. As was pointed out in Chapter 16, the reacting substances in an equilibrium need not be present in the exact ratio called for by the equation. They can be present in an unlimited combination of ratios. However, when they interact they always do so in the mole ratio represented by the equation. Thus, when Ag^+ ions react with Cl^- ions to form AgCl they always do so in the ratio of 1 mole of Ag^+ to 1 mole of Cl^-. However, the solution which is in equilibrium with the solid AgCl can contain Ag^+ and Cl^- ions in unlimited numbers of ratios. The only requirement is that the product of $[Ag^+]$ and $[Cl^-]$ at the particular temperature must always equal the K_{sp}.

21.2 A solution in equilibrium with a precipitate of Ag_2S was found, on analysis, to contain 6.3×10^{-18} mole of S^{--} per liter and 1.26×10^{-17} mole of Ag^+ per liter. Calculate the solubility product for Ag_2S.

SOLUTION:

S.P. for $Ag_2S = [Ag^+]^2 \times [S^{--}]$

$$= (1.26 \times 10^{-17} \text{ mole } Ag^+ \text{ per liter})^2$$
$$\times (6.3 \times 10^{-18} \text{ mole } S^{--} \text{ per liter})$$
$$= 1.0 \times 10^{-51} M^3$$

21.3 A solution in equilibrium with a precipitate of Ag_3PO_4 was found on analysis to contain 1.6×10^{-5} mole of PO_4^{---} per liter and 4.8×10^{-5} mole of Ag^+ per liter. Calculate the solubility product for Ag_3PO_4.

21.4 A solution in equilibrium with a precipitate of $Pb_3(PO_4)_2$ was found, on analysis, to contain 3.4×10^{-7} mole of PO_4^{---} per liter and 5.1×10^{-7} mole of Pb^{++} per liter. Calculate the solubility product of $Pb_3(PO_4)_2$.

NOTE: In comparing the solubility products in Problems 21.1, 21.2, 21.3, and 21.4 it will be noted that the units in which K_{sp} is expressed is a function of the number of ions involved in the equilibrium. The unit is "moles per liter" raised to a power equal to the number of ions per mole of solute. In subsequent problems in this chapter the units in which a particular solubility product is expressed will generally not be given.

21.5 A solution in equilibrium with a precipitate of Ag_3PO_4 was found, on analysis, to contain 1.52×10^{-3} g of PO_4^{---} per liter and 5.18×10^{-3} g of Ag^+ per liter. Calculate the solubility product of Ag_3PO_4.*

SOLUTION: First find the concentration of each ion in moles per liter. Then solve as in Problem 21.3.

21.6 Exactly 450 ml of 1.00×10^{-4} F $BaCl_2$ is placed in a beaker. In order to just start precipitation of $BaSO_4$ it is necessary to add, with constant stirring, exactly 350 ml of 2.00×10^{-4} F K_2SO_4. What is the solubility product of $BaSO_4$?

21.7 In each of the following a saturated solution was prepared by shaking the pure solid compound with pure water. The solubilities obtained are given. From these solubilities, calculate the solubility product of each solute.

(a) $AgCl = 1.67 \times 10^{-5}$ mole $AgCl$ per liter

SOLUTION: Since $AgCl$ ionizes, completely, as follows, $AgCl = Ag^+ + Cl^-$, a saturated solution containing 1.67×10^{-5} mole of $AgCl$ per liter will contain 1.67×10^{-5} mole of Ag^+ per liter, and 1.67×10^{-5} mole of Cl^- per liter.

$$S.P. = [Ag^+] \times [Cl^-]$$
$$= (1.67 \times 10^{-5} \text{ mole } Ag^+ \text{ per liter})$$
$$\times (1.67 \times 10^{-5} \text{ mole } Cl^- \text{ per liter})$$
$$= 2.8 \times 10^{-10}$$

*(b) $AgI = 2.2 \times 10^{-3}$ mg AgI per liter

(c) $AgBr = 5.7 \times 10^{-10}$ equivalent $AgBr$ per milliliter

*(d) $BaCrO_4 = 1.4 \times 10^{-5}$ millimole per milliliter

(e) $Ag_2SO_4 = 1.4 \times 10^{-2}$ mole Ag_2SO_4 per liter

SOLUTION: From the equation for the ionization of Ag_2SO_4

$$Ag_2SO_4 = 2\,Ag^+ + SO_4^{--}$$

it is evident that 1 mole of Ag_2SO_4 produces 2 moles of Ag^+ and 1 mole of SO_4^{--}.
Therefore, 1.4×10^{-2} mole of Ag_2SO_4 will produce 2.8×10^{-2} mole of Ag^+ and 1.4×10^{-2} mole of SO_4^{--}

$$S.P. = [Ag^+]^2 \times [SO_4^{--}]$$
$$= (2.8 \times 10^{-2})^2 \times (1.4 \times 10^{-2})$$
$$= 1.1 \times 10^{-5}$$

(f) $PbI_2 = 1.28 \times 10^{-3}$ M

21.8 What concentration of Ag^+ in moles per liter, must be present to just start precipitation of AgCl from a solution containing 1.0×10^{-4} mole of Cl^- per liter? The solubility product of AgCl is 2.8×10^{-10}.

SOLUTION: A substance will start to precipitate when the product of the concentrations of its ions equals (or just barely exceeds) the solubility product. No precipitate will form until the product of the concentrations of its ions equals the solubility product. In this particular problem precipitation of AgCl will not begin until the product of the mole concentrations of the ions involved equals the solubility product for AgCl.

$$S.P. = [Ag^+] \times [Cl^-] = 2.8 \times 10^{-10}$$

$$[Ag^+] = \frac{2.8 \times 10^{-10}}{[Cl^-]} = \frac{2.8 \times 10^{-10}}{1 \times 10^{-4} \text{ mole } Cl^- \text{ per liter}}$$

$$= 2.8 \times 10^{-6} \text{ mole } Ag^+ \text{ per liter}$$

21.9 What concentration of OH^-, in moles per liter, is necessary to start precipitation of $Fe(OH)_3$ from a solution containing 2×10^{-6} mole of Fe^{+++} per liter? The solubility product of $Fe(OH)_3$ is 6×10^{-38}.*

21.10 What concentration of sulfide ion, expressed in moles per liter, must be present to just start precipitation of the sulfide of the metal from each of the following solutions? The solubility product of each of the sulfides precipitated is given.

  (a) $1.0 \, F \, CuCl_2$; 4×10^{-36}

 *(b) $0.4 \, N \, FeCl_2$; 4×10^{-17}

  (c) $0.0010 \, F \, CdCl_2$; 6×10^{-27}

 *(d) $0.3 \, N \, BiCl_3$; 1×10^{-70}

21.11 The solubility of PbI_2 in water is 2×10^{-3} mole per liter. What concentration of lead ion would be required to just start precipitation of PbI_2 from $0.002 \, F \, KI$?*

21.12 The solubility product of Ag_3PO_4 is 1.8×10^{-18}. Assuming that a precipitate can be seen as soon as it begins to form, what is the minimum concentration of PO_4^{---} in milligrams per liter that can be detected by the addition of Ag^+ until the solution is $0.010 \, M$ in silver ions?

21.13 K_{sp} $BaSO_4$ = 1.5 × 10^{-9}; K_{sp} $Fe(OH)_3$ = 6 × 10^{-38}. Amounts of 0.00005 mole of soluble 100% ionized iron (III) sulfate and 0.00002 equivalent of soluble 100% ionized barium hydroxide are added to enough water to give a liter of solution. Will a precipitate form?*

21.14 A solution contains 0.010 mole Cl^- per liter and 0.0010 mole CrO_4^{--} per liter. The S.P. of AgCl is 1.56 × 10^{-10}, the S.P. of Ag_2CrO_4 is 9.0 × 10^{-12}. What will be the concentration of Cl^- in moles per liter when Ag_2CrO_4 just begins to precipitate by the continued addition of Ag^+, the volume of the solution at this point being exactly 1 liter?

SOLUTION: When Ag^+ ions are added to the solution represented by this problem, AgCl will begin to precipitate when the product of [Ag^+] and [Cl^-] equals the solubility product, 1.56 × 10^{-10}. Since [Cl^-] is 1 × 10^{-2}, the precipitation of AgCl will begin when [Ag^+] is 1.56 × 10^{-8}. Since the solubility product of Ag_2CrO_4 is 9.0 × 10^{-12} and [CrO_4^{--}] is 1 × 10^{-3}, precipitation of Ag_2CrO_4 will not begin until [Ag^+] is 9.5 × 10^{-5}; that means that, at the start, only AgCl precipitates. As more Ag^+ ions are added after precipitation of AgCl first begins, more AgCl will precipitate. As more AgCl precipitates the concentration of the Cl^- ions remaining in solution decreases, and as the concentration of Cl^- ions decreases the concentration of Ag^+ ions required to continue precipitation of AgCl increases; during the entire AgCl precipitation process the product of [Ag^+] and [Cl^-] must always be equal to 1.56 × 10^{-10}. Finally, the concentration of Cl^- ions will be low enough so that a Ag^+ ion concentration of 9.5 × 10^{-5} will be required to precipitate more AgCl. When that happens Ag_2CrO_4 will also begin to precipitate. Since [Ag^+] × [Cl^-] must always equal 1.56 × 10^{-10}, when [Ag^+] is 9.5 × 10^{-5}, [Cl^-] will be 1.56 × 10^{-10} ÷ 9.5 × 10^{-5} or 1.6 × 10^{-6} mole per liter.

21.15 A solution contains 0.000020 mole of Br^- per liter and 0.010 mole of Cl^- per liter. The S.P. of AgCl is 1.56 × 10^{-10}, the S.P. of AgBr is 3.25 × 10^{-13}. Which of these ions will start precipitating first when Ag^+ is added to the above solution? What will be its concentration when the other ion begins to precipitate?*

21.16 To a solution containing 0.010 mole of Ag^+, Cl^- was added, the final volume being 1000 cc; 7.0 × 10^{-3} mole of AgCl precipitated. How much Cl^- remained in solution? S.P. of AgCl is 2.8 × 10^{-10}.

21.17 The solubility product of $BaSO_4$ is 1.5×10^{-9}. To a solution containing 0.137 g of Ba^{++} per liter, H_2SO_4 was added until the concentration of SO_4^{--} was 1.00×10^{-4} M. How much $BaSO_4$ was precipitated?*

21.18 Calculate the concentration of Cl^- in a solution saturated with both AgCl and Ag_2CrO_4 and in which the concentration of chromate ion is 1.0×10^{-3} M. K_{sp} for $Ag_2CrO_4 = 1.7 \times 10^{-12}$, for AgCl $= 1.1 \times 10^{-10}$.

21.19 If to a certain solution 1.00×10^{-7} F in KI and 0.100 F in NaCl solid $AgNO_3$ is added, how many moles of AgI per liter will be precipitated before the solution is saturated with AgCl? Solubility products: AgI, 1.00×10^{-16}; AgCl, 1.10×10^{-10}.*

21.20 The solubility product of Ag_2CrO_4 is 5×10^{-12}, of $AgIO_3$ is 1×10^{-8}. Silver ions are added to a solution which is 0.001 F in KIO_3 and 0.001 F in K_2CrO_4 until one half of the chromate ions are precipitated as Ag_2CrO_4. What mole per cent of the total iodate ions is still in solution?

21.21 The solubility product of $Fe(OH)_3$ is 6×10^{-38}. How many equivalents of Fe^{+++} must be present in order that $Fe(OH)_3$ will just start to precipitate from a liter of solution whose pH is 8?*

21.22 A suspension of calcium hydroxide in water was found to have a pH of 12.3. Calculate the solubility product of $Ca(OH)_2$.

21.23 The molar concentration of the Cd^{++} in a solution in equilibrium with a precipitate of CdS was found to be four times as great as the molar concentration of the S^{--}. K_{sp} for CdS is 6×10^{-27}. What was the concentration of the Cd^{++}?

SOLUTION:

$$K_{sp} = [Cd^{++}] \times [S^{--}] = 6 \times 10^{-27}$$

Let X = concentration of Cd^{++}

$$\frac{X}{4} = \text{concentration of } S^{--}$$

Substituting these values in the S.P. equation

$$X \times \frac{X}{4} = 6 \times 10^{-27}$$

$$X^2 = 2.4 \times 10^{-26}$$

$$X = 1.6 \times 10^{-13} \ M$$

21.24 A liter of solution which is in equilibrium with a precipitate of $Cd(OH)_2$ contains four times as many moles of OH^- as Cd^{++}. How many moles of OH^- are present? S.P. of $Cd(OH)_2$ is 1.6×10^{-14}.

21.25 A solution in equilibrium with a precipitate of Ag_3PO_4 contains twice as many grams of PO_4^{---} as Ag^+. The solubility product of Ag_3PO_4 is 1.8×10^{-18}. How many grams of PO_4^{---} are present per liter of solution?*

21.26 From the respective solubility products at 20°C, calculate the solubility of each of the following in moles per liter. (By "solubility" is meant the quantity of solute that will go into solution when the pure solid is shaken with pure water, at 20°C, until a saturated solution is obtained.) The solubility product of each solute is given directly after its formula.

(a)   AgSCN; 1×10^{-12}

SOLUTION: When AgSCN dissolves, it is 100% dissociated into Ag^+ and SCN^-. Therefore,

moles of AgSCN dissolved = moles of Ag^+ = moles of SCN^-

Let X = moles of AgSCN dissolved

$$X = \text{moles of } Ag^+ \qquad X = \text{moles of } SCN^-$$
$$K_{sp} = [Ag^+] \times [SCN^-] = X^2 = 1 \times 10^{-12} \, M^2$$
$$X = 1 \times 10^{-6} \, M$$

*(b)   AgCl; 2.8×10^{-10}

(c) $Mg(OH)_2$; 8.9×10^{-12}

SOLUTION:

$$Mg(OH)_2 = Mg^{++} + 2 \, OH^-$$

Let X = moles of $Mg(OH)_2$ that dissolve

$$X = \text{moles of } Mg^{++} \qquad 2 \, X = \text{moles of } OH^-$$
$$K_{sp} = [Mg^{++}] \times [OH^-]^2 = X \times (2 \, X)^2 = 8.9 \times 10^{-12} \, M^3$$
$$4 \, X^3 = 8.9 \times 10^{-12} \, M^3$$
$$X = 1.3 \times 10^{-4} \, M$$

*(d) Ag_2SO_4; 1.1×10^{-5}

(e) $Al(OH)_3$; 5×10^{-33}

21.27 Silver oxide is in equilibrium with its saturated solution according to the reaction, $Ag_2O + H_2O \rightleftarrows 2 Ag^+ + 2 OH^-$. The solubility product for AgOH is $[Ag^+] \times [OH^-] = 2 \times 10^{-8}$. How many moles of Ag_2O will dissolve in a liter of solution whose pH is 11?*

21.28 Solid CdS is added to 0.001 F $Pb(NO_3)_2$ solution. S.P. of CdS is 6×10^{-27}; S.P. of PbS is 4×10^{-26}. Will PbS be precipitated?

21.29 In each of the first 3 parts set up 1 equation in 1 unknown, X, which when solved for the value of X will give the correct answer to the problem. Do not solve for the numerical value of X. In each case the substances are brought together in solution and the final volume of the solution is exactly 1 liter. Solve the last 3 parts as noted.*

(a) How many moles of Ag_2CrO_4 will be precipitated when 0.002 mole of Ag^+ is mixed with 0.0003 mole of CrO_4^{--}? S.P. for Ag_2CrO_4 is 1.9×10^{-12}.

(b) How many grams of Ag_3PO_4 will be precipitated when 0.01 mole of Ag^+ is mixed with 0.02 mole of PO_4^{--}? S.P. for Ag_3PO_4 is 1.8×10^{-18}.

(c) How many grams of Ag^+ ions must be mixed with 0.0004 mole of CrO_4^{--} to yield 0.0002 mole of precipitated Ag_2CrO_4? K_{sp} for Ag_2CrO_4 is 1.9×10^{-12}.

(d) A saturated solution formed by shaking solid Ag_2CrO_4 with water was found to contain X g of Ag^+ ions per liter. Calculate the solubility product of Ag_2CrO_4 as a function of X.

(e) Exactly 10.00 g of $Be(OH)_2$ were shaken with enough water to form a liter of saturated solution; X g of undissolved $Be(OH)_2$ remained as residue. Calculate the solubility product of $Be(OH)_2$ as a function of X.

(f) The solubility product of Ag_3PO_4 was determined by mixing 200 ml of 0.015 N Na_3PO_4 with 800 ml of 0.0050 F $AgNO_3$ and drying and weighing the Ag_3PO_4 that precipitated. The Ag_3PO_4 weighed m grams. Calculate the solubility product of Ag_3PO_4 as a function of m.

21.30 The solubility product of AgCl is 2.8×10^{-10}. How many moles of AgCl will dissolve in a liter of 0.010 N KCl? The KCl is 100% ionized.

SOLUTION:

$$[Ag^+] \times [Cl^-] = 2.8 \times 10^{-10}$$

$$[Ag^+] = \frac{2.8 \times 10^{-10}}{Cl^-} = \frac{2.8 \times 10^{-10}}{1 \times 10^{-2}} = 2.8 \times 10^{-8} \ M$$

To produce this 2.8×10^{-8} mole of Ag^+, 2.8×10^{-8} mole of AgCl must have gone into solution. In making this calculation the Cl^- derived from the AgCl has been ignored since its concentration is negligible, being about $2.8 \times 10^{-8} \ M$.

21.31 The solubility of $BaSO_4$ in water is $1 \times 10^{-5} \ M$. What is its solubility in $0.2 \ N \ K_2SO_4$?*

21.32 What volume in liters of $0.10 \ F \ MgCl_2$ is required to dissolve the same amount of Hg_2Cl_2 that will dissolve in 1.00 liter of pure water? K_{sp} for Hg_2Cl_2 is 4.0×10^{-18}.

21.33 When excess solid Ag_2CrO_4 is shaken with a liter of $0.10 \ F \ K_2CrO_4$, 0.723 mg of Ag_2CrO_4 dissolve. Calculate the solubility product of Ag_2CrO_4.*

21.34 The solubility product of PbI_2 at 30°C is 1×10^{-8}. The solubility product of $BaSO_4$ at 30°C is also 1×10^{-8}. How does the solubility of PbI_2 in moles per liter compare with the solubility of $BaSO_4$ in moles per liter?

21.35 250 ml of a solution containing 3.70×10^{-4} moles per liter of Ba^{++} is added to 250 ml of a solution $0.0008 \ N$ in Na_2SO_4. After precipitation of $BaSO_4$ it was found that the $[SO_4^{--}]$ was four times as great as the $[Ba^{++}]$. Calculate the solubility product for $BaSO_4$.*

21.36 An insoluble compound, AB, ionizes to give A^+ and B^-. The atomic weight of A is 50, of B is 80. When 50 ml of a solution containing 1.000 mg of A^+ per milliliter is mixed at 20°C with 50 ml of a solution containing 1.640 mg of B^- per milliliter, precipitation of AB continues until, at equilibrium, the number of moles of B^- in solution is exactly twice as great as the number of moles of A^+ in solution. Calculate the solubility product of AB at 20°C.

21.37 A 500 ml solution containing 1.391 g of Ag^+ was mixed, at 20°C, with 500 ml of a solution containing 0.927 g of BrO_3^-. When precipitation of $AgBrO_3$ was complete, the solution contained exactly twice as many grams of Ag^+ as BrO_3^-. Calculate the solubility product of $AgBrO_3$.*

Solubility Products and the Hydrogen Sulfide Equilibrium

A saturated solution of hydrogen sulfide in water at 18°C and standard barometric pressure is approximately 0.10 M in H_2S. Hydrogen sulfide is a very weak acid; hence, its per cent ionization is small. Although H_2S ionizes in two stages,

$$H_2S \rightleftarrows H^+ + HS^- \qquad K_1 = 1.0 \times 10^{-7}\, M$$

$$HS \rightleftarrows H^+ + S^{--} \qquad K_2 = 1.3 \times 10^{-13}\, M$$

the over-all ionization can be represented by one equation,

$$H_2S \rightleftarrows 2\, H^+ + S^{--}$$

The ionization constant for this over-all reaction is 1.3×10^{-20}. That is,

$$\frac{[H^+]^2 \times [S^{--}]}{[H_2S]} = 1.3 \times 10^{-20}\, M^2$$

When the concentration of H^+ is fixed, by addition of acid or base to the solution, this over-all ionization constant can justifiably be used to calculate $[S^{--}]$. Since the solution is saturated, the concentration of H_2S will be constant, namely 0.10 M. We can, therefore, combine this constant value with the ionization constant to get the equation,

$$\frac{[H^+]^2 \times [S^{--}]}{0.10} = 1.3 \times 10^{-20}\, M^2$$

$$[H^+]^2 \times [S^{--}] = 1.3 \times 10^{-21}\, M^3$$

This constant, $1.3 \times 10^{-21}\, M^3$, is the *ion product* for a saturated solution of H_2S. It is a very useful constant in calculations involving reactions in which an acidified or alkilinized saturated solution of hydrogen sulfide is either a reactant or a product.

Problems

21.38 Given solutions containing 1×10^{-6} mole per liter of Hg^{++}, Cu^{++}, Pb^{++}, Sn^{++}, Ni^{++}, Fe^{++}, and Mn^{++}, respectively. These solutions are saturated with H_2S at 18°C. The ion product, $[H^+]^2 \times [S^{--}]$, for a saturated (0.10 M) solution of H_2S is 1.3×10^{-21}. In each case what is the greatest H^+ concentration in moles per liter which will just allow precipitation of the sulfide to start? The solubility product for each sulfide is given.

(a) Hg^{++}; 1×10^{-50}

SOLUTION:

$$[Hg^{++}] \times [S^{--}] = 1 \times 10^{-50}$$

$$[S^{--}] = \frac{1 \times 10^{-50}}{1 \times 10^{-6} \text{ mole } Hg^{++} \text{ per liter}} = 1 \times 10^{-44} \, M$$

This is the concentration of S^{--} which must be present for precipitation of HgS to start from a solution containing 1×10^{-6} mole of Hg^{++} per liter.

$$[H^+]^2 \times [S^{--}] = 1.3 \times 10^{-21}$$

$$[H^+]^2 = \frac{1.3 \times 10^{-21}}{1 \times 10^{-44} \text{ mole } S^{--} \text{ per liter}} = 1.3 \times 10^{23}$$

$[H^+] = 3.6 \times 10^{11} \, M$. This is the concentration of H^+ which will be in equilibrium with 1×10^{-44} mole S^{--} per liter.

(b) Cu^{++}; 4.0×10^{-36} *(e) Ni^{++}; 1×10^{-22}

*(c) Pb^{++}; 4×10^{-26} (f) Fe^{++}; 4×10^{-17}

(d) Sn^{++}; 1.0×10^{-24} *(g) Mn^{++}; 8×10^{-14}

21.39 A solution containing 2×10^{-6} equivalents of Cd^{++} per liter was kept saturated with H_2S until precipitation was complete. The concentration of H^+ was kept at $0.2 \, N$ during the precipitation. How many grams of CdS were precipitated per liter of solution? S.P. for CdS is 6×10^{-27}.*

21.40 The solubility product of SnS is 1.1×10^{-24}. One liter of $0.00013 \, M$ Sn^{++} was kept saturated with H_2S until precipitation was complete, at which time 0.0135 g of SnS precipitated. What was the pH of the solution at the end of the precipitation?

21.41 How many grams of Ag^+ must be present per liter before Ag_2S will start to precipitate from a saturated solution of H_2S whose pH is 2.0? The solubility product of Ag_2S is 1×10^{-50}.*

21.42 The solubility product of Cu_2S is 4.4×10^{-49}. What must be the pH of a saturated solution of H_2S containing 2.0×10^{-18} mole of Cu^+ per liter if Cu_2S will just barely start precipitating?

21.43 The solubility product of SnS is 1×10^{-24}. If a 1×10^{-11} N solution of Sn^{++} whose pH is maintained at 4 is saturated with H_2S, will a precipitate form?*

21.44 A solution is 0.0000020 N with respect to Pb^{++} and 0.010 N with respect to Cu^{++}. If the solution is kept saturated with H_2S, what is the hydrogen-ion concentration which will permit the maximum precipitation of CuS but will not allow the precipitation of PbS? K_{sp} for CuS is 3.5×10^{-38} and for PbS is 1.0×10^{-29}.

21.45 If NiS just begins to precipitate from a 0.0010 F $NiCl_2$ solution saturated with H_2S when the pH is 1.0, what is the solubility product for NiS?*

21.46 The solubility product for SnS is 1.0×10^{-24}. A solution of $SnCl_2$ was of such concentration that 500 ml of this $SnCl_2$ solution reduced 20 ml of an acid solution of 0.0050 N $KMnO_4$. What concentration of hydrogen ions must be maintained in the above $SnCl_2$ solution if the precipitation of SnS is to be just prevented when it is saturated with H_2S?

21.47 The S.P. of $Mg(OH)_2$ is 8.9×10^{-12}. K_i for NH_4OH is 1.8×10^{-5} M. How many grams of NH_4^+ must be present in a liter of 0.10 F NH_4OH containing 0.30 g of Mg^{++}, to prevent $Mg(OH)_2$ from being precipitated?*

21.48 The S.P. of $Mn(OH)_2$ is 2.0×10^{-13}. How many grams of NH_4Cl must be present in 100 ml of 0.20 F NH_4OH to prevent precipitation of $Mn(OH)_2$ when the solution is added to 100 ml of 0.40 N $MnCl_2$?

21.49 The S.P. for $Fe(OH)_3$ is 6×10^{-38}. How much NH_4^+ must be present in order to prevent the precipitation of $Fe(OH)_3$ in a solution 0.1 F in NH_4OH and 0.0010 M in Fe^{+++}? Would it be possible to dissolve that much NH_4^+ in a liter?*

21.50 To a liter of 0.10 F NH_4OH containing 46.8 g of NH_4Cl are added 0.10 mole of Mn^{++} and 1.0 mole of Mg^{++}. The final volume of the solution is 1 liter. Will $Mg(OH)_2$ be precipitated? Will $Mn(OH)_2$ be precipitated?

21.51 s A liter of solution which was in equilibrium with a solid mixture of AgCl and AgI was found to contain 1×10^{-8} mole of Ag^+, 1×10^{-2} mole of Cl^-, and 1×10^{-8} mole of I^-. Enough Ag^+ ions were added, slowly and with constant stirring, to increase the concentration of Ag^+ to 10^{-6} mole per liter; the volume of the solution was kept constant at 1 liter. How many moles of AgCl were precipitated as a result of this addition of Ag^+ ions? How many moles of AgI were precipitated as a result of this addition of Ag^+?

21.52 s A liter of solution which was in equilibrium with a solid mixture of AgCl and Ag_2CrO_4 was found to contain 1.00×10^{-4} mole of Ag^+, 1.00×10^{-6} mole of Cl^-, and 8.00×10^{-4} mole of CrO_4^{--}. Ag^+ ions were added, slowly and with constant stirring, the volume being kept constant at 1 liter; 8.00×10^{-7} mole of AgCl was precipitated as a result of this addition of Ag^+. How many moles of Ag_2CrO_4 were precipitated as a result of this addition of Ag^+?

21.53 s (a) Exactly one millimole of silver chloride is shaken with a liter of water. What is the concentration of silver ion in the saturated solution?

(b) Solid potassium bromide is added to the solution. How many moles of potassium bromide are added to the solution at the point at which the first bit of silver bromide forms?

(c) How many moles of potassium bromide are added at the point at which the last bit of silver chloride disappears?

(d) At the point at which the solid is converted completely to silver bromide, addition of potassium bromide is terminated and ammonia is added until all the silver bromide dissolves. What is the concentration of ammonia in this solution?

K_{sp} for $AgCl = 1.8 \times 10^{-10}$, for $AgBr = 5.2 \times 10^{-13}$. Instability constant for $Ag(NH_3)_2^+ = 6.0 \times 10^{-8}$.

21.54 s One commonly used titrimetric method of determining the chloride ion content of a material utilizes the red color of silver chromate as an end point indicator. A solution of known volume, to which the chromate ion indicator has been added and which contains a weighed sample of the material, is titrated with a standard $AgNO_3$ solution until the red of the Ag_2CrO_4 just appears. From the measured and observed quantities and the appropriate solubility product constants, the amount of Cl^- present can be determined within a small error. Given the following data:

A 1.7750 g sample is dissolved in 203 ml of water.

1 cc of 0.00100 F K_2CrO_4 is added.

46.00 ml of 0.250 N $AgNO_3$ were required to produce the red end point.

K_{sp} of $AgCl = 1.50 \times 10^{-10}$

K_{sp} of $Ag_2CrO_4 = 9.00 \times 10^{-12}$

(a) What is the $[CrO_4^{--}]$ just as the red color appears?

(b) What is the $[Ag^+]$ at this end point?

(c) What is the $[Cl^-]$ at this end point?

(d) How many moles of Ag^+ were added?

(e) How many moles of $AgCl$ precipitated?

(f) What is the total amount of Cl^- present?

(g) What is the weight per cent of Cl^- in the original sample?

21.55 s The solubility products of $AgIO_3$ and $Ba(IO_3)_2$ are 1.0×10^{-8} and 6.0×10^{-10}, respectively. A solution is 8.6×10^{-4} molar in Ag^+ and 3.74×10^{-3} molar in Ba^{++}. Iodate ion is added to this solution, slowly and with constant stirring.

(a) Which cation precipitates as the iodate salt first? At what IO_3^- ion concentration does this precipitate just start to form?

(b) At what IO_3^- ion concentration does the second cation just start to precipitate as the iodate salt?

(c) What is the concentration of the first cation when the second cation just starts to precipitate?

21.56 s 2.667 moles of solid Na_2CrO_4 are added to 0.250 liter of 4.000 F Na_2SO_3; the resulting solution is diluted to a volume of 1.000 liter with a buffer solution of such composition that the pH of the diluted solution, both before and after the following reaction has taken place, is 8.

$$2\ CrO_4^{--} + 3\ SO_3^{--} + 5\ H_2O \rightarrow 2\ Cr(OH)_3 + 3\ SO_4^{--} + 4\ OH^-$$

This reaction goes to completion and is not affected by the buffer.

(a) What is the molar sulfate ion concentration in the final diluted solution after the above reaction has gone to completion?

(b) What is the formal Cr(VI) concentration in the final diluted solution after the above reaction has gone to completion?

(c) In any solution of CrO_4^{--} the following equilibrium is established and has the equilibrium constant noted. (There are practically no $HCrO_4^-$ ions.)

$$2\ CrO_4^{--} + 2\ H^+ \rightleftarrows Cr_2O_7^{--} + H_2O \qquad K = 1.00 \times 10^{16}$$

Calculate the molar concentrations of CrO_4^{--} and $Cr_2O_7^{--}$ in the final solution.

(d) How many moles of solid soluble $BaCl_2$ must be added to the final solution in order to just start the formation of a precipitate? What is this precipitate? K_{sp} for $BaSO_4$ is 1.0×10^{-10}, for $BaCrO_4$ is 2.4×10^{-10}. $BaCr_2O_7$ is soluble.

21.57 s The solubility product of $AgC_2H_3O_2$ is 4.0×10^{-4}. To 1 liter of a solution $1.0\ F$ in $HC_2H_3O_2$ and $0.10\ F$ in HNO_3 is added just enough solid $AgNO_3$ to start precipitation of $AgC_2H_3O_2$. How many moles of $AgNO_3$ are added?

21.58 s The equilibrium constants for the following reactions are:

$$Mg(OH)_2\ (s) \rightleftarrows Mg^{++} + 2\ OH^- \qquad K = 1.1 \times 10^{-11}$$

$$NH_4^+ \rightleftarrows NH_3 + H^+ \qquad K = 5.7 \times 10^{-10}$$

What concentration of magnesium ion exists in a solution $0.20\ F$ in NH_4NO_3 and $0.50\ F$ in NH_3 which is saturated with magnesium hydroxide?

21.59 s A solution was prepared by dissolving 1.80 moles of $NaC_2H_3O_2$ and 1.00 mole of $HC_2H_3O_2$ in enough water to give 1.00 liter of solution. What is the maximum concentration of Fe^{+++} that can exist in this solution without precipitation of $Fe(OH)_3$? Solubility product for $Fe(OH)_3 = 6.0 \times 10^{-38}$.

21.60 s The K_{sp} of $Fe(OH)_3$ is 6.0×10^{-38}; the ionization constant of NH_3 is 1.8×10^{-5}; the ionization constant of $HCOOH$ is 2.1×10^{-4}.

(a) What is the formal solubility of $Fe(NO_3)_3$ in a solution that is $0.20\ F$ in NH_3 and $0.36\ F$ in NH_4NO_3?

(b) What volume of this NH_3-NH_4NO_3 solution is needed to dissolve the same amount of $Fe(NO_3)_3$ that will dissolve 1.00 liter of a solution that is $0.10\ F$ in $HCOOH$ and $0.42\ F$ in $HCOOK$?

21.61 s When excess solid $Mg(OH)_2$ is shaken with 1 liter of $1.0\ F\ NH_4Cl$ the resulting saturated solution has a pH of 9.0. The net equation for the reaction that occurs is

$$Mg(OH)_2 + 2\ NH_4^+ = Mg^{++} + 2\ NH_4OH$$

Calculate the solubility product for $Mg(OH)_2$. K for NH_4OH $= 1.8 \times 10^{-5}$.

21.62 s When excess $Mg(OH)_2$ is shaken with a liter of $1.0\,F\,NH_4Cl$, 0.18 mole of $Mg(OH)_2$ dissolves. The resulting solution has a pH of 9.0. Calculate the solubility product of $Mg(OH)_2$ and the ionization constant of NH_4OH.

21.63 s Calculate the concentration of I^- in a solution obtained by shaking $0.100\,N$ KI with an excess of AgCl. K_{sp} of $AgCl = 1.1 \times 10^{-10}$, K_{sp} of $AgI = 1.0 \times 10^{-16}$.

SOLUTION: The two equilibria involved are:

(1) $AgCl\ (s) \rightleftarrows Ag^+ + Cl^-$

(2) $Ag^+ + I^- \rightleftarrows AgI\ (s)$

The net equation for the reaction is

(3) $AgCl\ (s) + I^- \rightleftarrows AgI\ (s) + Cl^-$

The equilibrium constant for Reaction (3) is

(4) $$K = \frac{[Cl^-]}{[I^-]} = 1.1 \times 10^6$$

Let $X = [I^-]$

$$0.100 - X = [Cl^-]$$

Substituting these values in Equation (4) gives us

$$\frac{0.100 - X}{X} = 1.1 \times 10^6$$

Since $[I^-]$ is only 10^{-6} as large as $[Cl^-]$, and since the maximum value of $[Cl^-]$ is $0.100\,M$, it is obvious that the value of X in the expression, $0.100 - X$, is so small that it can be dropped.

$$\frac{0.100}{X} = 1.1 \times 10^6$$

$$X = 9.1 \times 10^{-8}\,M = [I^-]$$

NOTE: Since $0.100\,M\,I^-$ is added to solid AgCl, a natural inclination, when substituting in Equation (4), is to let $X = [Cl^-]$ and $0.100 - X = [I^-]$. If this is done, X, being very large (about 0.100), cannot be dropped from the expression, $0.100 - X$. The equation will then be,

$$\frac{X}{0.100 - X} = 1.1 \times 10^6$$

Solving,

$$X = 1.1 \times 10^5 - 1.1 \times 10^6\, X$$

$$1.1 \times 10^6\, X + X = 1.1 \times 10^5$$

If X is dropped from the expression, $1.1 \times 10^6\, X + X$, the calculated value of X is 0.100. The value of $[I^-]$, since it is $0.100 - X$, will then be $0.100 - 0.100$, or zero. Obviously, X cannot be dropped in this instance.

The correct procedure in situations of this type is to *let X equal that quantity which we know is very small*; X, being very small, can then be dropped from expressions in which it is subtracted from or added to a number which is very large by comparison with X.

21.64 s Calculate the concentration of Ag^+ in a solution prepared by mixing 100 ml of a solution 0.200 N in both NaCl and KI with 100 ml of 0.100 N $AgNO_3$. K_{sp} for $AgCl = 1.1 \times 10^{-10}$, for $AgI = 1.0 \times 10^{-16}$.

21.65 s A solution is 0.10 M in Cl^-, in Br^-, and in I^-. To 1 liter of this solution is added 0.15 mole of $AgNO_3$. What are the final concentrations of Cl^-, Br^-, and I^- in the solution?

$$K_{AgCl} = 1.5 \times 10^{-10} \quad K_{AgBr} = 5.0 \times 10^{-13} \quad K_{AgI} = 8.3 \times 10^{-17}$$

21.66 s Excess solid AgCl is treated with 100 ml of 1 F NH_4OH. How many grams of AgCl will dissolve? The solubility product for AgCl is 1.0×10^{-10}. The instability constant for $Ag(NH_3)_2^+$ is 6.0×10^{-8}.

SOLUTION: The net equation for the reaction is, $AgCl + 2\,NH_3 \rightleftarrows Ag(NH_3)_2^+ + Cl^-$. Calculate K for this reaction. The value of $[Ag(NH_3)_2^+]$ can then be calculated.

21.67 s The first ionization of sulfuric acid, $H_2SO_4 = H^+ + HSO_4^-$, is 100% complete. The ionization constant for the second ionization, $HSO_4^- \rightleftarrows H^+ + SO_4^{--}$, is 1.2×10^{-2}. The solubility product for $BaSO_4$ is 1.0×10^{-10}. Excess solid $BaSO_4$ was shaken with a solution of sulfuric acid until a saturated solution of $BaSO_4$ was obtained. The pH of this saturated solution was 2. How many moles of $BaSO_4$ dissolved per liter of saturated solution?

21.68 s The divalent metal ion, M^{++}, forms an insoluble hydroxide, $M(OH)_2$, whose solubility product is 3.0×10^{-11} and an insoluble cyanide, $M(CN)_2$, whose solubility product is 1.0×10^{-6}. M^{++} does not form any stable hydroxo or cyano complexes. The ionization constant of HCN is 4.0×10^{-10}. When a small amount of soluble solid MCl_2 is added to a 0.30 F NaCN solution, with no change in the volume of the solution, which solid, $M(OH)_2$ or $M(CN)_2$, precipitates first? What is the molar M^{++} concentration when this precipitate just starts to form?

21.69 s To 1 liter of a 1 F solution of Na_2CO_3 is added 10^{-7} moles of $MgCl_2$. Will a precipitate form; and, if so, what is the precipitate?

For H_2CO_3; $K_1 = 4.2 \times 10^{-7}$ $K_2 = 4.7 \times 10^{-11}$.

K_{sp} for $MgCO_3 = 4.0 \times 10^{-5}$ K_{sp} for $Mg(OH)_2 = 1.3 \times 10^{-11}$

21.70 s A mixture of Na_2CO_3 and $Na_2C_2O_4$ totaling 2.60×10^{-3} moles was placed in a beaker. A quantity of $BaCl_2$ was added. When equilibrium was established the volume of the solution was exactly 1 liter and the mixture of $BaCO_3$ and BaC_2O_4 that had precipitated totaled 2.38×10^{-3} moles and weighed 0.5255 g. The solubility products of $BaCO_3$ and BaC_2O_4 are 1.60×10^{-9} and 1.60×10^{-8}, respectively. (Solution was buffered to prevent hydrolysis.)

(a) How many moles of $BaCO_3$ were present in the mixture of $BaCO_3$ and BaC_2O_4?

(b) How many moles of Na_2CO_3 were present in the mixture of Na_2CO_3 and $Na_2C_2O_4$?

(c) How many moles of $BaCl_2$ were added?

21.71 s A solution in equilibrium with solid CaC_2O_4 is 0.20 F in oxalate and has a pH of 4.0. Calculate the concentration of Ca^{++} ions in the solution. K_{sp} for $CaC_2O_4 = 1.3 \times 10^{-9}$. For $H_2C_2O_4$, $K_1 = 3.8 \times 10^{-2}$, $K_2 = 5.0 \times 10^{-5}$.

21.72 s When excess solid $BaSO_3$ is added to a liter of pure dilute HCl, 4.0×10^{-4} moles of $BaSO_3$ are dissolved. No SO_2 gas is evolved in the process, and no complex ions are formed. The pH of the resulting solution is 5.0. Calculate the solubility product for $BaSO_3$. For H_2SO_3 K_1 is 1.3×10^{-2} and K_2 is 5.6×10^{-8}. $Ba(HSO_3)_2$ is very soluble.

21.73 s A liter of solution known to contain Zn^{++} and Ni^{++} in equal molar concentrations was kept saturated with H_2S. When precipitation was complete it was found that

(a) the volume of the solution in equilibrium with the precipitate was 1 liter

(b) the pH of the solution was 4.000

(c) 99.000% of the Ni^{++} originally present was precipitated as NiS

What per cent of the Zn^{++} originally present was precipitated as ZnS? Solubility products: $ZnS = 1.3 \times 10^{-20}$, $NiS = 1.3 \times 10^{-22}$.

21.74 s A solution containing $0.01\ M\ Zn^{++}$, $0.1\ F$ acetic acid, and $0.05\ F$ $NaC_2H_3O_2$, is saturated with H_2S. What concentration of Zn^{++} remains in solution? K_{sp} for $ZnS = 1.3 \times 10^{-20}$.

21.75 s A solution contains $0.01\ F\ Ca(NO_3)_2$, $0.01\ F\ Sr(NO_3)_2$, and $0.5\ F$ oxalic acid. To what value should the hydrogen ion concentration be adjusted, by addition of HCl or NaOH, in order to precipitate as much as possible of the calcium while leaving all of the strontium in solution? K_{sp} for calcium oxalate $= 2.6 \times 10^{-9}$. K_{sp} for strontium oxalate $= 7.0 \times 10^{-8}$.

21.76 s The solubility product of $AgIO_3$ is 4.5×10^{-8}. When excess solid $AgIO_3$ is treated with 1 liter of $1\ F\ NH_4OH$ 85 g of $AgIO_3$ dissolve.

$$AgIO_3 + 2\ NH_3 \rightleftarrows Ag(NH_3)_2{}^+ + IO_3{}^-$$

Calculate the equilibrium constant for the reaction:

$$Ag(NH_3)_2{}^+ \rightleftarrows Ag^+ + 2\ NH_3$$

21.77 s K_{sp} for $Zn(OH)_2$ is 1×10^{-16}. When excess $Zn(OH)_2$ is treated with 1 liter of $0.4\ F$ KCN the reaction

$$Zn(OH)_2\ (s) + 4\ CN^- \rightleftarrows Zn(CN)_4{}^{--} + 2\ OH^-$$

occurs. When equilibrium is reached, the pH is 13. Calculate the equilibrium constant for the reaction,

$$Zn(CN)_4{}^{--} \rightleftarrows Zn^{++} + 4\ CN^-$$

21.78 s The solubility of $BaCO_3$ in water saturated with CO_2 at 1 atm is 0.01 mole per liter. The concentration of H_2CO_3 in this solution is $0.04\ M$. The net equation is, $BaCO_3\ (s) + H_2CO_3 \rightleftarrows Ba^{++} + 2\ HCO_3{}^-$. Calculate the equilibrium constant for this reaction and calculate the solubility product of $BaCO_3$.

21.79 s Excess solid $Ni(CN)_2$ is added to a liter of dilute HCl. When equilibrium is established, the pH of the saturated solution is 4 and exactly 0.010 mole of $Ni(CN)_2$ has dissolved. Calculate the solubility product of $Ni(CN)_2$.

21.80 s (a) Silver cyanide, AgCN, is soluble in water to the extent of 1.34×10^{-4} mgm per 100 ml of water. Assuming that when AgCN dissolves, the species present are Ag^+ and CN^-, what is the solubility product for AgCN?

(b) Actually a very stable complex is formed; the constant for the reaction, $Ag(CN)_2^- \rightleftarrows Ag^+ + 2\ CN^-$, is $K = 9.0 \times 10^{-22}\ M^2$. Considering this fact also, what is the true solubility product for AgCN?

21.81 s ZnS will precipitate from $0.010\ F\ Zn(NO_3)_2$ solution on saturation with H_2S only if the pH is greater than 1.00. ZnS will not be precipitated from a solution $0.010\ F$ in $Zn(NO_3)_2$ and $1.00\ M$ in CN^- unless the pH is greater than 9.00. Calculate K for the reaction $Zn(CN)_4^{--} \rightleftarrows Zn^{++} + 4\ CN^-$. A solution saturated with H_2S is $0.10\ M$ in H_2S. The over-all ionization constant for H_2S is 1.3×10^{-20}.

21.82 s Calculate the solubility of AgI in $0.1\ F\ Hg(NO_3)_2$. The main reaction is $AgI\ (s) + Hg^{++} \rightleftarrows HgI^+ + Ag^+$. For the equation, $HgI^+ \rightleftarrows Hg^{++} + I^-$, $K = 10^{-13}$. K_{sp} for AgI is 1×10^{-16}.

21.83 s The solubility product of AgCN is 2.6×10^{-19}. The instability constant of the dicyanoargentate(I) ion is $9.0 \times 10^{-22}\ M^2$. The ionization constant of HCN is $4.0 \times 10^{-10}\ M$. Calculate the molar concentrations of all ionic and molecular species in $0.100\ F$ HCN to which has been added sufficient solid AgCN to form a saturated solution.

SOLUTION: The main reaction is

$$AgCN\ (s) + HCN \rightleftarrows Ag(CN)_2^- + H^+$$

21.84 s To a liter of $0.1\ F$ HCN is added 9.9 g of CuCl. Assuming that there is no change in the volume of the solution when the CuCl is added, calculate the molar concentration of each species in the solution. K_i for $HCN = 4 \times 10^{-10}\ M$; K_{inst} for $Cu(CN)_2^- = 5 \times 10^{-28}\ M^2$; K_{sp} for CuCl $= 3.2 \times 10^{-7}$.

21.85 s In order to just prevent precipitation of BaF_2 in a solution which is $0.10\ F$ in $BaCl_2$ and $0.10\ F$ in KF it is necessary to adjust the pH to a value of 1.96 by addition of HCl. Calculate the solubility product of BaF_2. The ionization constant for HF is $6.9 \times 10^{-4}\ M$.

21.86 s Calculate the solubility of $CaCO_3$ in a solution buffered at a pH of 7.0. K_{sp} for $CaCO_3 = 7 \times 10^{-9}$. For H_2CO_3, $K_1 = 4 \times 10^{-7}$ M and $K_2 = 5 \times 10^{-11}$ M.

21.87 s The solubility product of $Ni(CN)_2$ is 6.4×10^{-17}. The ionization constant for HCN is 4.0×10^{-10}. You are asked to make up 1 liter of a solution 0.010 F in $NiCl_2$ and 0.010 F in NaCN. To what maximum value must the pH of the solution be adjusted by the addition of HCl, to just prevent precipitation of $Ni(CN)_2$? How many moles of HCl must be added per liter of solution to just prevent precipitation of $Ni(CN)_2$.

21.88 s A certain trivalent metal ion forms an insoluble hydroxide and an insoluble carbonate; the solubility products are 1.0×10^{-20} and 5.5×10^{-25}, respectively. If a mixture of a very small amount of these 2 solids is placed in 0.20 F Na_2CO_3, will the conversion hydroxide $\rightarrow$ carbonate occur, or will the reverse change take place?

21.89 s The following solubility equilibria apply to the insoluble precipitate $Zn(OH)_2$:

$$Zn(OH)_2 \text{ (s)} \rightleftarrows Zn^{++} + 2\ OH^- \qquad K_{sp} = 5.0 \times 10^{-17} M^3$$

$$Zn(OH)_2 \text{ (s)} + 2\ OH^- \rightleftarrows Zn(OH)_4^{--} \qquad K = 0.25\ M^{-1}$$

Over what pH range can $Zn(OH)_2$ be quantitatively precipitated in the sense that the total concentration of ions containing zinc in equilibrium with solid $Zn(OH)_2$ is less than 10^{-4} M?

21.90 s At 50°C the concentration of undissociated H_2S in equilibrium with H_2S gas at a partial pressure of 1.00 atm is 0.075 M. In 1.00 liter of solution buffered at pH 4.00, and which is 0.0045 F in $Ni(NO_3)_2$ and 0.500 F in NaCl, the partial pressure of H_2S gas required to just begin precipitation of NiS is 0.0333 atm. Assuming the Ks of H_2S and the K_{sp} for NiS given on pages 240–242 are applicable at 50°C, and that $NiCl^+$ is the only chloro complex of Ni^{++} formed, calculate the equilibrium constant for the reaction $NiCl^+ \rightleftarrows Ni^{++} + Cl^-$.

21.91 s The solubility of $CaCO_3$ in water at 25°C is 1.3×10^{-4} moles per liter. The solubility product, calculated from this solubility, is $4.8 \times 10^{-9} M^2$, not 1.7×10^{-8}. Explain.

$+$ $+$ $+$ $+$ $+$ $+$ $-$

Oxidation Potentials

Metals have a tendency to give off one or more electrons to form positive ions. Thus, when zinc is brought in contact with water, or an aqueous solution of some substance, the reaction

$$Zn = Zn^{++} + 2\ e$$

tends to take place.

Likewise, the reactions $Mg = Mg^{++} + 2\ e$, $Mn = Mn^{++} + 2\ e$, $Cu = Cu^{++} + 2\ e$, $Ag = Ag^{+} + e$, and so on, tend to occur. The energy or *potential* with which the electrons are expelled, that is the energy with which the metal reacts, varies from one metal to another.

If we list the metals in the order of the *potential* with which the electrons are given off, and include in this list other substances that give off electrons when they react, we obtain the sort of arrangement found in Table 5, page 244. The substance with the strongest tendency to lose electrons is at the top, the one with the weakest tendency is at the bottom.

In arriving at this table the potential of the reaction, H_2 (gas) $= 2\ H^+ + 2\ e$, is used as a standard of reference.

Potential is expressed in units of *volts*. The voltage of the reaction, $H_2 = 2\ H^+ + 2\ e$, is arbitrarily assigned a value of zero. That is,

$$H_2 = 2\ H^+ + 2\ e \qquad \text{Potential} = 0.00\ v$$

Any substance which has a stronger tendency to give off electrons than does H_2 has a positive voltage and lies above H_2 in the table; any substance whose tendency to lose electrons is less than that of H_2 has a negative voltage and falls below hydrogen. The voltage listed in the table gives the relative numerical value of this tendency. Thus, for the reaction, $Zn = Zn^{++} + 2\,e$, the potential is 0.763 v greater than that for H_2 while the potential of the reaction, $Cu = Cu^{++} + 2\,e$, is 0.337 v less than that for H_2.

When the reaction, $Zn = Zn^{++} + 2\,e$, occurs *zinc is oxidized*. The evidence is that its oxidation number is increased from 0 to +2, and two electrons are lost. *Oxidation involves* (1) *an increase in oxidation number of the element oxidized and* (2) *a loss of electrons by the element oxidized.*

In the above reaction zinc functions as a reducing agent. When any substance loses electrons and, for that reason, is oxidized, it functions as a *reducing agent*. We note, in Table 5, that all of the substances on the left in the table react by losing electrons. Therefore, all of the substances on the left are reducing agents. The higher the potential of a substance the greater its strength as a reducing agent.

The reaction, $Zn^{++} + 2\,e = Zn$, is the exact reverse of the reaction given in the previous paragraph. In this reaction zinc is reduced from Zn^{++} to Zn metal; Zn^{++} functions as an oxidizing agent.

If we examine the reactions in Table 5 we will find that, in every instance when the reaction proceeds from right to left the substance on the right functions as an *oxidizing agent*; in the course of the reaction the substance on the right is reduced.

Just as the substance on the left with the *highest potential* is the *strongest reducing agent* so the substance on the right with the *lowest potential* is the *strongest oxidizing agent*. The magnitude of the potential is thus a measure of the relative oxidizing strength of an oxidizing agent as well as the relative reducing strength of a reducing agent.

The reaction, $Zn = Zn^{++} + 2\,e$, will not go on by itself. It must be paired up with another reaction, one that will accept the two electrons. The same thing is true of every reaction in this table. Each is only a *half reaction* and must be coupled with another half reaction.

When zinc metal is added to a solution of copper sulfate the reaction

$$Zn + Cu^{++} = Zn^{++} + Cu$$

occurs. This over-all reaction is the sum of the two half reactions.

$$Zn = Zn^{++} + 2\,e \qquad 0.763\ v$$
$$Cu = Cu^{++} + 2\,e \qquad -0.337\ v$$

The substance with the higher potential (Zn) will function as the reducing agent while the substance with the lower potential (Cu^{++}) will function as the oxidizing agent. In effect, the second reaction is reversed and the over-all reaction is the sum of the two half reactions. Likewise, the potential of the over-all reaction is the sum of the potentials of the two half reactions. Since the second reaction is reversed, the sign of its potential is changed from -0.337 to $+0.337$. The potential of the over-all reaction is therefore, 1.100 v.

$$Zn = Zn^{++} + 2\ e \qquad\qquad 0.763\ v$$
$$Cu^{++} + 2\ e = Cu \qquad\qquad 0.337\ v$$
$$\overline{Zn + Cu^{++} = Zn^{+} + Cu \qquad 1.100\ v}$$

That the potential of this reaction is, in fact, 1.100 v, can be demonstrated by the following experiment.

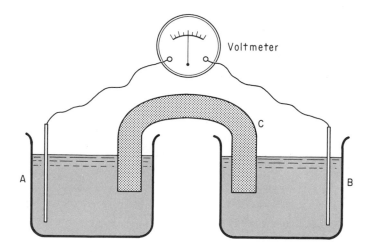

Voltmeter

Beaker A in the figure contains a strip of Zn metal in a 1-molal solution of $ZnSO_4$. Beaker B contains a strip of Cu metal in 1-molal $CuSO_4$. The U-shaped tube C contains a gel prepared with a solution of K_2SO_4. It is called a *salt bridge* and serves as a conducting medium between the two solutions. The strips of Cu and Zn are connected by copper wires through a voltmeter.

When the circuit is closed, the voltmeter registers 1.100 v. This proves that *the potential of the cell is the sum of the potentials of the two half reactions.*

A cell, made up as described above, is commonly designated by the notation $Zn | 1\ M\ Zn^{++} | 1\ M\ Cu^{++} | Cu$.

If a hydrogen gas electrode, prepared by keeping a piece of platinum immersed in 1 M H^+ and continually enveloped in hydrogen gas, is substituted for the Cu-CuSO$_4$ half cell the voltage is 0.763. This illustrates one method by which voltages in Table 5 were determined.

It should be emphasized that the voltages given in Table 5 are for systems in which the concentrations of all substances in solution are 1-molal. (Since molar and molal concentrations of aqueous solutions are very nearly the same, particularly for dilute solutions, it is common practice to consider that these solutions are 1 M.) The temperature is 25°C, and gases are at a pressure of 1 atm. Under these conditions the potentials are referred to as *Standard Electrode Potentials* and are designated by the symbol $E°$.

To determine the voltage for a pair of half reactions such as

$$Fe^{++} \rightleftarrows Fe^{+++} + e \qquad\qquad -0.771 \text{ v}$$

$$2\,Cr^{+++} + 7\,H_2O \rightleftarrows Cr_2O_7^{--} + 14\,H^+ + 6\,e^- \quad -1.33 \text{ v}$$

beaker A in the figure on page 226 contains a platinum electrode immersed in a solution 1 M in Fe^{++} and 1 M in Fe^{+++} while beaker B contains a platinum electrode immersed in a solution 1 M in $Cr_2O_7^{--}$, 1 M in Cr^{+++}, and 1 M in H^+.

If a battery is made up with a strip of Cu in a solution of $CuSO_4$ in one cell and a strip of Ag in Ag_2SO_4 in the other cell, its voltage is 0.462 v calculated as follows:

$Cu = Cu^{++} + 2\,e$	-0.337 v
$2\,Ag^+ + 2\,e^- = 2\,Ag$	$+0.799$ v
$Cu + 2\,Ag^+ = Cu^{++} + 2\,Ag$	$+0.462$ v

This is referred to as a $Cu|Cu^{++}|Ag^+|Ag$ cell.

Note, in this example, that doubling the number of moles of Ag^+ in the reaction, $2\,Ag^+ + 2\,e = 2\,Ag$, does not alter the voltage. The reason is that the voltage is a measure of the *work per electron*.

Note, also, that the substance with the lowest (most negative) potential, Ag^+ in this case, functions as the oxidizing agent. The Ag^+ half reaction has accordingly been reversed, resulting in its voltage being changed from -0.799 to $+0.799$. As a result, the sum of the voltages is positive $(+0.462)$. This illustrates how one can determine whether or not a certain oxidizing agent will react with a certain reducing agent. The rule is this: If the sum of the two potentials, written with the proper signs (sign of the potential of the oxidizing agent is reversed), is *positive*, the two substances *will* react with each other, if it is negative, they will not react.

Will Cu reduce Sn^{++++} to Sn^{++}, being itself oxidized to Cu^{++}?

$$Cu = Cu^{++} + 2\,e \qquad\qquad -0.337$$
$$Sn^{++++} + 2\,e = Sn^{++} \qquad\qquad +0.15$$
$$\overline{Cu + Sn^{++++} = Cu^{++} + Sn^{++} \qquad -0.19}$$

The sum is negative. Reaction will not occur.

Application of the above rule to Table 5 reveals these simple and useful relationships:

Any reducing agent of higher potential will reduce any oxidizing agent of lower potential. Any oxidizing agent of lower potential will oxidize any reducing agent of higher potential.

Any reducing agent on the left *will* reduce (be oxidized by) any oxidizing agent *below* itself and on the right. It *will not* be oxidized by an oxidizing agent above itself and on the right.

Any oxidizing agent on the right will oxidize (be reduced by) any reducing agent *above* itself and on the left. It *will not* oxidize a reducing agent *below* itself on the left.

In the reaction, $Zn + Cu^{++} = Zn^{++} + Cu$, Cu^{++} functions as the oxidizing agent and the half reaction, $Cu = Cu^{++} + 2\,e$, proceeds to the left. In the reaction, $Cu + 2\,Ag^+ \rightleftarrows Cu^{++} + 2\,Ag$, Cu is the reducing agent and the half reaction, $Cu = Cu^{++} + 2\,e$, proceeds to the right. This means that the reaction, $Cu = Cu^{++} + 2\,e$, is reversible, and, being reversible, it can reach a state of equilibrium.

What is true of the reaction, $Cu = Cu^{++} + 2\,e$, is true of all redox (oxidation-reduction) half reactions. They are reversible and can reach a state of equilibrium. For reactions with a high positive potential, indicating that the substance is a strong reducing agent, the equilibrium is far to the right. For reactions with a low potential (a large negative potential), meaning that the substance is a strong oxidizing agent, the equilibrium is far to the left.

Since the reactions are all reversible and can reach a state of equilibrium, they are written with conventional double arrows, $Cu \rightleftarrows Cu^{++} + 2\,e$.

Problems

22.1 Calculate the theoretical voltage of each of the following cells, assembled in the manner shown in the figure on page 226.

(a) $Zn|1\ M\ Zn^{++}|1\ M\ Ni^{++}|Ni$

*(b)   Al|1 M Al^{+++}|1 M Cu^{++}|Cu

(c)   Cu|1 M Cu^{++}|1 M Hg^{++}|Hg

*(d)   Pt|1 M Fe^{+++}, 1 M Fe^{++}|1 M MnO$_4^-$, 1 M Mn^{++}|Pt

22.2   State whether or not a reaction will occur when the following are brought together in acidic 1 M solution at 25°C.

(a)   MnO$_4^-$ and I$^-$

*(b)   Cr^{++} and Cu^{++}

(c)   Sn^{++} and H$_3$PO$_4$

*(d)   H$_2$S (at 1 atm) and Fe^{+++}

(e)   Sn and Sn^{++++}

Effect of Change of Concentration

Since each half reaction reaches a state of equilibrium it follows that the equilibrium, and, hence, the voltage, will change when the concentration of a reactant or product is changed. Thus for the reaction

$$Fe^{++} \rightleftarrows Fe^{+++} + e \qquad (-0.771 \text{ v})$$

an increase in concentration of Fe^{++} will shift the equilibrium to the right, thereby increasing the positive potential (decreasing the negative potential). If the concentration of Fe^{++} is reduced, the equilibrium will shift to the left and the potential will decrease. If the concentration of Fe^{+++} is increased the equilibrium will shift to the left and the potential will decrease while, if the concentration of Fe^{+++} is reduced, the equilibrium will shift to the right and the potential will increase.

The quantitative effect of change in concentration can be calculated by the use of the *Nernst equation*,

$$(1) \qquad E = E° - \frac{2.303 \, RT}{nF} \log \frac{[\text{product}]}{[\text{reactant}]}$$

In this formula $E°$ is the standard potential of the half reaction, E is its potential under the particular condition of the experiment, 2.303 is the *constant* for conversion from natural logarithms to logarithms to the base 10, R is the gas *constant*, F is the faraday (with a *constant* value of 96,500 coulombs), n is the number of electrons transferred in the half reaction, and T is the absolute temperature. Therefore, at constant temperature,

2.303 RT/F will be constant for all reactions; its value, at 25°C, is 0.059. Thus Equation (1) takes the simplified form

$$E = E° - \frac{0.059}{n} \log \frac{[\text{product}]}{[\text{reactant}]}$$

Since the product, Fe^{+++} in the above example, is in the oxidized state and the reactant, Fe^{++}, is in the reduced state, the formula is commonly written

$$E = E° - \frac{0.059}{n} \log \frac{[\text{oxidized state}]}{[\text{reduced state}]}$$

Suppose the concentration of Fe^{++} is 0.1 M and the concentration of Fe^{+++} is 1.0 M:

$$E = -0.771 - \frac{0.059}{1} \log \frac{1.0}{0.1} = -0.771 - 0.059 = -0.830 \text{ v}$$

If more than one reactant or more than one product is involved each species is included in the concentration term and, as in the standard equilibrium formula, each is raised to a power equal to the number of moles that react. Solid or liquid species are not included in the formulation and the concentration of H_2O is constant at 55.6 moles per liter. Thus, for the half reaction,

$$Cl^- + 3 H_2O \rightleftarrows ClO_3^- + 6 H^+ + 6 e \qquad -1.45 \text{ v}$$

$$E = -1.45 - \frac{0.059}{6} \log \frac{[ClO_3^-][H^+]^6}{[Cl^-]}$$

and for the reaction,

$$Zn \text{ (s)} \rightleftarrows Zn^{++} + 2 e \qquad 0.763 \text{ v}$$

$$E = 0.763 - \frac{0.059}{2} \log [Zn^{++}]$$

Note that, if all concentrations are 1 M, the term $[\text{oxid}]/[\text{red}] = 1$. Since $\log 1 = 0$, the entire term,

$$\frac{-0.059}{n} \log \frac{[\text{oxid}]}{[\text{red}]}$$

equals zero, and $E = E°$.

If $[\text{oxid}]$ is less than 1 or $[\text{red}]$ is greater than 1, making $[\text{oxid}]/[\text{red}]$ less than 1, the log will be negative. As a result, the term,

$$\frac{-0.059}{n} \times \log \frac{[\text{oxid}]}{[\text{red}]}$$

will be positive and E will be more positive than $E°$. This is exactly the conclusion that was reached in our qualitative inspection. If the ratio of [oxid] to [red] is greater than 1, the log will be positive, the term,

$$\frac{-0.059}{n} \log \frac{[oxid]}{[red]}$$

will be negative, and E will be less positive than $E°$.

Problems

22.3 Calculate the potential of the half reaction, $Zn = Zn^{++} + 2\,e$, when the concentration of the Zn^{++} ion is 0.10 M.*

22.4 Calculate the potential of the half reaction, $Fe^{++} \rightleftarrows Fe^{+++} + e$, when Fe^{++} and Fe^{+++} are, respectively, 0.40 M and 1.60 M.

Calculation of Equilibrium Constants

When equilibrium is established in a half reaction there is no net loss or gain of electrons. Hence, the voltage is zero. Therefore, at equilibrium, E in the Nernst formula is zero and [oxid]/[red] is the equilibrium constant for the reaction.

Therefore, at equilibrium,

$$E° = \frac{0.059}{n} \log K$$

$$\log K = \frac{nE°}{0.059} \quad \text{and} \quad K = 10^{\frac{nE°}{0.059}}$$

For the reaction, $Fe^{++} \rightleftarrows Fe^{+++} + e$, $E° = -0.771$ v

$$\log K = \frac{-0.771}{0.059} = -13$$

$$K = 10^{-13}$$

The extremely small value of K means that the reaction, $Fe^{++} \rightleftarrows Fe^{+++}$ is practically complete to the left.

The Nernst formula enables us, also, to calculate the equilibrium constant for the over-all oxidation-reduction reaction. Thus, suppose we set up a cell in the figure on page 226 with $Br_2 - Br^-$ in one beaker and $I_2 - I^-$ in the other, close the circuit, and allow the system to stand until the voltage drops to zero. The reaction, $Br_2 + 2I^- \rightleftarrows I_2 + 2\,Br^-$, will then have reached a state of equilibrium. When this point is reached, the potential generated by the reaction, $2\,Br^- = Br_2 + 2\,e$, will exactly equal the potential generated by the reaction, $2\,I^- = I_2 + 2\,e$.

But

$$E^{Br} = -1.065 - \frac{0.059}{2} \log \frac{[Br_2]}{[Br^-]^2}$$

and

$$E^{I} = -0.536 - \frac{0.059}{2} \log \frac{[I_2]}{[I^-]^2}$$

Then

$$-1.065 - \frac{0.059}{2} \log \frac{[Br_2]}{[Br^-]^2} = -0.536 - \frac{0.059}{2} \log \frac{[I_2]}{[I^-]^2}$$

$$\frac{0.059}{2}\left(\log \frac{[I_2]}{[I^-]^2} - \log \frac{[Br_2]}{[Br^-]^2}\right) = 1.065 - 0.536 = 0.529$$

$$\frac{0.059}{2} \log \frac{\dfrac{[I_2]}{[I^-]^2}}{\dfrac{[Br_2]}{[Br^-]^2}} = 0.529$$

$$\log \frac{[I_2] \times [Br^-]^2}{[I^-]^2 \times [Br_2]} = \frac{0.529 \times 2}{0.059} = 18$$

But $\dfrac{[I_2] \times [Br^-]^2}{[I^-]^2 \times [Br_2]}$ is the equilibrium constant, K, for the reaction $Br_2 + 2\,I^- \rightleftarrows 2\,Br^- + I_2$.

$$\log K = 18$$

$$K = 10^{18}$$

This means that the above reaction is practically complete to the right.

If we examine the calculations given above we will find that, for a reaction at equilibrium,

$$\log K = \frac{n \text{ (difference in the standard potentials of the two half reactions)}}{0.059}$$

and

$$K = 10^{\frac{n\Delta E^\circ}{0.059}}$$

where n is the number of electrons gained or lost in each balanced half reaction and ΔE° is the difference between the two standard potentials.

Problems

22.5 Calculate the equilibrium constants for each of the following reactions.

(a) $Cl_2 + 2\,Br^- \rightleftarrows 2\,Cl^- + Br_2$

*(b) $2\,Fe^{+++} + 2\,I^- \rightleftarrows 2\,Fe^{++} + I_2$

(c) $Cr_2O_7^{--} + 3\,Sn^{++} + 14\,H^+ \rightleftarrows 2\,Cr^{+++} + 3\,Sn^{4+} + 7\,H_2O$

*(d) $Zn + Cu^{++} \rightleftarrows Zn^{++} + Cu$

Calculation of the Potential of a Half Reaction from the Potentials of Other Half Reactions

We have learned that when two half reactions are combined to give a *complete reaction*, the voltage of the couple is the sum of the two voltages, due regard being given to the sign of each voltage.

When the potential of a third *half reaction* is calculated from two other half reactions we must keep in mind that (1) the expulsion of electrons requires energy, (2) that, since the potential of a reaction is a measure of the work per unit charge, the total energy in electron-volts will be the product of volts × electrons, and that (3) in any series of reactions the net change in energy is the algebraic sum of the energy change in each step.

Thus, suppose we wish to calculate the potential of the reaction, $BrO^- + 4\,OH^- = BrO_3^- + 2\,H_2O + 3\,e$, from the two half reactions, (1) and (2).

	Reaction	n	$E°$	Total energy
(1)	$6\,OH^- + Br^- = BrO_3^- + 3\,H_2O +$	$6\,e^-$	-0.61 v	$6 \times -0.61 = -3.66$ ev
(2)	$2\,OH^- + Br^- = BrO^- + H_2O +$	$2\,e^-$	-0.76 v	$2 \times -0.76 = -1.52$ ev
(3)	$4\,OH^- + BrO^- = BrO_3^- + 2\,H_2O +$	$4\,e$	-0.535 v	-2.14 ev

If we subtract Reaction (2) from Reaction (1), taking proper note of signs, we obtain Reaction (3). Note that, in Reaction (3), the total energy is -2.14 electron-volts. Since 4 electrons are given off per molecule of BrO^-, the potential, $E°$, in volts will be $-2.14 \div 4$ or -0.535.

Problems

22.6 Given the half reactions:

$$Cl^- + 3\ H_2O = ClO_3^- + 6\ H^+ + 6\ e^- \quad E° = -1.45\ v$$

$$2\ Cl^- = Cl_2 + 2\ e \quad\quad\quad\quad\quad\quad E° = -1.36\ v$$

Calculate $E°$ for the half reaction, $\frac{1}{2}\ Cl_2 + 3\ H_2O = ClO_3^- + 6\ H^+ + 5\ e^-$.

22.7 Given the half reactions:

$$S + 3\ H_2O = H_2SO_3 + 4\ H^+ + 4\ e^- \quad\quad E° = -0.45\ v$$

$$H_2SO_3 + H_2O = SO_4^{--} + 4\ H^+ + 2\ e^- \quad\quad E° = -0.17\ v$$

Calculate $E°$ for the half reaction,

$$*S + 4\ H_2O = SO_4^{--} + 8\ H^+ + 6\ e^-$$

22.8 The reactions in Group A below proceed substantially to completion in the direction written. On the basis of the information given in Group A state whether each reaction in Group B can proceed as written, cannot proceed as written, or is unpredictable.*

Group A	$Cd + Sn^{++++} = Sn^{++} + Cd^{++}$
	$Mn + Br_2 = Mn^{++} + 2\ Br^-$
	$Tl^+ + 2\ Co^{+++} = Tl^{+++} + 2\ Co^{++}$
	$Sn^{++} + Br_2 = Sn^{++++} + 2\ Br^-$
	$2\ Br^- + 2\ Co^{+++} = 2\ Co^{++} + Br_2$
Group B	$Cd^{++} + 2\ Co^{++} = Cd + 2\ Co^{+++}$
	$Cd + Br_2 = Cd^{++} + 2\ Br^-$
	$Tl^+ + Sn^{++++} = Sn^{++} + Tl^{+++}$
	$Mn^{++} + 2\ Co^{++} = Mn + 2\ Co^{+++}$
	$Cd + Mn^{++} = Cd^{++} + Mn$

22.9 s Uranium is known in oxidation states 0, 3, 4, 5, and 6. You are given the following standard oxidation potentials; for the purposes of this problem you may assume that all reactions that occur are rapid.

Half Reaction	E°
$U^{+++} + 2\,H_2O = UO_2^{++} + 4\,H^+ + 3\,e^-$	-0.02
$U = U^{+++} + 3\,e^-$	$+1.80$
$U^{++++} + 2\,H_2O = UO_2^+ + 4\,H^+ + e^-$	-0.62
$U^{++++} + 2\,H_2O = UO_2^{++} + 4\,H^+ + 2\,e^-$	-0.33
$Cd = Cd^{++} + 2\,e^-$	$+0.40$

(a) Calculate E° for the half reaction,

$$U^{+++} + 2\,H_2O = UO_2^+ + 4\,H^+ + 2\,e^-$$

(b) Will uranium (V) disproportionate to the two adjacent oxidation states?

(c) What oxidation state of uranium is produced when 1 M UO_2^{++} solution is treated with excess cadmium metal?

22.10 s The metal M has five oxidation states: 0, 2, 3, 4, and 5, which are related by the redox potentials given below; the potentials for zinc, iron, and tin are also included. Assume that all possible reactions are very rapid.

	Half Reaction	E°
A	$M = M^{++} + 2\,e^-$	$+0.80$
	$Zn = Zn^{++} + 2\,e^-$	$+0.76$
B	$M = M^{+++} + 3\,e^-$	$+0.70$
C	$M + H_2O = MO^{++} + 2\,H^+ + 4\,e^-$	$+0.60$
D	$M^{++} = M^{+++} + e^-$	$+0.50$
	$Fe = Fe^{++} + 2\,e^-$	$+0.45$
E	$M + 2\,H_2O = MO_2^+ + 4\,H^+ + 5\,e^-$	$+0.44$
F	$M^{++} + H_2O = MO^{++} + 2\,H^+ + 2\,e^-$	$+0.40$
G	$M^{+++} + H_2O = MO^{++} + 2\,H^+ + e^-$	$+0.30$
H	$M^{++} + H_2O = MO_2^+ + 4\,H^+ + 3\,e^-$	$+0.20$
	$Sn = Sn^{++} + 2\,e^-$	$+0.14$
I	$M^{+++} + 2\,H_2O = MO^+ + 4\,H^+ + 2\,e^-$	$+0.05$
J	$MO^{++} + H_2O = MO_2^+ + 2\,H^+ + e^-$	-0.20

(a) What is the potential of the reaction

$$3\,Sn^{++} + 2\,M^{++} + 4\,H_2O = 3\,Sn + 2\,MO_2^+ + 8\,H^+$$

(b) Will excess metallic Zn reduce M^{++} to M?

(c) Will excess metallic Zn reduce M^{+++} to M^{++}?

(d) Will excess metallic Zn reduce M^{+++} to M?

(e) What oxidation state of M is produced when 1 molal MO_2^+ is treated with

(1) excess metallic zinc?

(2) excess metallic tin?

(3) excess metallic iron?

(f) Will oxidation state $+3$ disproportionate to $+2$ and $+5$?

(g) Show how $E°$ for half reaction **H** can be calculated by appropriate combination of $E°$'s for

(1) half reactions **A** and **E**.

(2) half reactions **D**, **G**, and **J**.

(3) half reactions **J** and **F**

(4) half reactions **A**, **C**, and **J**.

22.11 s In acid solution will H_3PO_2 disproportionate to give PH_3 and H_3PO_4? (See Table 5.)

22.12 s Calculate the potential of the half reaction,

$$PH_3 + 3 H_2O \rightleftarrows H_2PO_3 + 7 H^+ + 7 e^-$$

22.13 s What oxidation state of chlorine will be formed when 1.0 M ClO_4^- is reduced with excess solid $Mn(OH)_2$ in alkaline solution? (See Table 6.)

22.14 s Calculate the potential of the half reaction,

$$Cl^- + 8 OH^- \rightleftarrows ClO_4^- + 4 H_2O + 8 e^-$$

22.15 s A cell is made up as illustrated in the figure on page 226, with a standard hydrogen electrode in beaker B. Beaker A contains Zn metal in contact with a solution prepared by adding a large excess of $Zn(OH)_2$ to 0.20 M NaOH. Calculate the theoretical voltage of the cell. K_{sp} for $Zn(OH)_2$ is 5.0×10^{-17}. K_{inst} for $Zn(OH)_4^{--}$ is 3.4×10^{-10}.

1
2
3
4
5
6
7
8
9
10
11
12
13
14
15
16
17
18
19
20
21
22

Appendix

Table 1   VAPOR PRESSURE OF WATER IN MILLIMETERS OF MERCURY

Degrees C	Pressures	Degrees C	Pressures
0	4.6	21	18.5
1	4.9	22	19.8
2	5.3	23	20.9
3	5.6	24	22.2
4	6.1	25	23.6
5	6.5	26	25.1
6	7.0	27	26.5
7	7.5	28	28.1
8	8.0	29	29.8
9	8.6	30	31.5
10	9.2	31	33.4
11	9.8	32	35.4
12	10.5	33	37.4
13	11.2	34	39.6
14	11.9	35	41.9
15	12.7	36	44.2
16	13.5	37	46.7
17	14.4	38	49.4
18	15.4	39	52.1
19	16.3	40	55.0
20	17.4	100	760.0

Table 2 IONIZATION CONSTANTS OF ACIDS AND BASES

(In units of moles/liter, M)

Acetic	$HC_2H_3O_2$	1.8×10^{-5}
Arsenic	H_3AsO_4	$K_1 = 2.5 \times 10^{-4}$
		$K_2 = 5.6 \times 10^{-8}$
		$K_3 = 3.0 \times 10^{-13}$
Arsenious	H_3AsO_3	$K_1 = 6 \ \times 10^{-10}$
Boric	H_3BO_3	$K_1 = 6.0 \times 10^{-10}$
Carbonic	H_2CO_3	$K_1 = 4.2 \times 10^{-7}$
		$K_2 = 4.8 \times 10^{-11}$
Chromic	H_2CrO_4	$K_1 = 1.8 \times 10^{-1}$
		$K_2 = 3.2 \times 10^{-7}$
Formic	$HCHO_2$	2.1×10^{-4}
Hydrocyanic	HCN	4.0×10^{-10}
Hydrofluoric	HF	6.9×10^{-4}
Hydrogen sulfide	H_2S	$K_1 = 1.0 \times 10^{-7}$
		$K_2 = 1.3 \times 10^{-13}$
Hypochlorous	$HClO$	3.2×10^{-8}
Nitrous	HNO_2	4.5×10^{-4}
Oxalic	$H_2C_2O_4$	$K_1 = 3.8 \times 10^{-2}$
		$K_2 = 5.0 \times 10^{-5}$
Phosphoric	H_3PO_4	$K_1 = 7.5 \times 10^{-3}$
		$K_2 = 6.2 \times 10^{-8}$
		$K_3 = 1.0 \times 10^{-12}$
Sulfurous	H_2SO_3	$K_1 = 1.3 \times 10^{-2}$
		$K_2 = 5.6 \times 10^{-8}$
Ammonium hydroxide	NH_4OH	1.8×10^{-5}

Table 3 COMPLEX ION EQUILIBRIA

Ligand	Equation	Instability Constant
Ammonia	$Cd(NH_3)_4^{++} \rightleftharpoons Cd^{++} + 4\,NH_3$	$7.5 \times 10^{-8}\ M^4$
	$Cu(NH_3)_4^{++} \rightleftharpoons Cu^{++} + 4\,NH_3$	$4.7 \times 10^{-15}\ M^4$
	$Co(NH_3)_6^{++} \rightleftharpoons Co^{++} + 6\,NH_3$	$1.3 \times 10^{-5}\ M^6$
	$Co(NH_3)_6^{+++} \rightleftharpoons Co^{+++} + 6\,NH_3$	$2.2 \times 10^{-34}\ M^6$
	$Ni(NH_3)_6^{++} \rightleftharpoons Ni^{++} + 6\,NH_3$	$1.8 \times 10^{-9}\ M^6$
	$Ag(NH_3)_2^{+} \rightleftharpoons Ag^{+} + 2\,NH_3$	$5.9 \times 10^{-8}\ M^2$
	$Zn(NH_3)_4^{++} \rightleftharpoons Zn^{++} + 4\,NH_3$	$3.4 \times 10^{-10}\ M^4$
Cyanide	$Cd(CN)_4^{--} \rightleftharpoons Cd^{++} + 4\,CN^-$	$1.4 \times 10^{-19}\ M^4$
	$Cu(CN)_2^{-} \rightleftharpoons Cu^{+} + 2\,CN^-$	$5.0 \times 10^{-28}\ M^2$
	$Fe(CN)_6^{----} \rightleftharpoons Fe^{++} + 6\,CN^-$	$1.0 \times 10^{-35}\ M^6$
	$Hg(CN)_4^{--} \rightleftharpoons Hg^{++} + 4\,CN^-$	$4.0 \times 10^{-42}\ M^4$
	$Ni(CN)_4^{--} \rightleftharpoons Ni^{++} + 4\,CN^-$	$1.0 \times 10^{-22}\ M^4$
	$Ag(CN)_2^{-} \rightleftharpoons Ag^{+} + 2\,CN^-$	$1.8 \times 10^{-19}\ M^2$
	$Zn(CN)_4^{--} \rightleftharpoons Zn^{++} + 4\,CN^-$	$1.3 \times 10^{-17}\ M^4$
Hydroxide	$Al(OH)_4^{-} \rightleftharpoons Al^{+++} + 4\,OH^-$	$1.0 \times 10^{-34}\ M^4$
	$Zn(OH)_4^{--} \rightleftharpoons Zn^{++} + 4\,OH^-$	$3.3 \times 10^{-16}\ M^4$
Chloride	$HgCl_4^{--} \rightleftharpoons Hg^{++} + 4\,Cl^-$	$1.1 \times 10^{-16}\ M^4$
Bromide	$HgBr_4^{--} \rightleftharpoons Hg^{++} + 4\,Br^-$	$2.3 \times 10^{-22}\ M^4$
Iodide	$HgI_4^{--} \rightleftharpoons Hg^{++} + 4\,I^-$	$5.3 \times 10^{-31}\ M^4$
Thiosulfate	$Ag(S_2O_3)_2^{---} \rightleftharpoons Ag^{+} + 2\,S_2O_3^{--}$	$3.5 \times 10^{-14}\ M^2$

Table 4 SOLUBILITY PRODUCTS AT 20°C

Aluminum hydroxide	$[Al^{+++}] \times [OH^-]^3$	5×10^{-33}
Barium carbonate	$[Ba^{++}] \times [CO_3^{--}]$	1.6×10^{-9}
Barium chromate	$[Ba^{++}] \times [CrO_4^{--}]$	8.5×10^{-11}
Barium sulfate	$[Ba^{++}] \times [SO_4^{--}]$	1.5×10^{-9}
Barium oxalate	$[Ba^{++}] \times [C_2O_4^{--}]$	1.5×10^{-8}
Bismuth sulfide	$[Bi^{+++}]^2 \times [S^{--}]^3$	1×10^{-70}
Cadmium hydroxide	$[Cd^{++}] \times [OH^-]^2$	2×10^{-14}
Cadmium sulfide	$[Cd^{++}] \times [S^{--}]$	6×10^{-27}
Calcium carbonate	$[Ca^{++}] \times [CO_3^{--}]$	6.9×10^{-9}
Calcium oxalate	$[Ca^{++}] \times [C_2O_4^{--}]$	1.3×10^{-9}
Calcium sulfate	$[Ca^{++}] \times [SO_4^{--}]$	2.4×10^{-5}
Chromium hydroxide	$[Cr^{+++}] \times [OH^-]^3$	7×10^{-31}
Cobalt sulfide	$[Co^{++}] \times [S^{--}]$	5×10^{-22}
Cupric hydroxide	$[Cu^{++}] \times [OH^-]^2$	1.6×10^{-19}
Cupric sulfide	$[Cu^{++}] \times [S^{--}]$	4×10^{-36}
Ferric hydroxide	$[Fe^{+++}] \times [OH^-]^3$	6×10^{-38}
Ferrous hydroxide	$[Fe^{++}] \times [OH^-]^2$	2×10^{-15}
Ferrous sulfide	$[Fe^{++}] \times [S^{--}]$	4×10^{-17}
Lead carbonate	$[Pb^{++}] \times [CO_3^{--}]$	1.5×10^{-13}
Lead chromate	$[Pb^{++}] \times [CrO_4^{--}]$	2×10^{-16}
Lead iodide	$[Pb^{++}] \times [I^-]^2$	8.3×10^{-9}
Lead sulfate	$[Pb^{++}] \times [SO_4^{--}]$	1.3×10^{-8}
Lead sulfide	$[Pb^{++}] \times [S^{--}]$	4×10^{-26}

Table 4 SOLUBILITY PRODUCTS AT 20°C—*cont.*

Magnesium carbonate	$[Mg^{++}] \times [CO_3^{--}]$	4×10^{-5}
Magnesium hydroxide	$[Mg^{++}] \times [OH^-]^2$	8.9×10^{-12}
Magnesium oxalate	$[Mg^{++}] \times [C_2O_4^{--}]$	8.6×10^{-5}
Manganese hydroxide	$[Mn^{++}] \times [OH^-]^2$	2×10^{-13}
Manganese sulfide	$[Mn^{++}] \times [S^{--}]$	8×10^{-14}
Mercurous chloride	$[Hg_2^{++}] \times [Cl^-]^2$	1.1×10^{-18}
Mercuric sulfide	$[Hg^{++}] \times [S^{--}]$	1×10^{-50}
Nickel hydroxide	$[Ni^{++}] \times [OH^-]^2$	1.6×10^{-16}
Nickel sulfide	$[Ni^{++}] \times [S^{--}]$	1×10^{-22}
Silver arsenate	$[Ag^+]^3 \times [AsO_4^{---}]$	1×10^{-23}
Silver bromide	$[Ag^+] \times [Br^-]$	5×10^{-13}
Silver carbonate	$[Ag^+]^2 \times [CO_3^{--}]$	8.2×10^{-12}
Silver chloride	$[Ag^+] \times [Cl^-]$	2.8×10^{-10}
Silver chromate	$[Ag^+]^2 \times [CrO_4^{--}]$	1.9×10^{-12}
Silver iodate	$[Ag^+] \times [IO_3^-]$	3×10^{-8}
Silver iodide	$[Ag^+] \times [I^-]$	8.5×10^{-17}
Silver phosphate	$[Ag^+]^3 \times [PO_4^{---}]$	1.8×10^{-18}
Silver sulfide	$[Ag^+]^2 \times [S^{--}]$	1×10^{-50}
Silver thiocyanate	$[Ag^+] \times [CNS^-]$	1×10^{-12}
Stannous sulfide	$[Sn^{++}] \times [S^{--}]$	1×10^{-24}
Zinc hydroxide	$[Zn^{++}] \times [OH^-]^2$	5×10^{-17}
Zinc sulfide	$[Zn^{++}] \times [S^{--}]$	1×10^{-20}

Table 5   SOME STANDARD OXIDATION POTENTIALS IN ACID SOLUTION*

	Half reaction	$E°$
1	$K (s) \rightleftarrows K^+ + e^-$	2.925
2	$Ca (s) \rightleftarrows Ca^{++} + 2 e^-$	2.87
3	$Al (s) \rightleftarrows Al^{+++} + 3 e^-$	1.66
4	$Mn (s) \rightleftarrows Mn^{++} + 2 e^-$	1.18
5	$H_2O + H_2PO_3 \rightleftarrows H_3PO_4 + H^+ + e^-$	0.9
6	$Zn (s) \rightleftarrows Zn^{++} + 2 e^-$	0.763
7	$P (s) + H_2O \rightleftarrows H_3PO_2 + H^+ + e^-$	0.51
8	$H_3PO_2 + H_2O \rightleftarrows H_3PO_3 + 2 H^+ + 2 e^-$	0.50
9	$Cr^{++} \rightleftarrows Cr^{+++} + e^-$	0.41
10	$H_3PO_3 + H_2O \rightleftarrows H_3PO_4 + 2 H^+ + 2 e^-$	0.276
11	$Ni (s) \rightleftarrows Ni^{++} + 2 e^-$	0.250
12	$Sn (s) \rightleftarrows Sn^{++} + 2 e^-$	0.136
13	$HS_2O_4^- + 2 H_2O \rightleftarrows 2 H_2SO_3 + H^+ + 2 e^-$	0.08
14	$H_2 (g) \rightleftarrows 2 H^+ + 2 e^-$	0.000
15	$PH_3 \rightleftarrows P (s) + 3 H^+ + 3 e^-$	−0.06
16	$H_2S \rightleftarrows 2 H^+ + S + 2 e^-$	−0.141
17	$Sn^{++} \rightleftarrows Sn^{++++} + 2 e^-$	−0.15
18	$H_2SO_3 + H_2O \rightleftarrows SO_4^{--} + 4 H^+ + 2 e^-$	−0.17
19	$Cu (s) \rightleftarrows Cu^{++} + 2 e^-$	−0.337
20	$S (s) + 3 H_2O \rightleftarrows H_2SO_3 + 4 H^+ + 4 e^-$	−0.45
21	$2 I^- \rightleftarrows I_2 + 2 e^-$	−0.5355
22	$MnO_4^{--} \rightleftarrows MnO_4^- + e^-$	−0.564

Table 5 SOME STANDARD OXIDATION POTENTIALS IN ACID SOLUTION*—*cont.*

	Half reaction	$E°$
23	$H_2O_2 \rightleftarrows O_2 + 2\,H^+ + 2\,e^-$	-0.682
24	$Fe^{++} \rightleftarrows Fe^{+++} + e^-$	-0.771
25	$Ag\,(s) \rightleftarrows Ag^+ + e^-$	-0.799
26	$NO_2 + H_2O \rightleftarrows NO_3^- + 2\,H^+ + e^-$	-0.80
27	$Hg\,(s) \rightleftarrows Hg^{++} + 2\,e^-$	-0.854
28	$NO + 2\,H_2O \rightleftarrows NO_3^- + 4\,H^+ + 3\,e^-$	-0.96
29	$NO + H_2O \rightleftarrows HNO_2 + H^+ + e^-$	-1.00
30	$2\,Br^- \rightleftarrows Br_2 + 2\,e^-$	-1.065
31	$Mn^{++} + 2\,H_2O \rightleftarrows MnO_2\,(s) + 4\,H^+ + 2\,e^-$	-1.23
32	$2\,Cr^{+++} + 7\,H_2O \rightleftarrows Cr_2O_7^{--} + 14\,H^+ + 6\,e^-$	-1.33
33	$2\,Cl^- \rightleftarrows Cl_2 + 2\,e^-$	-1.3595
34	$Cl^- + 3\,H_2O \rightleftarrows ClO_3^- + 6\,H^+ + 6\,e^-$	-1.45
35	$Mn^{++} + 4\,H_2O \rightleftarrows MnO_4^- + 8\,H^+ + 5\,e^-$	-1.51
36	$Mn^{++} \rightleftarrows Mn^{+++} + e^-$	-1.51
37	$Bi^{+++} + 3\,H_2O \rightleftarrows HBrO_3 + 5\,H^+ + 2\,e^-$	-1.70
38	$2\,H_2O \rightleftarrows H_2O_2 + 2\,H^+ + 2\,e^-$	-1.77
39	$2\,F^- \rightleftarrows F_2 + 2\,e^-$	-2.65
40	$2\,HF \rightleftarrows F_2 + 2\,H^+ + 2\,e^-$	-3.06

* For a complete list of oxidation potentials see *Oxidation Potentials*, Second Edition, by W. H. Latimer, Prentice-Hall, Inc., Englewood Cliffs, N. J., 1952.

Table 6   SOME STANDARD OXIDATION POTENTIALS IN ALKALINE SOLUTION

	Half reaction	$E°$
1	$Ca\ (s) + 2\ OH^- \rightleftarrows Ca(OH)_2\ (s) + 2\ e^-$	3.03
2	$H_2 + 2\ OH^- \rightleftarrows 2\ H_2O + 2\ e^-$	2.93
3	$K\ (s) \rightleftarrows K^+ + e^-$	2.925
4	$Al\ (s) + 4\ OH^- \rightleftarrows Al(OH)_4^- + 3\ e^-$	2.35
5	$P\ (s) + 2\ OH^- \rightleftarrows H_2PO_2^- + e^-$	2.05
6	$H_2PO_2^- + 3\ OH^- \rightleftarrows HPO_3^{--} + 2\ H_2O + 2\ e^-$	1.57
7	$Mn\ (s) + 2\ OH^- \rightleftarrows Mn(OH)_2\ (s) + 2\ e^-$	1.55
8	$Zn\ (s) + S^{--} \rightleftarrows ZnS\ (s) + 2\ e^-$	1.44
9	$Zn\ (s) + 4\ CN^- \rightleftarrows Zn(CN)_4^{--} + 2\ e^-$	1.26
10	$Zn\ (s) + 4\ OH^- \rightleftarrows Zn(OH)_4^{--} + 2\ e^-$	1.216
11	$HPO_3^{--} + 3\ OH^- \rightleftarrows PO_4^{---} + 2\ H_2O + 2\ e^-$	1.12
12	$S_2O_4^{--} + 4\ OH^- \rightleftarrows 2\ SO_3^{--} + 2\ H_2O + 2\ e^-$	1.12
13	$Zn\ (s) + 4\ NH_3 \rightleftarrows Zn(NH_3)_4^{++} + 2\ e^-$	1.03
14	$CN^- + 2\ OH^- \rightleftarrows CNO^- + H_2O + 2\ e^-$	0.97
15	$SO_3^{--} + 2\ OH^- \rightleftarrows SO_4^{--} + H_2O + 2\ e^-$	0.93
16	$Sn(OH)_4^{--} + 2\ OH^- \rightleftarrows Sn(OH)_6^{--} + 2\ e^-$	0.90
17	$PH_3 + 3\ OH^- \rightleftarrows P\ (s) + 3\ H_2O + 3\ e^-$	0.89
18	$Sn\ (s) + 4\ OH^- \rightleftarrows Sn(OH)_4^{--} + 2\ e^-$	0.76
19	$Ni\ (s) + 2\ OH^- \rightleftarrows Ni(OH)_2\ (s) + 2\ e^-$	0.72
20	$Fe(OH)_2\ (s) + OH^- \rightleftarrows Fe(OH)_3\ (s) + e^-$	0.56

Table 6 SOME STANDARD OXIDATION POTENTIALS IN ALKALINE SOLUTION—*cont.*

	Half reaction	$E°$
21	$S^{--} \rightleftarrows S + 2\ e^-$	0.48
22	$Cr(OH)_4^- + 4\ OH^- \rightleftarrows CrO_4^{--} + 4\ H_2O + 3\ e^-$	0.13
23	$H_2O_2 + 2\ OH^- \rightleftarrows O_2 + 2\ H_2O + 2\ e^-$	0.076
24	$Mn(OH)_2\ (s) + 2\ OH^- \rightleftarrows MnO_2\ (s) + 2\ H_2O + 2\ e^-$	0.05
25	$Cu(NH_3)_2^+ + 2\ NH_3 \rightleftarrows Cu(NH_3)_4^{++} + e^-$	0.0
26	$Mn(OH)_2\ (s) + OH^- \rightleftarrows Mn(OH)_3\ (s) + e^-$	-0.1
27	$Co(NH_3)_6^{++} \rightleftarrows Co(NH_3)_6^{+++} + e^-$	-0.1
28	$Co(OH)_2\ (s) + OH^- \rightleftarrows Co(OH)_3\ (s) + e^-$	-0.17
29	$ClO_2^- + 2\ OH^- \rightleftarrows ClO_3^- + H_2O + 2\ e^-$	-0.33
30	$ClO_3^- + 2\ OH^- \rightleftarrows ClO_4^- + H_2O + 2\ e^-$	-0.36
31	$4\ OH^- \rightleftarrows O_2 + 2\ H_2O + 4\ e^-$	-0.401
32	$I^- + 2\ OH^- \rightleftarrows IO^- + H_2O + 2\ e^-$	-0.49
33	$Ni(OH)_2\ (s) + 2\ OH^- \rightleftarrows NiO_2\ (s) + 2\ H_2O + 2\ e^-$	-0.49
34	$MnO_4^{--} \rightleftarrows MnO_4^- + e^-$	-0.564
35	$MnO_2\ (s) + 4\ OH^- \rightleftarrows MnO_4^- + 2\ H_2O + 3\ e^-$	-0.588
36	$MnO_2\ (s) + 4\ OH^- \rightleftarrows MnO_4^{--} + 2\ H_2O + 2\ e^-$	-0.60
37	$ClO^- + 2\ OH^- \rightleftarrows ClO_2^- + H_2O + 2\ e^-$	-0.66
38	$Br^- + 2\ OH^- \rightleftarrows BrO^- + H_2O + 2\ e^-$	-0.76
39	$2\ OH^- \rightleftarrows H_2O_2 + 2\ e^-$	-0.88
40	$Cl^- + 2\ OH^- \rightleftarrows ClO^- + H_2O + 2\ e^-$	-0.89

Table 7 FOUR-PLACE LOGARITHMS

N	0	1	2	3	4	5	6	7	8	9	1	2	3	4	5	6	7	8	9
10	0000	0043	0086	0128	0170	0212	0253	0294	0334	0374	4	8	12	17	21	25	29	33	37
11	0414	0453	0492	0531	0569	0607	0645	0682	0719	0755	4	8	11	15	19	23	26	30	34
12	0792	0828	0864	0899	0934	0969	1004	1038	1072	1106	3	7	10	14	17	21	24	28	31
13	1139	1173	1206	1239	1271	1303	1335	1367	1399	1430	3	6	10	13	16	19	23	26	29
14	1461	1492	1523	1553	1584	1614	1644	1673	1703	1732	3	6	9	12	15	18	21	24	27
15	1761	1790	1818	1847	1875	1903	1931	1959	1987	2014	3	6	8	11	14	17	20	22	25
16	2041	2068	2095	2122	2148	2175	2201	2227	2253	2279	3	5	8	11	13	16	18	21	24
17	2304	2330	2355	2380	2405	2430	2455	2480	2504	2529	2	5	7	10	12	15	17	20	22
18	2553	2577	2601	2625	2648	2672	2695	2718	2742	2765	2	5	7	9	12	14	16	19	21
19	2788	2810	2833	2856	2878	2900	2923	2945	2967	2989	2	4	7	9	11	13	16	18	20
20	3010	3032	3054	3075	3096	3118	3139	3160	3181	3201	2	4	6	8	11	13	15	17	19
21	3222	3243	3263	3284	3304	3324	3345	3365	3385	3404	2	4	6	8	10	12	14	16	18
22	3424	3444	3464	3483	3502	3522	3541	3560	3579	3598	2	4	6	8	10	12	14	16	17
23	3617	3636	3655	3674	3692	3711	3729	3747	3766	3784	2	4	6	7	9	11	13	15	17
24	3802	3820	3838	3856	3874	3892	3909	3927	3945	3962	2	4	5	7	9	11	12	14	16
25	3979	3997	4014	4031	4048	4065	4082	4099	4116	4133	2	4	5	7	9	10	12	14	16
26	4150	4166	4183	4200	4216	4232	4249	4265	4281	4298	2	3	5	7	8	10	11	13	15
27	4314	4330	4346	4362	4378	4393	4409	4425	4440	4456	2	3	5	6	8	9	11	12	14
28	4472	4487	4502	4518	4533	4548	4564	4579	4594	4609	2	3	5	6	8	9	11	12	14
29	4624	4639	4654	4669	4683	4698	4713	4728	4742	4757	1	3	4	6	7	9	10	12	13
30	4771	4786	4800	4814	4829	4843	4857	4871	4886	4900	1	3	4	6	7	9	10	11	13
31	4914	4928	4942	4955	4969	4983	4997	5011	5024	5038	1	3	4	5	7	8	10	11	12
32	5051	5065	5079	5092	5105	5119	5132	5145	5159	5172	1	3	4	5	7	8	9	11	12
33	5185	5198	5211	5224	5237	5250	5263	5276	5289	5302	1	3	4	5	7	8	9	11	12
34	5315	5328	5340	5353	5366	5378	5391	5403	5416	5428	1	2	4	5	6	8	9	10	11
35	5441	5453	5465	5478	5490	5502	5514	5527	5539	5551	1	2	4	5	6	7	9	10	11
36	5563	5575	5587	5599	5611	5623	5635	5647	5658	5670	1	2	4	5	6	7	8	10	11
37	5682	5694	5705	5717	5729	5740	5752	5763	5775	5786	1	2	4	5	6	7	8	9	11
38	5798	5809	5821	5832	5843	5855	5866	5877	5888	5899	1	2	3	5	6	7	8	9	10
39	5911	5922	5933	5944	5955	5966	5977	5988	5999	6010	1	2	3	4	5	7	8	9	10
40	6021	6031	6042	6053	6064	6075	6085	6096	6107	6117	1	2	3	4	5	6	8	9	10
41	6128	6138	6149	6160	6170	6180	6191	6201	6212	6222	1	2	3	4	5	6	7	8	9
42	6232	6243	6253	6263	6274	6284	6294	6304	6314	6325	1	2	3	4	5	6	7	8	9
43	6335	6345	6355	6365	6375	6385	6395	6405	6415	6425	1	2	3	4	5	6	7	8	9
44	6435	6444	6454	6464	6474	6484	6493	6503	6513	6522	1	2	3	4	5	6	7	8	9
45	6532	6542	6551	6561	6571	6580	6590	6599	6609	6618	1	2	3	4	5	6	7	8	9
46	6628	6637	6646	6656	6665	6675	6684	6693	6702	6712	1	2	3	4	5	6	7	7	8
47	6721	6730	6739	6749	6758	6767	6776	6785	6794	6803	1	2	3	4	5	6	7	7	8
48	6812	6821	6830	6839	6848	6857	6866	6875	6884	6893	1	2	3	4	5	6	7	7	8
49	6902	6911	6920	6928	6937	6946	6955	6964	6972	6981	1	2	3	4	4	5	6	7	8
50	6990	6998	7007	7016	7024	7033	7042	7050	7059	7067	1	2	3	3	4	5	6	7	8
51	7076	7084	7093	7101	7110	7118	7126	7135	7143	7152	1	2	3	3	4	5	6	7	8
52	7160	7168	7177	7185	7193	7202	7210	7218	7226	7235	1	2	3	3	4	5	6	7	7
53	7243	7251	7259	7267	7275	7284	7292	7300	7308	7316	1	2	2	3	4	5	6	6	7
54	7324	7332	7340	7348	7356	7364	7372	7380	7388	7396	1	2	2	3	4	5	6	6	7
N	0	1	2	3	4	5	6	7	8	9	1	2	3	4	5	6	7	8	9

Table 7 FOUR-PLACE LOGARITHMS—*cont.*

N	0	1	2	3	4	5	6	7	8	9	1	2	3	4	5	6	7	8	9
55	7404	7412	7419	7427	7435	7443	7451	7459	7466	7474	1	2	2	3	4	5	5	6	7
56	7482	7490	7497	7505	7513	7520	7528	7536	7543	7551	1	2	2	3	4	5	5	6	7
57	7559	7566	7574	7582	7589	7597	7604	7612	7619	7627	1	1	2	3	4	5	5	6	7
58	7634	7642	7649	7657	7664	7672	7679	7686	7694	7701	1	1	2	3	4	4	5	6	7
59	7709	7716	7723	7731	7738	7745	7752	7760	7767	7774	1	1	2	3	4	4	5	6	7
60	7782	7789	7796	7803	7810	7818	7825	7832	7839	7846	1	1	2	3	4	4	5	6	6
61	7853	7860	7868	7875	7882	7889	7896	7903	7910	7917	1	1	2	3	3	4	5	6	6
62	7924	7931	7938	7945	7952	7959	7966	7973	7980	7987	1	1	2	3	3	4	5	5	6
63	7993	8000	8007	8014	8021	8028	8035	8041	8048	8055	1	1	2	3	3	4	5	5	6
64	8062	8069	8075	8082	8089	8096	8102	8109	8116	8122	1	1	2	3	3	4	5	5	6
65	8129	8136	8142	8149	8156	8162	8169	8176	8182	8189	1	1	2	3	3	4	5	5	6
66	8195	8202	8209	8215	8222	8228	8235	8241	8248	8254	1	1	2	3	3	4	5	5	6
67	8261	8267	8274	8280	8287	8293	8299	8306	8312	8319	1	1	2	3	3	4	5	5	6
68	8325	8331	8338	8344	8351	8357	8363	8370	8376	8382	1	1	2	3	3	4	4	5	6
69	8388	8395	8401	8407	8414	8420	8426	8432	8439	8445	1	1	2	3	3	4	4	5	6
70	8451	8457	8463	8470	8476	8482	8488	8494	8500	8506	1	1	2	3	3	4	4	5	6
71	8513	8519	8525	8531	8537	8543	8549	8555	8561	8567	1	1	2	3	3	4	4	5	6
72	8573	8579	8585	8591	8597	8603	8609	8615	8621	8627	1	1	2	3	3	4	4	5	6
73	8633	8639	8645	8651	8657	8663	8669	8675	8681	8686	1	1	2	2	3	4	4	5	5
74	8692	8698	8704	8710	8716	8722	8727	8733	8739	8745	1	1	2	2	3	4	4	5	5
75	8751	8756	8762	8768	8774	8779	8785	8791	8797	8802	1	1	2	2	3	3	4	5	5
76	8808	8814	8820	8825	8831	8837	8842	8848	8854	8859	1	1	2	2	3	3	4	4	5
77	8865	8871	8876	8882	8887	8893	8899	8904	8910	8915	1	1	2	2	3	3	4	4	5
78	8921	8927	8932	8938	8943	8949	8954	8960	8965	8971	1	1	2	2	3	3	4	4	5
79	8976	8982	8987	8993	8998	9004	9009	9015	9020	9025	1	1	2	2	3	3	4	4	5
80	9031	9036	9042	9047	9053	9058	9063	9069	9074	9079	1	1	2	2	3	3	4	4	5
81	9085	9090	9096	9101	9106	9112	9117	9122	9128	9133	1	1	2	2	3	3	4	4	5
82	9138	9143	9149	9154	9159	9165	9170	9175	9180	9186	1	1	2	2	3	3	4	4	5
83	9191	9196	9201	9206	9212	9217	9222	9227	9232	9238	1	1	2	2	3	3	4	4	5
84	9243	9248	9253	9258	9263	9269	9274	9279	9284	9289	1	1	2	2	3	3	4	4	5
85	9294	9299	9304	9309	9315	9320	9325	9330	9335	9340	1	1	2	2	3	3	4	4	5
86	9345	9350	9355	9360	9365	9370	9375	9380	9385	9390	1	1	2	2	3	3	4	4	5
87	9395	9400	9405	9410	9415	9420	9425	9430	9435	9440	1	1	2	2	3	3	4	4	5
88	9445	9450	9455	9460	9465	9469	9474	9479	9484	9489	0	1	1	2	2	3	3	4	4
89	9494	9499	9504	9509	9513	9518	9523	9528	9533	9538	0	1	1	2	2	3	3	4	4
90	9542	9547	9552	9557	9562	9566	9571	9576	9581	9586	0	1	1	2	2	3	3	4	4
91	9590	9595	9600	9605	9609	9614	9619	9624	9628	9633	0	1	1	2	2	3	3	4	4
92	9638	9643	9647	9652	9657	9661	9666	9671	9675	9680	0	1	1	2	2	3	3	4	4
93	9685	9689	9694	9699	9703	9708	9713	9717	9722	9727	0	1	1	2	2	3	3	4	4
94	9731	9736	9741	9745	9750	9754	9759	9763	9768	9773	0	1	1	2	2	3	3	4	4
95	9777	9782	9786	9791	9795	9800	9805	9809	9814	9818	0	1	1	2	2	3	3	4	4
96	9823	9827	9832	9836	9841	9845	9850	9854	9859	9863	0	1	1	2	2	3	3	4	4
97	9868	9872	9877	9881	9886	9890	9894	9899	9903	9908	0	1	1	2	2	3	3	4	4
98	9912	9917	9921	9926	9930	9934	9939	9943	9948	9952	0	1	1	2	2	3	3	3	4
99	9956	9961	9965	9969	9974	9978	9983	9987	9991	9996	0	1	1	2	2	3	3	3	4
N	0	1	2	3	4	5	6	7	8	9	1	2	3	4	5	6	7	8	9

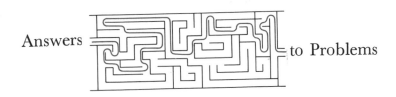

Answers to Problems

Answers are given to all unsolved problems except those marked with an asterisk (*). Units are given only when not specified in the problem. A list of answers to the unanswered problems is available for the use of instructors; requests for this list should be sent to the publishers or to the author.

2.1(a). 22.2 **2.2.(a).** 53.6. **2.3.** $-40°$. **2.5.** 73°.

3.1(a). 2.1×10^{10}; **(c).** 2.7×10^{-3}; **(e).** 1.0×10^{-1}. **3.2(a).** 2.69×10^{-1}.
3.3(a). 2.2×10^{-6}.

4.2. 30.42/40.08. **4.5.** 89.7 g. **4.7.** 45.1 g. **4.12.** 2.97×10^{24}. **4.14.** 34.5.
4.16. 6.83×10^{-4}. **4.18.** 1.42×10^{28}. **4.19.** 35.40. **4.20.** 12.5% of 24.1,
87.5% of 22.5.

5.5. CuO. **5.7.** $Na_2S_2O_3$. **5.9.** $Mg_2P_2O_7$. **5.10(b).** Fe_2O_3; **(d).** C_2H_6O. **5.17.**
20/17. **5.19.** 120/44. **5.23.** 1.70. **5.26.** 2.9. **5.30.** 8.57×10^{-4}. **5.33.** 373.
5.36. 17. **5.39.** 162. **5.42.** 3.72×10^{-4}. **5.46.** 6.62×10^{-2}. **5.48.** 3.34.
5.50(a). 48.0. **5.51.** 35.5. **5.52(a).** 1.62; **(b).** 360; **(c).** 117; **(d).** 51.4; **(e).**
2.44; **(f).** 0.36; **(g).** 10.2; **(h).** 1.47×10^{22}; **(i).** 8.82×10^{22}; **(j).** 58.5; **(k).** 1/6;
(l). 0.0697; **(m).** 14.4. **5.55.** (B). **5.57.** XY_3. **5.58.** 184.5; MCl_5; MCl_6.
5.59. $^{22}Na = 40\%$; $^{23}Na = 60\%$. **5.60.** XZ_2, $X_2 Z_5$, 3.18 times greater.

6.2. 845. **6.4.** 600. **6.7.** 575 cc. **6.9.** 606°. **6.11.** 45.5 l. **6.13.** 11.8 atm.
6.15. 0.84 liter.

7.2. 8.11. **7.6.** 2.91. **7.9.** 0.683. **7.11.** 236. **7.14.** 34.5. **7.17.** 7.03. **7.20.**
93.0. **7.22.** 34.9. **7.26.** 73.2. **7.30.** 48. **7.34.** 21.8. **7.36.** inversely proportional. **7.42.** 356. **7.44.** 14.6. **7.46.** 46. **7.48.** 1.205×10^{24}. **7.50.** 80;
infinite. **7.54.** 0.298 g/liter. **7.56.** 0.13 g/liter. **7.58.** 109 cu ft. **7.60.** 564.
7.62. 9.4. **7.64.** 20 mm. **7.66.** 0.25. **7.68.** 15 mm. **7.70.** 70. **7.72.**

1400 mm. **7.74.** 148 mm. **7.76.** 2220 mm. **7.80(a).** 44; **(b).** 1.36; **(c).** 18; .**(d).** 5.1; **(e).** 79.2; **(f).** 9.82; **(g).** 1.45×10^{25}; **(h).** 8.20×10^{23}; **(i).** 4.5; **(j).** 0.22; **(k).** 160; **(l).** 5.35×10^{24}; **(m).** 67.2 liters; **(n).** 17.5 liters; **(o).** 6.25; **(p).** 168 g; **(q).** 1.96; **(r).** 81.8; **(s).** 200 mm; **(t).** 1.0; **(u).** 0.272; **(v).** 0.82. **7.84.** $d_B = 10.2 \times d_A$. **7.86.** 33.8. **7.88.** 0.195. **7.89.** 0.320 g. **7.90(a).** 0.664 atm; **(b).** 1.34 atm. **7.91.** 21.46. **7.92.** 25; 28. **7.93.** 0.012 g. **7.94.** 1.0. **7.95(a).** 112 mm; **(b).** none; **(c).** 0.12. **7.96(a).** 740 mm; **(b).** 0.017; **(c).** 68%. **7.97.** 11.2 mm. **7.98.** 2nd vol = $7.79 \times$ 1st vol. **7.99.** 22. **7.100.** 0°C. **7.101.** 134.4 atm. **7.102.** 0.089 g/liter. **7.103.** 228. **7.104.** 2.4. **7.105.** O_2. **7.106.** HF; HCl.

8.8. 4.20; 2.40; 3.60. **8.10.** 1.90. **8.12.** 12. **8.14.** 1.13. **8.16.** 2.47. **8.18.** 163. **8.20.** 74.8. **8.22.** 37.8. **8.24.** 625; 500; 750. **8.26.** 421; 1050. **8.30.** 102. **8.32.** 55. **8.34.** 22.6. **8.36.** 27.8. **8.38.** 80.0. **8.40.** 64%. **8.42.** 15.4. **8.44.** 2.96%. **8.46.** 23. **8.48.** $Pb_3O_4 + 4\ H_2 = 3\ Pb + 4\ H_2O$. **8.50.** ZnI_2. **8.52.** 84.4. **8.54.** 128. **8.55.** 36. **8.56.** 3.8. **8.57.** 75 mm. **8.58.** 494 mm. **8.59.** C_3H_8. **8.60.** 114 mm. **8.61.** C_3H_8. **8.62.** C_3H_8S. **8.63.** C_4H_{10}. **8.64.** $2\ C_6H_{14} + 15\ O_2 = 4\ CO_2 + 8\ CO + 14\ H_2O$. **8.65.** wt of $C_2H_4 = 2.33 \times$ wt of C_5H_{12}. **8.66.** 0.938 to CO_2; 0.062 to CH_4. **8.67.** $2\ H_2S = 2\ H_2 + S_2$. **8.68.** 25%. **8.69.** 0.58. **8.70.** CH_4O. **8.71.** 15. **8.72.** 30.9. **8.73.** 0.32. **8.74.** $2\ CrCl_3 + 3\ H_2 = 2\ Cr + 6\ HCl$. **8.75.** 87.6; 127. **8.76.** 14.0; 107.9. **8.77.** $Zr + 4\ HCl = ZrCl_4 + 2\ H_2$. **8.78.** I_2. **8.79.** $SiH_4 + 4\ M_2O_5 = SiO_2 + 2\ H_2O + 8\ MO_2$ (or $4\ M_2O_4$). **8.80.** 42.0.

9.4. 2.72. **9.6.** 26.2. **9.8.** 13.6. **9.10.** 44.5. **9.16.** 46.1. **9.18.** 10.7. **9.20.** 37. **9.22.** 2. **9.24.** 75. **9.25.** 128 mm. **9.26.** 3.36. **9.27.** 1.5 moles CH_4, 0.4 mole C_2H_4, 1.1 moles C_2H_2. **9.28.** 1.5 atm. **9.29.** 0.55. **9.30.** 50% $CaCO_3$; 10% $NaHCO_3$; 40% Na_2CO_3. **9.31.** 21.7. **9.32.** $C_5H_{11}OC_5H_{11}$; C_5H_{12}. **9.33.** C_4H_6; $C_5H_{11}OH$.

10.2. 80. **10.6.** 10.8. **10.8.** 69. **10.10.** 731.6. **10.12.** 1.37×10^4. **10.14.** 1.5 g. **10.15.** 1.98. **10.16.** 228. **10.17.** 77.6 kcal/mole. **10.18.** 9,850. **10.19.** 66.2 kcal/mole. **10.20.** 70.2 kcal/mole.

11.2. 24, 12, 2. **11.4(a).** $^{228}_{88}Ra$; **(c).** $^{220}_{86}Rn$. **11.5(a).** beta. **11.7.** 13, 7, 5, N. **11.8(b).** $^{29}_{15}P$. **11.9(a).** ^4_2He; **(c).** ^1_0n. **11.10(b).** ^4_2He. **11.11.** 8 alpha, 6 beta. **11.12.** $^{207}_{82}Pb$. **11.13.** $^{237}_{93}Np = ^{205}_{83}Bi + 8\ ^4_2He + 6\ ^{\ 0}_{-1}e$. **11.14.** 54 min. **11.15.** 35.5 g. **11.16.** 4.15×10^{-3} atm. **11.17.** 2.25 atm. **11.18.** 300°K. **11.19.** 6.0×10^{23}. **11.20.** $^3H/^1H = 2.0$; $N = 6.4 \times 10^{23}$. **11.21.** 900 mm.

12.10. 11.7.   **12.12.** 29.   **12.14.** 18.   **12.16.** 10.

13.6. 2.7.   **13.8.** 0.27.   **13.10.** 4.57.   **13.12.** 1.83.   **13.18(a).** 0.5;   **(b).** 0.8.
13.20. 254 mm.   **13.22.** 1.83.   **13.24.** 128; 4.59.   **13.26.** 0.32.   **13.28.** 2.24.
13.30. 2.00.   **13.32.** 3 atm.   **13.34.** 4.76.   **13.36.** 8.96.   **13.37.** 1500.   **13.38.**
3.5   **13.39.** 4.0.   **13.40.** Na_2CO_3, 0.250 M; $NaHCO_3$, 0.125 M.   **13.41.** 2000.
13.42. 81.   **13.43.** 1790.   **13.44.** 30.   **13.45.** 0.050; 0.10.   **13.46.** 0.050; 0.10.
13.47. 0.69.

14.2. 129.   **14.4.** 141.   **14.6.** 119.   **14.8.** 5°/mole.   **14.10.** 1.30 g/ml.   **14.11.**
3.88.   **14.12.** 4.3.   **14.13.** 192; 56.5%.   **14.14.** C_4H_6; C_4H_{10}.

15.4. 32.042.   **15.6.** 16.042.   **15.7.** 70.13.   **15.8.** 28.054.

16.2. 0.2 PCl_3; 0.2 Cl_2; 0.8 PCl_5.   **16.6.** 267.   **16.8.** 0.521.   **16.10.** 0.96.   **16.12.**
0.68.   **16.14.** 16.   **16.20.** 0.7.   **16.26.** 0.12, 0.32, 0.78.   **16.28.** 0.18.   **16.30(a).**
17.5;   **(b).** 121 atm.   **16.31.** 300 liters.   **16.32.** 1.6×10^{-2} mole/liter.   **16.33.**
1.41.   **16.34.** S_2Cl_2; 1.2×10^2 liters^2 × mole^{-2}.   **16.35(a).** 6.00;   **(b).** 3.46.
16.36. 55, 14, 0.50.   **16.37.** $\zeta = 25$; $[NH_3] = 5.0$; $[N_2] = 1.0$; $[H_2] = 1.6$.
16.38. 8.1.   **16.39.** 0.56 liter.   **16.40.** 18 liters.   **16.41.** $K_1 = 6.9$ liters^2/mole^2;
$K_2 = 0.38$ mole/liter; $K_2 = 1/\sqrt{K_1}$.   **16.42.** $N_2O_5 = 0.94$; $N_2O_3 = 1.62$; $N_2O = 1.44$.   **16.44(a).** $K_p = K_c$;   **(b).** $K_p < K_c$;   **(c).** $K_p > K_c$.   **16.45.** 1 atm.   **16.46.**
$K_p = 8.8 \times 10^{-2}$ atm^2; $K_c = 3.5 \times 10^{-6}$ (mole/liter)^2.   **16.47.** $K_c = 1.94 \times 10^{-2}$ mole/liter; $K_p = 0.954$ atm.   **16.48.** 0.0343.   **16.49.** 1.15×10^4 mm.

17.2(a). $1.7 \times 10^{-5} M$;   **(b).** $1.8 \times 10^{-5} M$;   **(c).** $4 \times 10^{-10} M$.   **17.4.** $FX^2/1 - X$.
17.6. 0.10 F; $1.36 \times 10^{-3} M$.   **17.8.** $1.3 \times 10^{-3} M$.   **17.12.** $3.2 \times 10^{-7} M$.   **17.14.**
1.8×10^{-5}.   **17.16.** 8×10^{-5}.   **17.18(a).** 5.0×10^{-4}; 2.8×10^{-10}; 8.4×10^{-22}.
17.20(b). (1). 2.5×10^{-4}; (2). $3.1 \times 10^{-4} + \gamma$.   **17.21.** 2.8×10^{-10}.   **17.22.**
1.18×10^{-2}.   **17.26.** 0.134.   **17.27.** 1.1 ml of HCl and 2.9 ml of water.   **17.28.**
0.70 F.   **17.29(a).** $a = 0.20$; $b = 0.25$; $c = 0.30$; **(b).** 51. **17.30.** $1.0 \times 10^{-6} M$.

18.3(a). 1.7×10^{-7}.   **18.4(a).** 5.0×10^{-10}.   **18.7(a).** 8;   **(c).** 2.5;   **(e).** 11.3.
18.8(b). 11.6.   **18.11(a).** 3.2×10^{-2}.   **18.12(a).** 4.0×10^{-11}.   **18.13.** (b).
18.16. 8.3.   **18.18.** 0.11 M; $2.2 \times 10^{-5} M$.   **18.21.** 5×10^{-2}.   **18.22.** 5×10^{-4}.
18.24(a). $HC_2H_3O_2 = 0.36$ F; $NaC_2H_3O_2 = 0.64$ F;   **(b).** $[H^+] = 1 \times 10^{-5} M$;
$[OH^-] = 1 \times 10^{-9} M$; $[HC_2H_3O_2] = 0.36 M$; $[C_2H_3O_2^-] = 0.64 M$; $[Na^+] = 0.64 M$.   **18.25.** $[H^+] = 1 \times 10^{-4}$; $[OH^-] = 1 \times 10^{-10}$; $[H_2C_2O_4] = 1.9 \times 10^{-5}$;
$[HC_2O_4^-] = 1.2 \times 10^{-2}$; $[C_2O_4^{--}] = 7.6 \times 10^{-3}$.   **18.26.** 8.4.   **18.27.** 1.53.

18.28(a). 2.3; **(b).** 5.14. **18.29(a).** 4×10^{-8}; **(b).** $[NH_3] = 0.20$; $[Na^+] = [C_2H_3O_2^-] = 0.20$; $[NH_4^+] = [OH^-] = 1.9 \times 10^{-3}$; $[HC_2H_3O_2] = 5.9 \times 10^{-8}$; $[H^+] = 5.3 \times 10^{-12}$; **(c).** $[Na^+] = [CN^-] = 0.20$; $[NH_3] = 0.20$; $[NH_4^+] = 1.2 \times 10^{-3}$; $[HCN] = 1.7 \times 10^{-3}$; $[OH^-] = 2.9 \times 10^{-3}$; $[H^+] = 3.5 \times 10^{-12}$. **18.30.** 11; 1×10^{-9}. **18.31.** 6×10^{-8}. **18.32.** 1/3. **18.33.** 666 ml NH_3 and 333 ml HCl. **18.34.** $1 \times 10^{-6} M$. **18.35.** 42.5. **18.36(a).** $[H^+] = 5.0 \times 10^{-8}$; $[OH^-] = 2.0 \times 10^{-7}$; $[S^{--}] = 5.2 \times 10^{-8}$; $[H_2S] = 0.010$; $[Na^+] = 0.020$; **(b).** $[NH_4^+] = [S^{--}] = 4.1$; $[NH_3] = 0.94$; $[OH^-] = 4.2 \times 10^{-6}$; $[H^+] = 2.4 \times 10^{-9}$; $[H_2S] = 0.10$. **18.37(a).** $7.3 \times 10^{-3} M$; **(b).** 6.0×10^{23}. **18.38.** 1.5. **18.39.** 0.0048. **18.40.** 0.337. **18.41(a).** $[H^+] = 5.0 \times 10^{-6}$; $[OH^-] = 2.0 \times 10^{-9}$; $[Na^+] = 0.080$; $[A^-] = 0.080$; $[HA] = 0.240$; $K = 1.67 \times 10^{-6} M$; **(b).** $[A^-] = 0.070$; $[HA] = 0.250$; $[Na^+] = 0.080$; $[Cl^-] = 0.010$; $[H^+] = 5.9 \times 10^{-6}$; $[OH^-] = 1.7 \times 10^{-9}$. **18.42(a).** 0.1; **(b).** 1 pH unit higher; **(c).** 10 times as great. **18.43(a).** 100 times as great; **(b).** same value; **(c).** 4 units greater. **18.44(a).** 4.0; **(b).** 0.050 mole; **(c).** 7.9; **(d).** 0.26 moles. **18.45(a).** 11.3; **(b).** 7.7×10^{-2}. **18.46.** 0.0022 atm. **18.47.** $K_3 = 4.3 \times 10^{-9}$; K_1 and K_2 are very large. **18.48.** 12; $H_2PO_4^- = 3.3 \times 10^{-5}$; $HPO_4^- = 2.14$; $PO_4^{---} = 2.25$; $H_3PO_4 = 4.2 \times 10^{-15}$. **18.49.** 2.8.

19.12. 0.04. **19.14.** 1.6. **19.16.** 0.83. **19.18.** 83. **19.20.** 2.24. **19.21(b).** 36.5; **(d).** 0.005; **(f).** 0.25; **(h).** 0.90. **19.24.** dilute 10.0 ml to 400 ml. **19.26(a).** 4.7; **(c).** 12.3. **19.28.** 1.6. **19.30.** 0.91. **19.32.** 65. **19.34(a).** basic; **(b).** 0.52. **19.38.** 12.2. **19.40.** 73.3. **19.42.** 24. **19.44.** 1.60×10^{-19}. **19.46.** 34. **19.47.** 408. **19.48.** 7.5. **19.49.** 0.50. **19.50.** 7.0 ml. **19.51.** 333. **19.52.** 1.15 g Na; 13.74 g Ba. **19.53.** 0.4. **19.54.** 1.53; 66.7. **19.55.** 55.9. **19.56.** 25. **19.57(a).** 9,650; **(b).** 2.6 liters; **(c).** 1.2×10^{23}; **(d).** 800 ml. **19.58.** 3.21 h. **19.59.** 386. **19.60.** MCl_3. **19.61.** 3.62. **19.62.** K_2MoO_4. **19.63.** 4. **19.64.** 6.5×10^{23}. **19.65(a).** $Y_2(SO_4)_3$; **(b).** 27 min; **(c).** 189 cc.

20.2. 12.00. **20.4.** 12.0. **20.8.** 22.997. **20.9.** 114. **20.10.** 126.9. **20.11.** 65.4. **20.12(a).** 140; **(b).** $Ce_2(SO_4)_3$; **(c).** 0.0100. **20.13.** MF_6. **20.14.** 137.4; 35.5. **20.15.** 127; 108. **20.16.** 24.3.

21.3. $1.8 \times 10^{-18} M^4$. **21.4.** $1.5 \times 10^{-32} M^5$. **21.6.** 4.92×10^{-9}. **21.7(c).** 3.3×10^{-13}; **(f).** 8.38×10^{-9}. **21.10(a).** 4×10^{-36}; **(c).** 6×10^{-24}. **21.12.** 1.7×10^{-7}. **21.16.** 9.3×10^{-8} mole. **21.18.** $2.7 \times 10^{-6} M$. **21.20.** 10. **21.22.** 4×10^{-6}. **21.24.** 4.0×10^{-5}. **21.26(e).** $4 \times 10^{-9} M$. **21.28.** yes. **21.32.** 10 billion. **21.34.** 13.6 times as great. **21.36.** 1.25×10^{-7}. **21.38(b).** 1.8×10^4; **(d).** 3.6×10^{-2}; **(f).** 5.7×10^{-6}. **21.40.** 0.66. **21.42.** 4.0. **21.44.** 11 M.

21.46. 0.36 M.   **21.48.** 14.   **21.50.** $Mn(OH)_2$ precipitates, $Mg(OH)_2$ not.
21.51. $9.9 \times 10^{-3}; 9.9 \times 10^{-9}$.   **21.52.** 7.68×10^{-4}.   **21.53(a).** $1.34 \times 10^{-5} M$;
(b). 3.88×10^{-8}; **(c).** 1×10^{-3}; **(d).** 0.35 M.   **21.54(a).** 4×10^{-6} M; **(b).**
1.5×10^{-3} M; **(c).** 1.00×10^{-7} M; **(d).** 1.15×10^{-2}; **(e).** 1.11×10^{-2}; **(f).**
$(1.11 \times 10^{-2}) + (2.5 \times 10^{-8})$ mole; **(g).** 22.2.   **21.55(a).** Ag^+; $1.2 \times 10^{-5} M$;
(b). 4.0×10^{-4} M; **(c).** 2.5×10^{-5}.   **21.56(a).** 1.000 M; **(b).** 2.000 F; **(c).**
$0.78 M$; $0.61 M$; **(d).** 1×10^{-10} mole; $BaSO_4$.   **21.57.** 2.2.   **21.58.** $5.8 \times 10^{-3} M$.
21.59. 6×10^{-11} M.   **21.60(a).** 6.0×10^{-23} F; **(b).** 1.2×10^{14} liters.   **21.61.**
1.8×10^{-11}.   **21.62.** 1.8×10^{-11}; 1.8×10^{-5}.   **21.64.** $2.0 \times 10^{-15} M$.   **21.65.**
$[Cl^-] = 0.10$ M; $[Br^-] = 0.05$ M; $[I^-] = 8.3 \times 10^{-6}$.   **21.66.** 0.55.   **21.67.**
2.8×10^{-8}.   **21.68.** $M(OH)_2$; 4.0×10^{-6}.   **21.69.** yes; $Mg(OH)_2$.   **21.70(a).**
3.8×10^{-4}; **(b).** 4.0×10^{-4}; **(c).** 2.46×10^{-3}.   **21.71.** $2.0 \times 10^{-8} M$.   **21.72.**
8.4×10^{-10}.   **21.73.** 0%.   **21.74.** $5 \times 10^{-9} M$.   **21.75.** 0.5 M.   **21.76.** $8 \times$
10^{-8}.   **21.77.** 3×10^{-16}.   **21.78.** 1×10^{-4}; 1×10^{-8}.   **21.79.** 6.4×10^{-17}.
21.80. 1×10^{-16}; 1.5×10^{-19}.   **21.81.** 1×10^{-16}.   **21.82.** $1 \times 10^{-2} M$.   **21.83.**
$[H^+] = [Ag(CN)_2^-] = 1.1 \times 10^{-4}$; $[OH^-] = 9.3 \times 10^{-11}$; $[Ag^+] = 7.0 \times 10^{-13}$;
$[HCN] = 0.10$; $[CN^-] = 3.7 \times 10^{-7}$.   **21.84.** $[H^+] = 0.1$; $[Cl^-]$ 0.05; $[Cu(CN)_2^-]$
$= 0.05$; $[HCN] = 5 \times 10^{-4}$; $[Cu^+] = 6 \times 10^{-5}$; $[CN^-] = 2 \times 10^{-12}$; $[OH^-] =$
1×10^{-13}.   **21.85.** 3.2×10^{-6}.   **21.86.** $4 \times 10^{-3} M$.   **21.87.** 4.3; $1 \times 10^{-2} +$
5×10^{-5}.   **21.88.** Reverse.   **21.89.** $7.85 - 12.30$.   **21.90.** 3.4×10^{-6}.

22.1(a). 0.513 v; **(c).** 0.517 v.   **22.2(a).** yes; **(c).** no; **(e).** yes.   **22.4.** -0.806
v.   **22.5(a).** 1×10^{10}; **(c).** 1×10^{120}.   **22.6.** -1.47 v.   **22.9(a).** -0.01 v;
(b). yes; **(c).** $+4$.   **22.10(a).** 0.06 v; **(b).** no; **(c).** yes; **(d).** no; **(e1).** $+2$;
(e2). $+4$; **(e3).** $+3$; **(f).** no.   **22.11.** yes.   **22.12.** 0.140 v.   **22.13.** -1.
22.14. -0.56 v.   **22.15.** 1.2 v.

Index

THE PRENTICE-HALL **H**ow **To S**olve SERIES

Simple explanations and step-by-step solutions